STUDY GUIDE TO ACCOMPANY
MICROBIOLOGY
PELCZAR, REID, AND CHAN

McGraw-Hill Book Company ● New York ● St. Louis ● San Francisco ● Auckland
Bogotá ● Düsseldorf ● Johannesburg ● London ● Madrid ● Mexico
Montreal ● New Delhi ● Panama ● Paris ● São Paulo ● Singapore
Sydney ● Tokyo ● Toronto

STUDY GUIDE TO ACCOMPANY

MICROBIOLOGY

PELCZAR, REID, AND CHAN   FOURTH EDITION

Ronald M. Weiner

ASSOCIATE PROFESSOR OF MICROBIOLOGY
UNIVERSITY OF MARYLAND

Study Guide
to accompany Pelczar, Reid, and Chan:
Microbiology

ISBN 0-07-049232-8

1 2 3 4 5 6 7 8 9 0 V H V H 7 8 3 2 1 0 9 8 7

This book was set in Press Roman by Allen Wayne Technical Corp. The
editors were William J. Willey and Thomas A. P. Adams; the designer
was Hermann Strohbach; the production supervisor was Joe Campanella.
Von Hoffmann Press, Inc., was printer and binder.

To Adele and Karl

Contents

Four / Control of Microorganisms

Five / Microorganisms and Disease

Six / Environmental and Industrial Microbiology

To the Student: How to Use This Study Guide

ORIENTATION As a beginning student in microbiology you have probably had considerable exposure to a number of other disciplines: English, mathematics, perhaps the biology of visible plants and animals, and so forth. It is equally likely that you have had very little exposure to the study of microorganisms, which are generally not visible to the naked eye. Consequently you will be encountering a vocabulary of technical terms, species names, and basic concepts that may be entirely new to you. Because they are new, it is all the more important that you concentrate— from the beginning—on learning these essential "building blocks" of the subject of microbiology. Later, this information will enable you to better understand, among other things, how micro- organisms cause disease; how they can be controlled; how their activities can be (and have been) made to serve a variety of purposes; and how they fit into the ecology of our planet.

Since you are taking an introductory course, almost every chapter of the text will expose you to an entire subdiscipline within microbiology. Such fundamental information may serve as a springboard that will enable you to further your knowledge of individual subject areas. This is especially true should you specialize in microbiology. If your interests lie in a related discipline, the knowledge you accumulate will prove invaluable, for no biological, medical, environmental, or agricultural study is complete unless it takes microorganisms into consideration. Should your interests lie outside of science, then this course will still prepare you to deal more knowledgeably with certain issues and problems that affect you directly. You will learn when to take certain vac- cines and antibiotics, the proper temperature at which to set a refrigerator or freezer, some ways to maintain plant health, the best way to treat a cut, and so on.

No matter what you expect from this course, the acquisition of knowledge demands your utmost commitment. Your instructor has a similar commitment to help you acquire that knowl- edge. Your text has been written to aid both you and your instructor in this joint enterprise. The purpose of this study guide is to enable you, the student, to better comprehend the text *and* to evaluate for yourself your progress in learning the subject. It may also serve as a set of study notes to allow you to set and accomplish your learning goals more easily.

How to Use the Sections of the Study Guide

Each chapter of this study guide consists of an *introduction*, an *outline*, a *summary*, and two types of *tests*.

INTRODUCTION   The introduction should be read first. It will focus your general understanding and help you to direct your study effort. As appropriate, some or all these topics will be included:

1. Rationale for inclusion of the chapter.
2. How the chapter relates to other sections of the text.
3. The main emphasis of the chapter.
4. A preview of the information contained in the chapter.
5. Why it is important for you to know the information.
6. What you should get out of the chapter.

EXPANDED OUTLINE   This section serves two purposes. The first is as a study framework and organizational guide. In the beginning of each chapter of your text, there is an outline of the major topics. (In the study guide, these are designated with roman numerals.) The study guide outline includes also subtopics (capital letters) and the key points within each subtopic (arabic numerals). As you scan this outline, you can quickly see the overall pattern of the subject matter and the material that is most likely to require your greatest concentration.

The second function of the expanded outline is to provide you with a set of study notes. (You will notice that the expanded outline has been *written* as a set of notes. That is, the information outlined is presented in the form of complete sentences, single phrases, basic definitions, lists of characteristics, one-word headings, and even tables.) As you read it, you should constantly ask yourself questions. Some likely questions might be: What is the meaning of this word? How does this fact relate to that fact? Are there any valid generalizations I can make from this information?

SUMMARY   After you have read the previous sections you should read the summary. It contains the main concepts described in the text. Often, where appropriate, the summary is combined with the expanded outline (small letters, small roman numerals). This combination format then turns into a highly abbreviated form of the text to enable you to quickly review any chapter. Key figures and tables (mostly from the text) are included in these combined sections. Figures and tables from the text are numbered as in the text, while new figures are lettered. (For example, Fig. 10-1 in this guide is Fig. 10-1 in the text. But Fig. 10-A is found only in this guide.)

In several instances, the summary includes somewhat more detailed discussion of some material and/or philosophy. Where this is done, it is because it is felt that explanations of a few key examples will lead to better comprehension of all information.

PROGRAMMED SELF-TEST   This should be taken immediately after reading the text and the previous portions of the study guide. Its purposes are:

1. To enable you to evaluate your comprehension of the material.
2. To reinforce your mastery of technical words, terms, and concepts.

Therefore, the required information is somewhat detailed. The format is such that if you miss several questions in any section you can easily find the corresponding portion of the text and reread it to remedy any weaknesses.

To test yourself on the chapter take the Programmed Self-Test. The correct answer to any question is located to the right and opposite the next question (i.e., the answer to Question 4 will be found to the right of Question 5). Therefore, take a piece of paper or cardboard and place it under the question. Write your answer to the question in the blank. As you shift the paper down to begin the next question, the correct answer will appear to the right. Usually one word per blank will suffice, though two and sometimes three may be necessary. Don't guess the answer by the number of blanks! Try to be as precise as possible. If you plan to look at the printed answer before fully attempting the question—*DON'T*. You will be cheating yourself out of valuable information: what you know and what you don't know. Sometimes you may write a synonym of the correct answer or an equally precise correct answer. That is fine, but a vague answer is unacceptable. Remember, while you are the one who will judge your performance in this study guide, the results will eventually show up on the exams you take. And someone else will be marking them!

MULTIPLE-CHOICE TEST   These questions can be answered days after you have assimilated your instructor's lecture, read the text, and reinforced the information using the study guide. The multiple-choice test will help prepare you for any objective test. It will help you also diagnose your own understanding of the material. Essay and thought-provoking questions are presented at the end of each chapter of your text. Therefore, they are not duplicated in this study guide. However, you should write out answers to these subjective questions as well.

Once you can recall most of the terminology and detail (Programmed Self-Test), correctly answer many of the objective questions, and integrate the material and theory (essay test), you will rightly be confident of your mastery of microbiology. One sure road to success and the pride and excitement that comes with it is to follow a study procedure like that suggested below.

GENERAL STUDY METHODS   The assigned portion of the text should be read *before* each corresponding lecture. An initial glance at either the text outline or the expanded outline of this study guide will provide you with an overview and mentally prepare you for the task ahead. After reading the text, read the corresponding chapter of the study guide. This will enable you to highlight key information, reinforce what you have learned, and evaluate your own degree of comprehension.

When you attend class, take accurate notes. As soon as possible after class, rewrite your notes. As you rewrite your notes, again consult the text and study guide to help you to organize, fill in gaps, crystallize your thoughts, and expand your knowledge. Such rewriting (which is itself a memory aid) will further reinforce your learning and provide the most accurate and complete set of notes. If you find you do not understand any information, the time to seek assistance is during this process and not just prior to exams. It requires far less effort to assimilate knowledge when it has recently been presented than after a period of time has elapsed.

If you follow this procedure, your examination study will actually be a review, not a desperate attempt to organize, assimilate, relate, and understand the material in an impossibly short time. The suggested program of study will lead to better grades because you will know more, because the information will become a part of you and you will think *in* microbiology and not *of* microbiology.

Ronald M. Weiner

STUDY GUIDE TO ACCOMPANY
MICROBIOLOGY
PELCZAR, REID, AND CHAN

Chapter 1
The Scope of Microbiology

INTRODUCTION: The discipline of microbiology is introduced. Because the subject is ordinarily not emphasized in precollege curricula and because microorganisms are not readily "visible," as are other biological entities, this may be an entirely new dimension of knowledge for you. This chapter offers a glimpse into that dimension. As you read you should begin to think in the language of microbiology and become aware that unseen microorganisms interact in all spheres of nature and influence the human condition considerably.

Expanded Outline

I. Microbiology and Biology.
   A. Microorganisms as biological models.
      1. Microorganisms are much like other forms of life. Similar physiological, genetic, and biochemical characteristics.
      2. They are relatively easy to grow and handle.
   B. Microorganisms as uniquely important entities.
      1. Diverse and ubiquitous, and play useful or harmful roles.

II. The Place of Microorganisms in the Living World (Introduction to Taxonomy)
   A. Microbes cannot be conveniently grouped with either plants or animals.
   B. Eucaryotic and procaryotic cells.
      1. Eucaryotic microorganisms (higher protists) includes protozoa, fungi, and algae.
      2. Procaryotic microorganisms (lower protists) include bacteria and blue-green algae (often referred to now as blue-green bacteria).
   C. Whittaker's five-kingdom concept.
      1. Monera (includes procaryotes)—lack ingestive mode of nutrition.
      2. Protista—unicellular eucaryotic microorganisms.
      3. Plantae—multicellular green plants and higher algae.
      4. Animalia—multicellular animals.
      5. Fungi—multinucleate higher fungi.

      D.   Bergey's Manual of Determinative Bacteriology, 8th ed.
         1.   Standard reference for bacterial taxonomy.
         2.   Kingdom Procaryotae—two divisions: blue-green algae; bacteria.

III.   Groups of Microorganisms.
      A.   Algae.
         1.   Unicellular: aggregates of undifferentiated cells or specialized multicellular forms.
         2.   All have chlorophyll and are capable of photosynthesis.
      B.   Bacteria.
         1.   Unicellular or simple associations of similar cells; procaryotic
      C.   Fungi.
         1.   Usually multicellular but all relatively undifferentiated; eucaryotic.
         2.   No chlorophyll, no photosynthesis.
      D.   Protozoa.
         1.   Single-celled eucaryotic protists.
      E.   Viruses
         1.   Acellular.

IV.   Distribution of Microorganisms in Nature.
      A.   Basically found everywhere, including other forms of life and unique habitats (i.e., they are ubiquitous).

V.   Applied Areas of Microbiology (Some subdisciplines).
      A.   Medical—disease-producing microorganisms and prevention and control of disease (e.g., chemotherapy, immunization, epidemiology, diagnostic procedures).
      B.   Aquatic—marine, estuarine, and freshwater microorganisms.
      C.   Domestic water and sewage—fresh and waste-water treatment.
      D.   Air.
      E.   Milk—associated with food and dairy industry.
      F.   Food—safe storage, preservation, and production of edible products.
      G.   Soil—fertility and crop health.
      H.   Industrial—production of medicines, food supplements, alcoholic beverages, enzymes, organic acids.
      I.   Insects—control of insects and insect vectors (i.e., disease carriers).
      J.   Space (exobiology)—occurrence of microorganisms and requirements for maintaining them in space vehicles and extraterrestrial environments.
      K.   Geochemical transformations—e.g., formation of coal, petroleum.

VI.   Microbiology and the Origin of Life.
      A.   Process: Inorganic compounds $\longrightarrow$ organic compounds

           "life" $\longleftarrow$ protein $\longleftarrow$ polypeptides $\longleftarrow$ peptides $\longleftarrow$ amino acids
      B.   Mediated by ultraviolet light, electrical discharge, and/or high temperature.

Summary

MICROBIOLOGY AND BIOLOGY: In some respects, microorganisms are much like any other forms of life, and what is found to be true of microorganisms is often true of other life forms.

Therefore, because microorganisms are relatively easy to manipulate in the laboratory, it is often convenient to use them to study basic life processes. Microorganisms are also extremely important biological entities in any study of communicable disease, the environment, food manufacture, and numerous other subjects. The importance of microorganisms cannot be overestimated.

THE PLACE OF MICROORGANISMS IN THE LIVING WORLD: It is difficult to classify microorganisms as either animals or plants. Therefore, several other systematic schemes have been suggested. One such scheme places all microorganisms in the kingdom Protista. According to this scheme, the higher protista include the eucaryotic microorganisms (algae, fungi, and protozoa), the lower protista include the procaryotic microorganisms (bacteria and blue-green algae), the viruses, being acellular, are left out of this scheme of organization. An alternative scheme of classification, Whittaker's five-kingdom concept, is also discussed in the text (Fig. 1-5).

GROUPS OF MICROORGANISMS: Algae, fungi, protozoa, bacteria, blue-green "algae" (or bacteria), and viruses are all considered to be microorganisms. Each group of organisms has distinguishing characteristics that make it unique among all life forms.

AREAS OF MICROBIOLOGY: Microbiology, though a subdiscipline of biology, has many disciplines of its own. One can specialize in the study of a certain group of microorganisms (e.g., protozoology or virology), or in what microorganisms do to people (medical microbiology), or what they do for people (industrial microbiology), or in a specific environmental niche (marine microbiology), or in any one of a number of subspecialties.

Programmed Self-Test

Do not begin this self-test before reading the corresponding chapter in the text.

MICROBIOLOGY AND BIOLOGY (Text pages 4 to 6)

Microorganisms can conveniently be grown in _____.	
Some rapidly multiplying bacteria go through almost _____ generations in a 24-h period.	test tubes *or* flasks
Yeasts utilize glucose in essentially the same manner as _____ cells.	100
Bacteria, in particular, are able to utilize a great variety of chemical substances as their energy source, substances ranging from simple _____ to complex _____.	mammalian
Viruses that grow and reproduce in bacteria are called _____.	inorganic materials; organic substrates

THE PLACE OF MICROORGANISMS IN THE LIVING WORLD (Text pages 6 to 10)

Haeckel placed microorganisms into a new kingdom called _____.	bacteriophages
Whittaker's five-kingdom scheme of classification is based on three levels of _____ as well as three modes of _____.	Protista
Procaryotes are included in Whittaker's kingdom _____; they lack the _____ mode of nutrition.	cellular organization; nutrition
Bergey's Manual calls the kingdom Monera _____ which is divided into _____ division(s).	Monera; ingestive

GROUPS AND DISTRIBUTION OF MICROORGANISMS (Text pages 10 to 13)

Unlike other protista, all algae cells contain _____.	procaryotae; two
True fungi are composed of filaments and masses of cells which make up the "body," known as a _____.	chlorophyll
Protozoa are single-celled _____ protists.	mycelium
Viruses can be cultivated only in _____.	eucaryotic
Microorganisms can be found _____.	living cells

AREAS OF MICROBIOLOGY (Text pages 13 to 17)

Mycology is a branch of microbiology that deals with _____.	nearly everywhere
Some microorganisms are used in the production of _____, _____, and other dairy products.	fungi
Microorganisms grow profusely where they synthesize proteins and vitamins and digest _____.	cheese; buttermilk
	cellulose

Multiple-Choice Test

Underline the correct answer.

1. The ability to react to changes in the environment is termed: (a) reproduction; (b) ingestion; (c) irritability; (d) sensitivity.

2. Of the following types of organism, which do not have a membrane surrounding the DNA? (a) Algae; (b) bacteria; (c) fungi; (d) protozoa.

3. A microorganism that does not have a cellular structure is a: (a) yeast; (b) protozoa; (c) blue-green algae; (d) virus.

4. "The mechanisms by which organisms (or their cells) utilize energy are _____ throughout the biological world." (a) Highly varied; (b) fundamentally the same; (c) unknown.

5. Which of the following are *not* included among the higher protists? (a) Bacteria; (b) fungi; (c) protozoa; (d) algae.

6. In Whittaker's five-kingdom system, bacteria are placed in the kingdom: (a) Protista; (b) Fungi; (c) Monera; (d) Plantae.

7. Algae are most commonly found in: (a) humans; (b) the desert; (c) the air; (d) aquatic environments.

8. Which is the largest molecule? (a) Polypeptide; (b) protein; (c) peptide.

Answers: 1. (c); 2. (b); 3. (d); 4. (b); 5. (a); 6. (c); 7. (d); 8. (b).

Chapter 2
The Evolution of Microbiology

INTRODUCTION: Discoveries which had a great impact on microbiology are discussed. While this chapter could be subtitled "A Brief History of Microbiology," it could also be called "The Curiosity of the Human Mind." After you read it, you will better appreciate the circumstances that combine with genius to yield the precious commodity called knowledge.

Expanded Outline

For this chapter, the outline is presented as a synoptic table of important discoveries and principles.

Topic	Scientist(s)	Theory of Discovery	Century
The Micro-scope	Aristotle	Postulated cellular structure of living things	4th B.C.
	Bacon	Postulated disease caused by invisible living creatures	13th
	Fracastoro of Verona	Postulated disease caused by invisible living creatures	16th
	Plenciz	Different germs cause different diseases	Mid 18th
	Kircher	"Invisible worms" in decaying bodies, etc.	Mid 17th
	Hooke	Saw and described cells	Mid 17th
	Leeuwenhoek	Built microscopes; saw and described bacteria	Mid 17th
Spontaneous Generation vs. Biogenesis	Aristotle	Espoused spontaneous generation theory	4th B.C.
	Redi	Experiments to show flies come from maggots (biogenesis)	17th
	Needham	Experiments erroneously showed bacteria were spontaneously generated	Mid 17th
	Spallanzani	Experiments that attempted to prove Needham wrong. Boiled contents of flask	Later 18th
	Schulze	Experiments disprove spontaneous genera-tion—air through acid	Early 19th
	Schwann	Experiments disprove spontaneous gener-ation—air through red hot tubes	Early 19th

Topic	Scientist(s)	Theory or Discovery	Century
Spontaneous Generation vs. Biogenesis (continued)	Shroder and von Dusch	Experiments disprove spontaneous generation—air through cotton	Mid 19th
	Pouchet	Still adhered to theory of spontaneous generation	Mid 19th
	Pasteur	Experiments once and for all disprove spontaneous generation—air through undulating gooseneck opening	Mid 19th
	Tyndall	Demonstrated dust carries germs	Later
Germ Theory of Disease	Holmes	Puerperal fever caused by germs	Late 19th
	Semmelweis	Antiseptics to reduce obstetrical mortality	Late 19th
	Pasteur	Heat to "remove" microbes; isolated parasite of silkworm disease	Late 19th
	Koch	Proved specific bateria cause specific disease, e.g., anthrax, tuberculosis	Late 19th
Pure-Culture Concept	Lister	Obtained first pure culture by serial dilution	Late 19th
	Koch	Developed solid culture medium	Late 19th
	Winogradsky	Found that some organisms are better studied in mixed culture	Late 19th
Immunization	Pasteur	"Accidently" stumbled onto immunization with attenuated organisms; developed rabies vaccine	
	Jenner	Developed smallpox vaccine	Late 18th
Widening Horizens	Klebs and Loeffer	Discovered diphtheria bacillus	Turn of the 20th
	von Behring and Kitasato	Antitoxins against diphtheria and Tetanus	
Applied Micro-biology	Metchnikoff	Discovered phagocytosis	
	Ehrlich	Immunity from soluble substances in blood; chemotherapy	
	Lister	Aseptic surgical technique	
	Reed	Yellow fever transmitted by mosquito vector	
	Hellriegel and Wilfarth	Symbiotic relationship between bacteria and legumes	
	Beijerinck	Free-living N-fixing bacteria	
	Hansen	Pure cultures of organisms in vinegar manufacture (industrial starter cultures)	
	Burrill	Fireblight in pears caused by bacterium	
	Ivanowski	Viral nature of some plant diseases	
Widening Horizons: Molecular Biology	Enders, Robbins, Weller	Cultured polio virus	20th
	Salk, Cox, Koprowski, Sabin	Polio vaccines	
	Lippman and Krebs	Physiology and metabolism	
	Lederberg, Beadle, and Tatum	Action of the genetic code	
	Avery, et al.	Bacterial transformation; evidence that DNA is carrier of genetic code	
	Ochoa and Kornberg	Synthesized RNA and DNA	
	Holly	Structure of tRNA	
	Khorana	Genetic code triplet	
	Nirenberg	Deciphered genetic code	

Topic	Scientist(s)	Theory or Discovery	Century
Widening Horizons:	Delbruck, Hershey and Luria	Action of bacteriophages	20th
Molecular Biology (continued)	Edelman and Porter	Chemical structure of antibodies	
	Claude, Bordet, Palade, and deDuve	Techniques and discoveries in tissue culture	
	Dulbecco, Temin, and Baltimore	"Reverse transcriptase" as it relates to cancer viruses	

Summary

Microbiology became a science after the invention of the first microscopes and the observations of single-celled organisms in the mid-seventeenth century. During the seventeenth, eighteenth, and nineteenth centuries, efforts were made to prove or disprove the idea that organisms, particularly invisible ones, are generated from nonliving matter. After Needham, using septic technique, showed showed that broths could give rise to living matter, it took experiments conducted over a span of two centuries to show that cells come from preexisting cells. At first broths were heated; then, so as not to destroy the "vital force," air that had been "sterilized" by acid, by heat, by cotton filtration was allowed to come in contact with broths. Finally, in the 1860s, Pasteur settled the issue in favor of biogenesis. Also in this era, Pasteur, Koch, and others demonstrated that specific microorganisms cause specific diseases. Culture techniques were invented, vaccines were prepared; and with these events, microbiology blossomed into an important theoretical and applied science. The The food industry began to use pure-culture microorganisms, and diseases of plants and animals were studied and often controlled. In the 1960s, a century after Pasteur's experiments on biogenesis, the genetic code was broken as microorganisms yielded their secrets in a series of landmark investigations.

Programmed Self-Test

Do not begin this self-test before reading the corresponding chapter in the text.

THE MICROSCOPE (Text pages 21 to 34)

The first accurate descriptions of observations of bacteria and protozoa were written by _____.	
Leeuwenhoek's microscopes were capable of magnifications up to _____.	Antony van Leeuwenhoek
Leeuwenhoek called free-living protozoa _____.	200X to 300X

SPONTANEOUS GENERATION VS. BIOGENESIS (Text pages 24 to 26)

Francesco Redi showed that _____ could not be spontaneously generated from meat.	animalcules
Even after Schroder and von Dusch disproved Needham's data and the theory of spontaneous generation, _____ published a paper proving its occurrence.	maggots
In Pasteur's experiment, nutrient solutions were heated in the flask; air, _____ and _____, could pass in or out.	Pouchet

GERM THEORY OF DISEASE (Text pages 26 to 28)

That "germs" cause disease was postulated by _____ _____ and by _____ even before proof came from experiments by Koch and Pasteur.	untreated; unfiltered
Koch proved, for the first time, that a bacterium was the cause of an animal disease. This disease was _____.	Fracastoro of Verona; Plenciz of Vienna
Pasteur found that the problem of proper fruit fermentation involved _____, while the silkworm disease, pepbrine, was caused by a _____.	anthrax

PURE-CULTURE CONCEPT (Text pages 28 to 29)

In purifying cultures, the development of _____ _____ may be considered "one of Koch's greatest contributions."	yeasts; protozoan
Joseph Lister obtained the first pure culture of a bacterium and named the organism _____.	solid culture media

IMMUNIZATION (Text pages 29 to 31)

Pasteur accidentally used attenuated organisms responsible for _____.	*Bacterium lactus*

The first vaccine developed, by Jenner, protected people from _____.	chicken cholera
Pasteur developed a vaccine to protect animals and people against _____.	smallpox

WIDENING HORIZONS (Text pages 31 to 37)

Emil von Behring and Shibasaburo Kitasato prepared antitoxins against _____and_____.	rabies
Elie Metchnikoff, observing leucocytes (white blood cells), described an important line of defense against infection called _____.	diphtheria; tetanus (lockjaw)
Paul Ehrlich explained _____on the basis of soluble substances in the blood and developed the first _____ _____ agent.	phagocytosis
Emil Christian Hansen opened the way to the study of _____.	immunity; chemotherapeutic
The construction of the Panama Canal was facilitated by the conquest of the disease _____.	industrial fermentation
The _____ was the first virus to be purified (crystalized).	yellow fever
In 1944, Avery et al demonstrated in transformation experiments with pneumococcus that _____ _____,	tobacco mosaic virus
Much of the genetic code was deciphered by _____, while the chemical structure of tRNA was determined by _____.	DNA carries genetic material
RNA tumor viruses may contain an enzyme that can make a copy of _____ from _____.	Nirenberg; Holly
	DNA; RNA

Multiple-Choice Test

Underline the correct answer.

1. "I discovered, in a tiny drop of water, incredibly many very little animalcules, and these of diverse sorts and sizes. They moved with bendings, as an eel always swims with its head in front, and never tail first, yet these animalcules swam as well backwards as forwards, though their motion was very slow." These words were written by: (a) Galileo; (b) Salk; (c) Aristotle; (d) Leeuwenhoek.

2. Who opposed the theory of biogenesis? (a) Redi; (b) Spallanzani; (c) Pouchet; (d) Pasteur.

3. The controversy of spontaneous generation vs. biogenesis may have led to important practical developments involving: (a) virus propagation; (b) aseptic culture technique; (c) genetic engineering; (d) the invention of the microscope.

4. These words may have signalled the death knell of _____. "There is no condition known today in which you can affirm that microscopic beings come into the world without germs, without parents like themselves. They who allege it have been the sport of illusions, of illmade experiments, vitiated by errors which they have not been able to perceive and have not known how to avoid." (a) The theory of spontaneous generation; (b) the germ theory of disease; (c) Koch's postulates; (d) the pure-culture concept.

5. Which statement is not one of Koch's postulates? (a) A specific organism can always be found in association with a given disease. (b) The organism can be isolated and grown in pure culture in the laboratory. (c) The pure culture will produce the disease when inoculated into a susceptible animal. (d) It is possible to recover the organism in pure culture from the experimentally infected animal. (e) Death of the experimentally infected animal is proof that the agent has caused the disease.

6. Winogradsky, Hellriegel, Wilfarth, and Beijerinch all worked on: (a) plant viruses; (b) eradication of yellow fever; (c) bacteriology of plants and the nitrogen cycle; (d) the genetic code.

7. An enzyme that could make DNA from an RNA template was found in a: (a) bacterium; (b) protozoa; (c) white blood cell; (d) virus.

Answers: 1. (d); 2. (c); 3. (b); 4. (a); 5. (e); 6. (c); 7. (d).

Chapter 3

Characterization and Classification of Microorganisms

INTRODUCTION: When knowledge is organized, learning is facilitated; when organisms are clearly characterized and classified, their identities, roles, and niches become more readily apparent. Generalizations from one organism (or group of organisms) to another then becomes possible, and patterns of life become clearer. In this chapter the characteristics, methods, and rationale of microbial taxonomy are introduced. Familiarity with these aspects of microbiology is essential if you are to master later topics.

Expanded Outline

I. Major Characteristics of Microorganisms
    A. Cultural characteristics—nutritional and physical requirements for growth; specifically the culture medium, or material and nutrients in (on) which microorganisms are grown in the lab.
    B. Microscopic characteristics—morphology. Cell size arrangement and other distinguishing traits.
    C. Metabolic (biochemical) characteristics—specific chemical reactions to each microorganism. Usually involves an examination of which nutrients are used and what end-products are produced.
    D. Chemical characteristics—identification of major chemical components comprised in the cell. For example, does a given virus contain RNA or does it instead contain DNA?
    E. Antigenic characteristics—serological relationships among organisms. As you will learn in Chap. 27, this involves specific antibodies that react with specific macromolecular cell components (antigens).
    F. Genetic characteristics—analysis of base composition (% G + C) and base sequences of DNA ("hybridization").

II. Microbial Taxonomy, Nomenclature, and Classification.
    A. Taxonomy—"systematic" arrangement of organisms into groups, or *taxa*.
        1. Classification—The orderly arrangement of units into groups.

2. Nomenclature—naming of the classified units.
3. Identification—comparison of the characteristics of "unknown" units to those of known units.
B. Nomenclature—uniform rules of naming.
1. Principles—each distinct kind of organism is classified as a species and designated by a scientific, binomial name to provide an international label.
2. Scientific names of bacteria—species are given two-word names which are *italicized*.
   a. Genus (Latin or Greek)—first letter capitalized.
   b. Species—not capitalized and usually descriptive of the bacterium.
3. Common names of bacteria—some bacteria may also have a common name (e.g., *Neisseria gonorrhoeae* may be called gonococcus).
C. Taxonomic categories.

TAXON	DEGREE OF RELATEDNESS
Species	Organisms of one and the same kind
Genus	A group of related species
Tribe	A group of related genera
Family	A group of related tribes or genera
Order	A group of related families
Division or class	A group of related orders
Phylum	A group of related classes or divisions
Kingdom	A group of related phyla

D. Classification schemes—these may be artificial, designed solely to identify the organism, or phylogenetic, with organisms arranged according to supposed evolutionary relationships. As evolutionary relationships are extremely difficult to determine in microbiology, artificial schemes are increasingly used.
1. Skerman key—a series of yes-no questions about the characteristics of an organism which results in the generic identification of that organism.
2. Adansonian classification
   a. Compare as many characteristics of each organism as possible.
   b. Each characteristic is given equal weighting.
   c. The more characteristics common to two organisms, the more related are the organisms.

Summary

MAJOR CHARACTERISTICS OF ORGANISMS: Like all things, microorganisms are identified on the basis of distinguishing characteristics. In some cases, a few traits may be sufficient, but in many instances numerous traits are required for identification. Microorganisms differ with respect to growth requirements and growth patterns (cultural characteristics), the way their cells look (morphological characteristics), their biochemistry (metabolic characteristics), the chemical composition of their substance, the antigens they possess, and the base sequences in their genetic code. Differences in the genetic code produce differences among organisms. Therefore, scrutiny of the genome can provide a direct "fingerprint" of each organism. Some information can be gained by examining the ratio of two molecules in the genetic code, guanosine (G) and cytosine (C), to all four bases that appear in DNA (adenine + thymine + G + C). This is called *DNA base composition,* and is routinely used in taxonomic study. Organisms that have different base ratios must be different; however, two different organisms can have identical base ratios. Therefore an even more sensitive test is required, in which the order of bases in the genome of any one organism is compared with the order of bases in the genome of another organism (DNA hybridization). Identical organisms have exactly the same base-sequence order; unrelated organisms will differ in at least some of their base sequences. The degree of similarity between base sequences indicates the degree of relatedness between the two organisms.

MICROBIAL TAXONOMY, NOMENCLATURE, AND CLASSIFICATION: Taxonomy involves the identification of organisms, their nomenclature (orderly naming), and their classification into larger related groups (see expanded outline). Uniquely different organisms are called *species,* and a group of closely related species are said to belong to the same *genus.* Thus, bacteria are given two names, e.g., *Staphylococcus* (genus) *aureus* (species). Note that the genus is capitalized while the species begins with a lower-case letter, and that both are italicized. The species name is generally descriptive of the organism (in this example, *aureus* means "yellow"). To be internationally consistent, Latin or Greek words are used.

It is difficult to classify microorganisms according to their evolutionary relatedness (as is usually done in the case of animals and plants). Therefore artificial classification schemes are most often employed. Though microbial taxonomy is still in a state of flux, two such schemes are most often used. The Skerman key (text p. 49) is used in *Bergey's Manual of Determinative Bacteriology,* while adansonian classification is the basis for numerical taxonomy. In numerical taxonomy, all characteristics are given about equal weight and many characteristics are used (often over 300). The question is then asked, how many traits does organism *A* have in common with organisms *B, C, D,* etc.? If all characteristics are identical, the organisms are considered identical (i.e., of the same species). Organisms sharing fewer common traits are considered to be more distantly related. If more than 30 percent of the traits are different, the organisms are usually considered to be entirely unrelated.

Programmed Self-Test

Do not begin this self-test before reading the corresponding chapter in the text.

MAJOR CHARACTERISTICS OF MICROORGANISMS (Text pages 41 to 44)

The material on or in which microorganisms are grown in the
laboratory is called a _____.

Rickettsias and viruses only multiply in _____.   culture medium

---

Light microscopes can provide magnifications up to approximately _____ diameters.	living cells
One μm is equivalent to _____ in.	1,000
A major distinction among viruses is made on the basis of _____.	0.0000004
The DNA base composition is calculated from the formula _____.	the kind of nucleic acid they possess
The % G + C of different species of bacteria ranges from _____.	$\dfrac{G + C}{A + T + G + C} \times 100$ $= \% \, G + C$

MICROBIAL TAXONOMY, NOMENCLATURE, AND CLASSIFICATION (Text pages 44 to 50)

Have most of the existing species of protozoa been described and classified? _____	23 to 75
The term taxonomy has sometimes been used interchangeably with the term _____.	No
Each distinct kind of organism is called a _____.	systematics
Bacillus is a Latin word meaning _____.	species
Sarcina means _____.	small rod
The common name of *Neisseria gonorrhoeae* is _____.	packet *or* bundle
The Skerman classification scheme appears in _____ _____.	gonococcus
A classification scheme in which the overall similarity of two organisms is a function of the proportion of features (equally weighted) they have in common was developed by _____.	*Bergey's Manual*
	Adanson

Multiple-Choice Test

Underline the correct answer.

1. A culture that consists of a single kind of microorganism (one living species), regardless of the number of individuals, in an environment free of other living organisms is technically called: (a) an axenic culture; (b) a pure culture; (c) a mixed culture; (d) a tissue culture.

2. The experimental procedure in which single strands of DNA from two bacterial species are compared with respect to base sequences is called: (a) antigenic characterization; (b) hybridization; (c) taxonomy; (d) numerical taxonomy.

3. Which taxon encompasses the broadest diversity of organisms? (a) Species; (b) class; (c) genus; (d) tribe.

4. The Skerman classification scheme: (a) evolved from adansonian classification; (b) is a phylogenetic scheme; (c) is utilitarian; (d) Comprises 73 orders of bacteria.

5. Two hundred characteristics of organisms A and B are identified. One hundred and fifty of them are found to be common to both organisms. The remainder differ. Based on adansonian principles, what is the percent similarity between the two organisms? (a) 100; (b) 50; (c) 25; (d) 75.

6. In which genus of bacteria has the number of species increased in the period between 1948–1974? (a) *Bacillus;* (b) *Pseudomonas;* (c) *Escherichia;* (d) *Streptomyces.*

Answers: 1. (a); 2. (b); 3. (b); 4. (c); 5. (d); 6. (d).

Chapter 4

The Microscopic Observation of Microorganisms

INTRODUCTION: As unicellular microorganisms are invisible to the naked eye, prior to the invention of the microscope their existence was postulated but never proven. Therefore in one, sense, microbiology was born when the brightfield microscope was "born" and virology blossomed when the electron microscope was invented. This chapter introduces you to these essential microbiological tools. You should become familiar with their applications, capabilities, and associated methodology (e.g., staining).

Expanded Outline

I. Microscopes and Microscopy.
   A. Systems based on optical lenses (light microscopes).
      1. Brightfield microscopy—field brightly lighted; objects appear darker. Magnification: X 1000.
         a. Resolving power—ability to distinguish two adjacent points as distinct and separate.

$$\text{R. P.} = \frac{\lambda}{NA_{obj} + NA_{cond}}$$

         b. Use of oil-immersion objective.
      2. Dark-field microscopy—dark background against which objects are brilliantly illuminated. Unlike most brightfield microscopy in that staining is not required.
      3. Ultraviolet microscopy—resolving power about twice as great as brightfield.
      4. Fluorescence microscopy—use of ultraviolet microscope and fluorescent dyes. An important example in microbiology is immunofluorescence, or the fluorescent-antibody technique, which involves the use of a fluorescent dye, chemically attached to an antibody (discussed in Chap. 27).
      5. Phase-contrast microscopy—widely used in study of living cells because staining is unnecessary. Works on principle of differing refractive indices between cells, cell parts, and surrounding media.

B. Systems based on magnets which focus electron beams.
1. Transmission electron microscopy—resolving power 100 times that of light microscope, but the specimen cannot be viewed live.
   a. Shadow casting—deposit of thin metal layer produces topographical representation of surface of specimen.
   b. Ultrathin sectioning.
   c. Negative staining—electron-dense material (e.g., phosphotungstic acid) outlines object.
   d. Freeze etching—specimen sectioned while frozen. Carbon replicas of exposed surfaces reveal structures.
   e. Localization of cell constituents—use of ferritin-labeled antibody.
   f. Localization of enzymes—deposit of small, dense particles in the tissue as the end product of controlled chemical reaction. Allows correlation of fine structure and function.
   g. Autoradiography—chemical constituents of tissues can be localized by noting the position of radioactive material incorporated in the specimen.
2. Scanning electron microscoscopy (SEM)—has lower resolution than transmission electron microscopy, but provides "three-dimensional images."

II. Preparations for Light-Microscopic Examination
A. Wet-mount and hanging-drop techniques—examination of living organisms suspended in fluid. Used to study morphology, motility, cytological changes, cell inclusion bodies.
B. Fixed stained smears—observation of morphological characteristics of bacteria and rickettsias.
1. Microbiological stains—acid dyes (negative charge) for staining basic cell components; basic dyes (positive charge) for staining acidic cell components; neutral dyes.
   a. Simple staining—one dye used. Shows size, shape, and arrangement of cells.
   b. Differential staining—more than one reagent used to visualize differences between bacterial cells or parts of a bacterial cell.
      i. Gram staining—categorizes bacteria into one of two groups. *Gram-positive* cells retain crystal violet after being washed with alcohol, and *gram-negative* cells lose the crystal violet, are counterstained by safranin, and hence appear red. Gram-staining differences among species may be due to differences in cell-wall composition and structure.
      ii. Acid-fast staining—many Mycobacteria differ from other cells in that they are *acid-fast,* which means that they retain carbolfuchsin after being washed with acid alcohol.
      iii. Giemsa staining—useful for demonstrating rickettsias, protozoa in blood, and nuclear material.
      iv. Staining to reveal cell structure—structures include flagella, capsules, nuclear materials, granules, and endospores.
   c. Negative staining—as under a dark-field microscope, organisms so stained appear light against a darker background. Useful for study of morphology without harsh cell treatment. Two such stains commonly used are india ink and nigrosine.

Summary

There are a wide variety of microscopes that facilitate the study of microorganisms. Perhaps the most commonly used is the brightfield microscope which allows one to see gross morphological features of all microorganisms except viruses. However, to increase contrasts, and therefore practical resolution, the specimens must be stained. A great variety of simple, differential and negative staining procedures have been devised to allow one to see cells and parts of cells and to differentiate among groups of organisms. Many of these staining techniques kill the cells and may even cause distortion. Therefore, to observe cells without resorting to stains, the dark-field microscope may be used, and to observe some cell structures phase-contrast microscopes are helpful. Fluorescence microscopy is a powerful technique which can be used to identify organisms and parts of cells and has other numerous applications as well. To resolve objects smaller than about 0.2 μm (viruses and cell fine structure) requires electron microscopes. Unfortunately, however, only dead, and thus potentially distorted, specimens may be viewed.

Programmed Self-Test

Do not begin this self-test before reading corresponding chapter in the text.

MICROSCOPES AND MICROSCOPY (Text pages 53 to 67)

The ability to distinguish two adjacent points as distinct and separate is termed _____.	
Air has a refractive index of _____.	resolving power
Dark-field microscopy is particularly valuable for the examination of _____.	1
Ultraviolet microscopes are capable of about _____ greater resolution than that obtainable with the conventional light microscope.	unstained microorganisms
The phenomenon whereby substances absorb the energy of ultraviolet waves and emit it as visible waves of greater length is called _____.	two times
Structures or units in a cell which have a similar refractive index and are not, therefore, discernible by light microscopy can be distinguished by _____ microscopy.	fluorescence

The microscope that is capable of giving the best resolving power is the _____.	phase-contrast
A cytochemical method, utilizing the electron microscope, in which the location of the chemical constituents of tissues is studied by recording the position of radioactive material incorporated in the specimen is called _____.	transmission electron microscope

PREPARATIONS FOR LIGHT-MICROSCOPIC EXAMINATION (Text pages 67 to 72)

In the examination of exudates suspected of containing the spirochete that causes syphilis, the wet preparations are often examined by _____ microscopy.	autoradiography
An acid, or anionic, dye generally stains _____ cell components.	dark-field
The coloration of bacteria by applying a *single* solution of stain to a fixed smear is termed _____.	basic
After the gram-stain procedure, gram-negative bacteria appear _____.	simple staining
Gram-positive bacteria retain the dye _____ after washing with ethanol.	red
The most plausible explanations of the mechanism of the gram reaction implicate the structure and composition of the _____.	crystal violet
In the gram reaction, a complex is formed between _____ _____ and _____.	cell wall
Protoplasts are cells with "all" _____ removed.	crystal violet; iodine
Acid-fast bacteria belong to the genus _____.	cell-wall material
Two reagents used for negative staining are _____ and _____.	*Mycobacterium*
	india ink; nigrosine

Multiple-Choice Test

Underline the correct answer.

1. What is the best resolution that can be obtained with a microscope that has a condenser with a numerical aperature of 1.3, an objective lens with a numerical aperture of 1.4, and a light source with a wavelength of 0.55 μm (micrometers)? (a) 2 μm; (b) 0.1 μm; (c) 203 nm (nanometers); (d) 0.87 μm.

2. If the microscope described above had its condenser removed or was improperly focused, what would be its best resolution? (a) 0.50 μm; (b) the resolution would remain the same; (c) 0.39 μm; (d) 0.01 μm.

3. Of the following microscopes, which one can resolve the smallest objects? (a) Brightfield microscope; (b) ultraviolet microscope; (c) phase-contrast microscope; (d) dark-field microscope; (e) transmission electron microscope; (f) scanning electron microscope.

4. Which microscope has enough resolution to enable one to visualize bacteria? (a) Brightfield; (b) dark-field; (c) phase-contrast; (d) electron; (e) all the above.

5. A gram-negative cell: (a) usually produces powerful exotoxins; (b) holds the crystal violet–iodine (CV-I) complex when washed with 95% ethyl alcohol (ETOH); (c) releases the CV-I complex when washed with 95% ETOH; (d) weights slightly less than 1 g.

6. Gram-positive bacteria that have their cell walls removed or badly damaged stain: (a) gram-positive; (b) gram negative; (c) acid-fast; (d) the same as their species with cell walls intact.

7. Which of these techniques is not used in electron microscopy? (a) Shadow casting; (b) ultra-thin sectioning; (c) freeze etching; (d) immunofluorescence.

8. The gram-stain reaction is a _____ stain reaction. (a) Simple; (b) negative; (c) complex; (d) differential.

Answers: 1. (c); 2. (c); 3. (e); 4. (e); 5. (c); 6. (b); 7. (d); 8. (d).

Chapter 5

The Morphology
and Fine Structure
of Bacteria

INTRODUCTION: This chapter deals with the fine structure of bacterial (predominantly eubacterial) cells. In many ways this structure is similar to that found in cells of higher organisms. However, bacteria are procaryotes, and thus basic differences also exist. A knowledge of the structure of bacterial cells is important in identification, taxonomy, and numerous other facets of study. An appreciation of the differences between procaryotic and eucaryotic cells is the forerunner to understanding such applied topics as chemotherapy. Therefore, the material in this chapter is not only inherently important but, as in preceding textual material, provides the foundation upon which the practice of bacteriology rests.

Expanded Outline

I. The Size, Shape, and Arrangement of Bacterial Cells.
   A. Shape and arrangement of commonly studied bacterial cells (eubacteria).
      1. Cocci (spherical or ellipsoidal).
      2. a. Irregular masses (e.g., *Staphylococci*).
         b. Packets of fours (e.g., *Sarcina*).
         c. Pairs or longer in chains (e.g., *Pneumococci* and *Streptococci*).
      2. Bacilli (cylindrical or rodlike)
         a. Usually as single, unattached cells.
         b. Pairs (e.g., *Diplobacilli*).
         c. Chains (e.g., *Streptobacilli*).
      3. Spirilla (spiral-shaped)—unattached, individual cells.
         a. Short, incomplete spirals (e.g., *Vibrio*).
         b. Long, exhibiting series of twists.
   B. Shape and arrangement of other bacterial cells—show considerable variation. Some examples: *Saprospira* form helical filaments (length, up to 500 μm), *Caulobacter* are rod-shaped and form a stalk, *Streptomycetes* growth "mimics" that of molds.

      C.   Size of bacterial cells. Those most frequently studied measure 0.5 to 1.0 by 2.0 to
5.0 μm (average size). Largest unicellular bacteria are some spiral-shaped organisms
(e.g., *Thiospirellum*) with a diameter of 4 to 5 μm and a length of 30 to 40 μm or
longer. Smallest bacteria include some forms of the mycoplasmas, 0.1 to 0.3 μm.

  II.   Bacterial Structures.
      A.   Structures external to the cell wall.
          1. Flagella—thin, hairlike appendages, composed of protein, that function in motility.
Present on some species.
             a. Taxis response—bacterial reaction to stimuli.
          2. Pili (fimbriae)—thin, hairlike appendages that enable bacteria to adhere to surfaces.
One or more types may be found on any species. F-pili—function in conjugation;
(see Chap. 1).
          3. Capsules—one or more kinds may surround a bacterium. Composition is species-
specific, mostly some type of polypeptide or other material. Some capsules may
be protective, others a reservoir of stored food.
      B.   The cell wall—rigid structure surrounding cell that is protective and serves in cell growth
and division, as a "backbone" for flagella motion, as a "template" for cell-wall growth,
and as a receptor cite for some bacteriophages.
          1. Chemical composition and structure—backbone of *peptidoglycan*. Gram-positive
cells also have *teichoic acid* and some polysaccharide material. Gram-negative
cells also have, besides peptidoglycon, polysaccharides, protein, and *lipopoly-
saccharide* (LPS). Cell wall of gram-positive organisms is thicker than that of gram-
negative organisms.
             a. Peptidoglycan structure—Composed of acetylglucosamine (AGA), acetylmuromic
acid (AMA), and a peptide of four or five amino acids.
      C.   Structures internal to the cell wall.
          1. Protoplasts, spheroplasts—protoplasts have all cell-wall material and spheroplasts
some cell-wall material (peptidoglycan) removed by treatment with lysozyme or
penicillin. In isotonic medium, cells remain viable, but lose functions normally
associated with cell wall.
          2. The cytoplasmic (protoplasmic) membrane—thin (7.5 μm) layer, composed of pro-
tein and phospholipid, that is essential to cell viability, functioning as a permeability barrier, in active transport, and as a metabolic center.
          3. Membranous intrusions and membrane systems (mesosomes)—may function during
cell division, DNA replication and segregation, and in other vital areas.
          4. The cytoplasm—"cell soup" which includes vital structures (e.g., ribosomes), en-
zymes, and dissolved nutrients.
          5. Cytoplasmic inclusions—concentrated deposits of certain substances like volutin
(poly-meta-phosphate), poly-β-hydroxybutyric acid, starch, sulfur, or other compounds.
          6. Nuclear material—double-stranded DNA about 1.2 μm long x 20 $^{\circ}$A wide. As in
eucaryotic cells, "storehouse of the genetic code."
          7. Endospores—cells of *Bacillus* and *Clostridium* can differentiate into this
thick-walled, extremely resistant structure containing relative large amounts
of dipicolinic acid and Ca^{2+} but small concentrations of water. In this

dormant state the organism can survive adverse conditions that would kill other forms of life.

Summary

SIZE, SHAPE, AND ARRANGEMENT OF BACTERIAL CELLS: Bacterial cells are generally smaller than eucaryotic cells. The smallest bacteria (some mycoplasmal cells) are less than a micrometer (μm) long, or over 1000 times smaller than the naked eye can resolve, while the largest unicellular bacteria (some spiral organisms) are over 40 μm long. An "average"-size bacteria like *Escherichia coli* measures about 0.5 to 1.0 μm in width and 2.0 to 5.0 μm in length. Some filamentous bacteria grow over 100 μm long (one tenth of a millimeter), but their diameter is still comparatively small, about 1 μm. Because bacteria rank among the smallest organisms, their surface-area-to-volume ratio is high, which, in part, accounts for their high rates of metabolism and growth.

As a group, the Procaryotae are very diverse. Some grow in long filaments that are surrounded by a sheath (e.g., *Sphaerotilus*), others form stalks (e.g., *Caulobacter*), and some grow as a well-developed branched mycelium (e.g., *Streptomyces*). This morphological diversity is discussed further in Chaps. 13 and 14. Bacteria frequently studied in the laboratory (formerly called eubacteria) have one of three general forms: ellipsoidal, or spherical; cylindrical, or rodlike; and spiral, or helical. The first forms, cocci, grow singly, in irregular masses, in packets of four or eight, and/or in short or long chains. These organisms are in part classified by cellular arrangement. Rodlike forms, bacilli, generally occur singly but may also be found in short or long chains. Spiral-shaped bacteria include those that look like small commas (vibrios) and those that are very long and contain many helices (spirillum). Spiral-shaped bacteria occur predominantly as unattached individual cells.

BACTERIAL STRUCTURES: *Structures external to the cell wall: Flagella* are proteinaceous organs of motility. They are generally several times longer than the cell but have diameters of only 10 to 10 nm (0.01 to 0.02 μm). Depending on the species and growth conditions, cells may have no flagella, or one or more flagella emanating from one or both poles (polar flagellation), or flagella emanating from the entire surface area (peritrichous flagellation). *Pili (fimbriae)* are proteinaceous hairlike extensions that function during certain "mating" events and enable some cells to adhere to surfaces. There are several types of pili, and a species may possess one or more types. *Capsules* surround the cell wall. Depending on the species and growth conditions, cells may be uncapsulated, have a thick, viscous capsule (slime layer), and/or have a thinner, more organized capsule (microcapsule). Also depending on the species, capsules vary considerably in chemical composition. Many are polysaccharides (e.g., dextran, levan, or cellulose), a few are polypeptides (e.g., poly-D-glutamic acids produced by *Bacillus anthracis*), and occasionally they consist of other compounds (e.g., polyphosphate capsule produced by *Haemophillus influenzae*). The functions of capsules may also vary. Some organisms may store nutrients external to the cell wall as a capsule, while in *Pneumococci* the capsule is protective in the sense that uncapsulated cells are more readily phagocytized and killed by mammalian defense mechanisms.

The cell wall: The cell wall is a rigid structure that protects, permits growth and division, permits motility (in those cells having flagella), permits attachment of some bacteriophages, and acts as a template for the addition of new cell-wall material during cell growth and division. The backbone of both gram-positive and gram-negative bacterial cell walls is peptidoglycan, which is composed of *acetylglucosamine, acetylmuramic acid,* and peptides, consisting of 4-5-D-configuration amino acids. In addition to peptidoglycan, thicker gram-positive cell walls contain teichoic acid, while the thinner gram-negative cell walls contain carbohydrates and lipids (LPS) and protein. Removal of all cell-wall material from gram-positive cells by lysozyme yields osmotically fragile *protoplasts.* In gram-negative cells, lysoyzme removes some cell-wall material (peptidoglycan), yielding osmotically fragile *spheroplasts.*

Structures internal to the cell wall: In most bacteria the cytoplasmic membrane—and invaginations thereof—is the only membrane. If it is severely damaged, the cell dies. To underscore the importance of this structure, some researchers theorize that when the first membrane formed, the first "life" arose out of the mire of primordial earth. The membrane surrounds and "holds" the cell soup (cytoplasm), which contains ribosomes (protein synthesis), enyzmes, nutrients, perhaps inclusions (concentrated deposits of, usually, metabolically important substances), and other life-associated chemicals. The membrane also controls active transport of nutrients into the cell and waste products out of the cell. It probably has a central function as the spatial organizer in procaryotic cells, as enyzmatic systems mediating metabolism are associated with certain portions of the membrane. Some invaginations of the membrane (mesosomes) may play a role in chromosome (DNA) replication and segregation and in septum formation. Numerous cell-membrane invaginations are found in photosynthetic bacteria, and these are probably sites of photosynthesis.

Endospores: These are formed during the life cycle of cells belong to the genera *Bacillus* and *Clostridium.* The function is protective rather than reproductive, as one cell usually forms a dormant spore which, in turn, when conditions are favorable, germinates into a single cell. The numerous layers and coats surrounding the cell membrane, coupled with the presence of disproportionate amounts of Ca^{2+} and an unusual compound, dipicolinic acid, contribute to the endospores' resistance to harsh environmental conditions (boiling, ultraviolet irradiation, toxic chemicals, etc.).

Programmed Self-Test

Do not begin this self-test before reading the corresponding chapter in the text.

SIZE, SHAPE, AND ARRANGEMENT OF BACTERIAL CELLS (Text pages 78 to 82)

Size, shape, structure, and arrangement constitute cell _____.	
Spherical, or ellipsoidal, bacterial cells are called _____.	morphology
Cylindrical, or rodlike, bacterial cells are called _____.	cocci
Cells that appear as short, incomplete spirals are called _____.	bacilli

One of the longest filamentous bacteria, *Saprospira,* may be as long as _____.	vibrios
A genus of bacteria that grows as branched mycelium is _____.	500 μm
The smallest bacteria belong to the order _____.	*Streptomyces*
Staphylococci have diameters of about _____.	Mycoplasmatales
Bacteria may grow and metabolize exceedingly rapidly because the surface-area-to-volume ratio is comparatively _____.	1 μm

BACTERIAL STRUCTURES (Text pages 83 to 100)

Appendages that function in bacterial motility are called _____.	high
The three parts of a flagellum are _____, _____and _____.	flagella
Pseudomonas is characterized by _____ flagella and *Escherichia* by _____ flagella.	basal structure; hooklike structure; long wavy filament;
Bacterial movement in response to certain stimuli is called _____.	polar; peritrichous
Pili can be visualized only by a(n) _____ microscope.	taxis
Some types of pili may allow bacteria to _____, while the F pilus functions during bacterial _____.	electron
A viscous substance forming a covering layer around the cell is called _____.	adhere to surfaces; mating
The *Bacillus anthracis* capsule is a polymer of _____.	a capsule
The _____ are divided into more than 70 distinguishable types on the basis of slight differences in the chemical composition of the capsule.	D-glutamic acid

The cell wall may account for as much as _____ of the dry weight of a bacteria.	pneumococci
Cells whose walls have been removed are called_____.	10 to 40 percent
A polymeric substance known as _____ imparts rigidity to the cell wall.	protoplasts
Peptidoglycans are composed of the building blocks _____ _____, _____ and _____.	peptidoglycan
A substance not found anywhere but in cell walls of gram-positive organisms is _____, and a substance only found in gram-negative cell walls is _____ _____.	acetylglucosomine; acctylmuramic acid; a 4- or 5-amino acid peptide
The lipopolysaccharide is also known as _____ material.	teichoic acid; lipopolysaccharide (LPS)
Lysozyme degrades _____.	endotoxin
When a gram-negative cell is exposed to lysozyme, a _____ forms.	peptidoglycan
The terms semipermeable, selective, location of cytochromes refer to the _____.	spheroplast
One type of membrane intrusion is called a _____.	cytoplasmic membrane
Ribosomes are composed of _____ and _____.	mesosome
Concentrated deposits of certain substances that are detectable in some cells are called _____.	RNA; protein
Volutin granules are also known as _____ _____.	cytoplasmic inclusions
The nucleus of a procaryotic cell is structurally_____ the nucleus of a eucaryotic cell.	metaclumatic granules
Endospores are produced by the genera _____ and _____.	unlike

The function of the endosphere is_____.   *Bacillus;*
                                                          Clostridium

All bacterial endospores contain large amounts of _____   protective
_____, whereas this substance is undetectable in
vegetative cells.

                                                         dipicolinic acid

Multiple-Choice Test

Underline the correct answer.

1. Which organelle is believed to play a key role in DNA replication *and* segregation? (a) Ribosome; (b) mesosome; (c) cell wall; (d) nuclear membrane.

2. Of the following, the most *abundant* chemical component (by weight) of bacteria is: (a) protein; (b) nucleic acids (RNA and DNA); (c) water; (d) carbohydrates;

3. Cell walls of gram-negative bacteria generally lack: (a) mucopeptide (peptidoglycan); (c) protein; (d) lipid.

4. Which one of these should not be listed among the functions of the subacterial cell wall? (a) Rigidity and shape of the cell; (b) cell division; (c) active transport of nutrients; (d) indirect aiding in cell motility; (e) site of bacteriophage attachment; (f) providing template for new cell-wall synthesis.

5. Bacterial spheroplasts and protoplasts stain: (a) gram-positive; (b) gram-negative; (c) gram-variable.

6. Which genus of bacteria has peritrichous flagellation? (a) *Desulfovibrio;* (b) *Pseudomonas;* (c) *Spirillum;* (d) *Escherichia.*

7. The endospore has at least two properties that make it resistant to many harsh environmental conditions. They are: (a) high water content and high motility; (b) an abundance of outer membranes (coats, etc.) and low water content; (c) lack of DNA and heat-labile protein; (d) ability to multiply rapidly and produce energy.

8. A eubacterium can be motile without which one of the following structures; (a) Pili; (b) flagellum; (c) cell wall; (d) cell membrane.

9. In pneumococcus the function of the capsule is: (a) extracellular storage of nutrients; (b) protective (against phagocytosis); (c) to enable the organism to survive in the soil; (d) to mediate active transport of nutrients.

10. Mucopeptides, polysaccharides, protein, and lipid (but no teichoic acid) is descriptive of the chemical composition of: (a) the capsule of *Bacillus anthracis;* (b) the capsule of many gram-negative bacteria; (c) the cell wall of gram-negative bacteria; (d) the cell wall of gram-positive bacteria.

11. Motility among eubacteria is dependent on the presence of: (a) flagella; (b) pili;; (c) capsule; (d) mesosome.

12. Which structure is absolutely essential for the survival of any bacterial cell under any circumstances? (a) Capsule; (b) cell wall; (c) cell membrane; (d) flagella.

13. Because of its ability to form a specific heat-resistance structure, which genus requires autoclaving (rather than simply boiling) to achieve complete sterilization? (a) *Escherichia;* (b) *Staphylococcus;* (d) *Streptococcus* (d) *Bacillus.*

14. Which structure may be physically connected to the eubacterial genome ("chromosome")? (a) Nuclear membrane; (b) mesosome; (c) flagella; (d) granule or cytoplasmic inclusion.

15. Nonrandom bacterial motion is termed: (a) instinct response; (b) tropism; (c) responsive reflex; (d) taxis.

Answers: 1. (b); 2. (c); 3. (b); 4. (c); 5. (b); 6. (d); 7. (b); 8. (a); 9. (b); 10. (b); 11. (a); 12. (c); 13. (d); 14. (b); 15. (d).

Chapter 6

The Cultivation of Bacteria

INTRODUCTION: Since the era of Koch and Pasteur, microorganisms have for the most part been studied, controlled (by vaccines), and successfully used (in starter cultures) only after they have been propagated in the laboratory. Studies *in situ* are also important, of course, for organisms may behave differently in "captivity" than they would in the "wild." But to date, microbiology has progressed as organisms have been cultivated in carefully controlled environments. This chapter lays the foundation for you to knowledgeably cultivate a variety of bacteria and thereby acquire an essential microbiological skill.

Expanded Outline

I. Nutritional Requirements (factors required by all living organisms).
  A. Energy source.
    1. Radiant energy—phototrophs, e.g., green plants.
    2. Oxidation of chemical compounds—chemotrophs, e.g., animal life.
  B. Carbon source.
    1. Carbon dioxide as sole carbon source—autotrophs.
      a. Photoautotrophs—obtain energy from light.
      b. Chemoautotrophs—obtain energy from oxidizing chemical compounds.
    2. Organic carbon source also required—heterotrophs.
  C. Nitrogen source.
    1. Inorganic—e.g., KNO_3 or even atmospheric nitrogen.
    2. Organic—e.g., proteins and their degradation products.
  D. Sulfur and phosphorus sources.
    1. Inorganic—e.g., hydrogen sulfide or sulfur; phosphates.
    2. Organic—e.g., cysteine.
  E. Metallic elements. In some instances trace amounts are required.
  F. Vitamins and vitaminlike compounds. Some bacteria synthesize these compounds

and therefore do not require them in the culture medium; others cannot synthesize one or more vitamins, and so these must be provided.

    G. Water.

II. Nutritional Types of Bacteria.

    A. Phototrophs.

       1. Photolithotrophs—CO_2 principal source of carbon.

       2. Photoorganotrophs—require organic carbon source.

    B. Chemotrophs.

       1. Chemolithotrophs—oxidize inorganic compounds to fulfill energy need and fix CO_2 to fulfill carbon need.

       2. Chemoorganotrophs—energy by oxidation of organic compounds.

    C. Autotrophs and heterotrophs.

       1. Autotrophs—includes photolithotrophic and chemolithotrophic bacteria. From relatively simple inorganic compounds these organisms synthesize the complex biochemical compounds that constitute the living cell.

       2. Heterotrophs—includes photoorganotrophic and chemoorganotrophic bacteria. Wide spectrum. Some species require only one relatively simple organic compound, while others require numerous complex organic compounds. This most widely studied group of bacteria includes most pathogens.

III. Bacteriological Media—chemical composition known (synthetic or defined) or unknown (nonsynthetic), liquid or solid (inclusion of agar).

    A. Types of media—nonsynthetic media for cultivation of heterotrophs.

       1. Enriched—addition of blood, serum, or other complex growth factors to support growth of fastidious heterotrophs.

       2. Selective—addition of certain substances to prevent growth of one group of bacteria without inhibiting others (e.g., specific concentrations of crystal violet prevent growth of gram-positive bacteria but not gram-negative bacteria).

       3. Differential—addition of reagents that allow one to differentiate between types of bacteria (e.g., blood agar for degree of hemolysis).

       4. Assay—testing for amounts of vitamins, amino acids, and antibiotics; also for testing disinfectants.

       5. Enumeration—for determining numbers of bacteria in milk, water, etc.

       6. Characterization—to determine growth patterns and chemical reactions of bacteria.

       7. Maintenance—for longer term storage of bacteria.

    B. Preparation of media—ingredients or dehydrated medium are dissolved in distilled water, pH is adjusted if necessary, and media are dispensed into containers which are capped and sterilized.

IV. Physical Conditions Required for Growth.

    A. Temperature—each species can grow within certain limits and grows most rapidly over a narrower range (optimum temperature).

       1. Psychrophiles—about -5 to 15°C.

       2. Mesophiles—about 25 to 40°C.

       3. Thermophiles—about 45 to 90°C.

          a. Facultative or eurithermophiles—also grow in the mesophilic range.
          b. Obligate or stenothermophiles—true thermophiles that do not grow below
             about 45°C.

   B. Gaseous requirements—on the basis of responses to free oxygen (O_2).
      1. Aerobic bacteria—grow in presence of O_2.
      2. Anaerobic bacteria—grow in absence of O_2.
      3. Facultatively anaerobic bacteria—grow with or without O_2.
      4. Microaerophilic bacteria—grow in presence of minute quantities of free O_2.

   C. Acidity or alkalinity (pH)—most bacteria have an optimum pH of 6.5 to 7.5 and grow in the range from about pH 4 to 9. Because pH shifts as bacterial end products are produced, buffers must be included in the growth medium.

   D. Miscellaneous physical requirements.
      1. Illumination—especially for photosynthetic autotrophs.
      2. Osmotic or hydrostatic pressure—salt concentration, water pressure.
         a. Halophiles—require 10 to 15% salt concentration.

V.   Choice of Media and Conditions of Incubation.
   A. Suitable growth medium based on nutritional requirements of organism.
   B. Incubation of inoculated medium in appropriate conditions.

Summary

NUTRITIONAL REQUIREMENTS: All living organisms require an energy source, C, H, N, O, P, S, metallic elements, and sometimes cofactors for growth. At one end of this spectrum, fastidious heterotrophs may require numerous complex organic compounds; at the other, certain autotrophs may require only light and essentially a "pinch of salts." It is important to determine what that species requires and then provide it.

NUTRITIONAL TYPES OF BACTERIA: Metabolically, bacteria are even more diverse than eucaryotes. *Photolithotrophs* are species whose main energy source is light; they have the capability of anabolizing all large organic compounds starting from CO_2. *Photoorganotrophs* also derive energy from light but are capable of using organic compounds as carbon sources. *Chemolithotrophs* derive energy from the oxidation of inorganic compounds (e.g., *Nitrobacter* oxidizes nitrite to nitrate) and fix CO_2 to build large molecules associated with life. *Chemoorganotrophs* derive energy by oxidation and fermentation of organic carbon compounds and may or may not synthesize complex biochemical molecules from simpler organic molecules. There is a wide spectrum of chemoorganotrophs, ranging from those that may, for example, require only glucose to those that require vitamins, amino acids, nucleotides, and many other molecules already synthesized by other life forms. Such organisms are called *fastidious* and are in this sense metabolic cripples. At this extreme end of the nutritional spectrum we find pathogenic bacteria as well as animals. Photolithotrophs and chemolithotrophs are also called *autotrophs,* while photoorganotrophs and chemoorganotrophs are called *heterotrophs.*

BACTERIOLOGICAL MEDIA: All media, liquid or solid (agar), fall into the two main categories of synthetic or nonsynthetic. All the ingredients—and quantities of ingredients—of synthetic media are known. One must ascertain the needs of a particular species and then satisfy those needs, be they salts and/or hundreds of biochemicals. Synthetic media are useful for metabolic and genetic studies and for the cultivation of autotrophic bacteria. In nonsynthetic media, complex raw materials (not totally analyzed with respect to exactly what is present and in what quantities) such as peptones and yeast extract are provided. Such media support the growth of many heterotrophs and can be prepared to serve one of many purposes, as indicated in III.A of this chapter's expanded outline. Prior to use, all media must be hydrated, adjusted to an appropriate pH, and sterilized in suitable containers.

PHYSICAL CONDITIONS REQUIRED FOR GROWTH: Just as the correct nutrients must be provided, so must the organism be cultivated in an appropriate physical environment. The main factors include temperature, concentration of O_2, pH, osmotic and hydrostatic pressure, and perhaps light source. As with nutritional requirements, the optimal physical conditions for bacteria as a group are extremely heterogeneous. The optimum growth condition is defined as that at which a given species grows fastest. Some bacteria have a temperature optimum below 20°C (psychrophiles), others between 25 and 40°C (mesophiles), while still others can grow between about 30 and 60°C (facultative thermophiles or eurithermophiles), and a few grow best above 60°C (true thermophiles, obligate thermophiles, or stenothermophiles). Incubators that maintain constant temperatures are routinely used in microbiology laboratories.

Aerobic bacteria grow in the presence of O_2, *anaerobic bacteria* grow in its absence, *facultatively anaerobic bacteria* grow in the presence or absence of O_2, and *microaerophilic bacteria* grow in minute quantities of O_2. In the laboratory, aerobic bacteria are cultivated in vessels that allow a large interface between medium and air. Aeration is increased by shaking the inoculated liquid medium or by forcing sterile air through it. For the growth of anaerobic bacteria, O_2 must be removed by the addition of a reducing compound (e.g., sodium thioglycolate) to the medium, by pumping air out of the vessel and another gas in, or by a chemical reaction that confines most O_2 in a compound. Many types of anaerobic vessels and incubators can be commercially purchased.

Most bacteria have an optimum pH of between 6.5 and 7.5 and a growth range of pH 4 to pH 9. Because bacteria often produce acidic or basic end products, many media are buffered (e.g., with KH_2PO_4 and K_2HPO_4) to stabilize the pH. Additionally, salt concentrations and levels of light often must be carefully regulated.

CHOICE OF MEDIA AND CONDITIONS OF INCUBATION: All the above factors must be considered before a species of bacteria can be grown. When the species is unknown, some reasoning and perhaps some experimentation may be required before suitable growth conditions can be provided. For example, if one wishes to cultivate a bacterium from the human intestine, it would be proper to "duplicate" this ecological niche. One should provide a rich supply of nutrients (a nonsynthetic medium may be used), temperature of around 37°C, neutral to slightly alkaline pH, microaerophilic or anaerobic conditions, and perhaps small quantities of bile salts in a nutrient solution approximating physiological saline.

Programmed Self-Test

Do not begin this self-test before reading the corresponding chapter in the text.

NUTRITIONAL REQUIREMENTS; NUTRITIONAL TYPES OF BACTERIA (Text pages 103 to 108)

Forms of life that use radiant energy as an energy source are called

_____.

Forms of life that oxidize chemical compounds to obtain energy and are incapable of utilizing radiant energy are called _____.	phototrophs
Organisms that require CO_2 as their sole carbon source are called _____.	chemotrophs
Organisms that require an organic form of carbon are called _____.	autotrophs
Phototrophic bacteria that utilize CO_2 as their principal source of carbon are called _____.	heterotrophs
An example of a photolithotrophic species of bacteria is _____.	photolithotrophs
An example of a photoorganotrophic bacterium is _____.	*Chromatium*
Bacteria of the genus *Nitrobacter* are able to oxidize nitrite to _____ and to fix _____ to fulfill energy and carbon needs.	*Rhodopseudomonas palustis*
Species that require organic carbon compounds as energy and carbon sources are called _____.	nitrate; CO_2
Photolithotrophic and chemolithotrophic bacteria are commonly referred to as _____.	chemoorganotrophs
Photoorganotrophic and chemoorganotrophic species are called _____.	autotrophs
A medium composed of known chemical compounds is _____ or _____.	heterotrophs

All species that cause disease are, metabolically,_____ bacteria.	chemically defined; synthetic
Though *E. coli* and *Lactobacillus* spp. are both heterotrophic, _____ require(s) much more complex nutrient media for growth.	heterotrophic

BACTERIOLOGICAL MEDIA (Text pages 108 to 111)

_____media are used to support the growth of fastidious heterotrophs.	*Lactobacillus* spp.
Media to which specific chemical substances that inhibit the growth of some, but not all, types of bacteria have been added are called _____.	Enriched
Some concentrations of crystal violet inhibit the growth of _____ bacteria without affecting the growth growth of _____ varieties.	selective
The incorporation of certain chemicals into media may result in a kind of growth or change, after inoculation and incubation, which permits the observer to differentiate between types of bacteria. This kind of medium is called _____.	gram-positive gram-negative
Media of special composition, called _____, are available for testing disinfectants.	differential
Semisolid media contain_____ or less agar.	assay
Growth media are generally sterilized by _____.	0.5%

PHYSICAL CONDITIONS REQUIRED FOR GROWTH (Text pages 111 to 116)

Bacteria that grow below 20°C are called _____.	autoclaving
_____ grow best in a temperature range of approximately 25 to 40°C.	psychrophiles
Stenothermophiles grow best above _____.	Mesophiles

Eurithermophiles grow in the thermophilic and _____ temperature ranges.	60°C
At the optimum temperature, bacteria grow _____ _____.	mesophilic
A bacterium that can grow in the presence or absence of O_2 is called _____.	most rapidly
An example of a reducing compound that is used in anaerobic culture media is _____.	facultatively anaerobic
For most bacterial species, the minimum and maximum growth limits fall somewhere between pH ____ and pH____.	sodium thioglycolate
KH_2PO_4 and K_2HPO_4 are often used together in media as _____.	4; 9
Organisms that require 10% salt for growth are termed _____.	buffers
	halophilic

Multiple-Choice Tests

Underline the correct answer.

1. Which heterotrophic bacterium does not require any amino acids or vitamins to support its growth? (a) *Escherichia coli;* (b) *Staphylococcus aureus;* (c) *Proteus vulgaris;* (d) *Lactobacillus acidophilus.*

2. What source of energy and source of carbon (respectively) does a chemolithotroph require for growth? (a) Light, CO_2; (b) light, organic compound; (c) oxidation of inorganic compounds, CO_2; (d) oxidation of organic compound, organic compound.

3. Photoorganotrophs are also called: (a) halophilic; (b) mesophilic; (c) autotrophs; (d) heterotrophs.

4. An autotrophic type of medium includes: (a) glucose; (b) amino acids; (c) folic acid; (d) water.

5. A bacterial genus that exemplifies the chemolithotrophic type of metabolism is: (a) *Chromatium;* (b) *Rhodopseudomonas;* (c) *Thiobacillus;* (d) *Escherichia.*

6. Organisms are inoculated into a jar filled with sterile nutrient broth containing thioglycolate. The jar is then sealed so that no additional air is allowed to enter. All other conditions being equal, which of the following types of bacteria is most likely to multiply for the longest period of time? (a) Aerobic; (b) microaerophilic; (c) facultative; (d) anaerobic.

7. A bacterial pathogen is most likely to be: (a) a heterotroph; (b) an autotroph; (c) a thermophile; (d) a halophile.

8. A hypothetical bacterial growth medium permits only anaerobic sporeforming organisms to grow. Of these, the nonpathogenic members are purple while the pathogens are white. Such a hypothetical medium is: (a) enriched; (b) selective; (c) differential; (d) selective and differential.

9. Which type of microorganism can be found growing deep inside a wound *and* on its surface? (a) Aerobic; (b) microaerophilic; (c) facultatively anaerobic; (d) anaerobic.

10. Which of the following types of organisms cannot survive in the presence of a lot of oxygen or in its complete absence (requires minute amounts of O_2)? (a) Aerobic; (b) microaerophilic; (c) anaerobic; (d) thermophilic.

11. In the laboratory, you have been incubating some of your bacterial cultures at 37°C (human body temperature). This is the *optimum* growth temperature for many kinds of bacteria. At the optimum growth temperature, bacteria: (a) undergo fewest mutations; (b) form the largest colonies; (c) survive longest; (d) grow at the fastest rate.

12. A wound is infected with an unknown bacterial agent. The pus is swabbed onto nutrient agar, selective media and differential media, but after suitable incubation no colonies appear on any of these media. Which kind of medium should be employed to try to achieve growth? (a) Synthetic; (b) differential; (c) selective; (d) enriched.

13. Four petri plates, each containing a different medium, are left open in a hospital ward for 1h. The plate containing _____ is most likely to allow the growth of the widest assortment of species of bacteria. (a) Nutrient agar; (b) blood agar; (c) nutrient agar + crystal violet; (d) nutrient agar + bile salts.

14. An organism is isolated from a hot (87°C) sulfur spring in Yellowstone National Park at a depth of 25 m, where there is little, if any, free oxygen. The organism is characterized as: (a) an aerobic psychrophile; (b) an anaerobic psychrophile; (c) an anaerobic thermophile; (d) an anaerobic mesophile.

Answers: 1. (a); 2. (c); 3. (d); 4. (d); 5. (c); 6. (d); 7. (a); 8. (d); 9. (c); 10. (b); 11. (d); 12. (d); 13. (b); 14. (c).

Chapter 7

Reproduction and Growth

INTRODUCTION: Compared with other organisms, most bacteria grow and multiply extremely rapidly. This chapter deals with the characteristics and laboratory measurements of bacterial growth and division. One must understand these processes as they occur in a single cell and in entire cultures. Without such understanding it would be difficult to utilize some bacteria to advantage and to control those that may be destructive.

Expanded Outline

I. Reproduction
   A. Cell division (binary fission and other types).
      1. Binary fission—most common process. Asexual. Single cell divides in two after developing transverse cell wall.
      2. Reproductive spores, e.g., *Streptomyces*.
      3. Fragmentation of filaments, e.g., *Nocardia*.
      4. Budding, e.g., *Hyphomicrobium*.
   B. New cell formation (macromolecular synthesis).
      1. Nutrients enter cell.
      2. Biochemical macromolecules synthesized (e.g., DNA).
      3. Cell mass and cell size increases.
      4. New cell-wall substance synthesized.
      5. Division processes initiated.

II. Growth
   A. Growth rate and generation time.
      1. Actively growing populations increase geometrically (e.g., one cell becomes two, two become four, four become eight, etc.).
      2. Generation time—the time interval between cell divisions or population doublings; varies from species to species and from one set of growth conditions to another.

Working formula for calculating the generation time of a logarithmically growing population:

$$G = \frac{t}{3.3 \log (b/B)}$$

where G = the generation time
  t = the time interval between measurement of the number of cells in the population at one moment (B) and then again at another moment (b)
  B = the initial population
  b = the population after time t
  $\log = \log_{10}$
  $3.3 = \log_2$ to $\log_{10}$ conversion factor

B. Normal growth cycle (growth curve) of bacterial culture. The organisms are growing in batch culture (a relatively closed system where nutrients are not renewed and waste products are not removed).
   1. *The lag phase.* Cells not multiplying. May be very long or almost nonexistent, depending on the species and condition of inoculum, growth media, and many other factors. Cells eliminating waste, being derepressed (see Chap. 9), synthesizing macromolecules, and/or growing in size in preparation for division.
   2. *The logarithmic, or exponential, phase.* Cells divide steadily at a constant rate and are most nearly balanced or uniform in terms of chemical composition, metabolic activity, etc. Therefore, "log" populations are most commonly studied in the lab.
   3. *The stationary phase.* Reproduction rate equals death rate, due to depletion of nutrients, accumulation of waste products, and other detrimental conditions.
   4. *The phase of decline or death.* Cells die faster than new ones are produced. Factors leading to stationary phase are now augmented.
C. Synchronous growth. Theoretically all cells in the population are uniform and are doing the same things uniformly (e.g., metabolism, growth, and division). All cells divide simultaneously. Important experimental condition that may be temporarily induced via cell-size sorting, use of mutants, biochemical inhibitors, etc.
D. Continuous culture. Growth in an open vessel. Nutrients renewed and waste products removed. Cells in *steady state* or *balanced growth.*
   1. Turbidostat—turbidity of culture kept constant by regulation of nutrient inflow.
   2. Chemostat—flow of nutrients kept constant (and limiting) so that cell growth remains constant.

III. Quantitative Measurement of Bacterial Growth
   A. Commonly used procedures for determining cell numbers and cell mass.
      1. Direct microscopic count. Viable and nonviable cell number determined. E.g., Petroff-Hausser counting chamber—accurately ruled slide of known dimensions. Average number of cells within each small square times 2×10^7 equals number of cells per milliliter in the culture.
      2. Determination of the number of cells which will multiply under certain defined conditions, by the plate count. Viable cell numbers determined. One organism gives rise to one colony (mass of cells). Appropriate dilutions of culture placed in and/or on solid medium. Number of colonies times the dilution factor approximates the number of cells per milliliter in the original culture.

3. Membrane-filter count. As above, but known volume of medium, air, or water is passed through filters which trap bacteria. The filters, with trapped organisms, are placed on appropriate media so colonies may form.
4. Determination of cell density by turbidimetric determination. Measures both living and dead cell mass, cell components, and debris, all of which add to the density of cell suspensions. Rapid method for following cell growth, as under most conditions optical density (OD) is proportional to cell density.
5. Determination of the cell concentration by measurement of nitrogen content. Indicates approximate mass of viable and nonviable cells (bacteria are about 14 percent nitrogen by dry weight). Research-oriented technique.
6. Determination of the dry weight of cells. Most direct approach for quantitative measurement of the mass of viable and nonviable cells.
7. Determination of the cell mass by measurement of a specific chemical change produced on a constituent of the medium—e.g., amount of acid end product is roughly proportional to the number of viable cells.

B. Turbidity measurements and direct expressions of growth. Standard curve—experimentally determined OD values equated with experimentally determined weights of cells per milliliter (or with other direct measurements). Then, under similar experimental conditions, an easily obtained OD value can be related to cell weight, cell number, or any other previously standardized value.
C. The selection of a procedure to measure growth. (See text, Table 7-2.)
D. Importance of quantitative measurement of growth.

Summary

REPRODUCTION: Bacteria take up nutrients, synthesize necessary macromolecular components, enlarge the cell wall and envelope, replicate the chromosome, form crosswalls (septa), and then divide. Asexual fission is the predominant mode of reproduction, and in many bacteria only binary fission occurs.

GROWTH AND MULTIPLICATION: A population of cells, dividing by binary fission, doubles at intervals (generation time) that vary according to the species, nutrient supply, and physical conditions. Binary fission leads to geometric population proliferation ($1 \rightarrow 2 \rightarrow 4 \rightarrow 8 \rightarrow 16$, etc.). During logarithmic (balanced) growth, the generation time can be calculated according to the formula

$$G = \frac{t}{3.3 \log (b/B)}$$

When cells are inoculated into a fresh medium in a semiclosed environment (batch culture), a characteristic pattern of changes in viable cell numbers is noted. Initially, populations remain static (lag phase), then increase exponentially (logarithmic phase), then become static once more (stationary phase), and finally decline (death phase). Some reasons are as follows. At first newly inoculated cells may rid themselves of waste products and take up fresh nutrients and only then synthesize necessary biochemicals, allowing for growth that occurs before division commences. This is followed by a period of rapid division, during which time cells are metabolizing and dividing at roughly equivalent rates (balanced growth). Finally, when nutrient concentrations become limiting and toxic end products accumulate, cell divisions approximate cell deaths. Eventually, conditions become more intolerable, and cells may die as rapidly as they once multiplied. Other factors such as bacteriophage infection may also precipitate the death phase.

During balanced growth, cells are metabolizing and dividing at the same rates, but they are not doing so in unison. When cells synthesize DNA, etc., and divide simultaneously, the population is termed synchronous. Populations may be synchronized by cell-size sorting or by the regulation of their metabolism, but synchrony seldom lasts for more than one or two generations.

The stationary and decline phases of growth are characteristic of batch growth (closed system) and may be eliminated in cultures or populations that grow in an open environment.

Under these conditions, nutrients are continuously available to the culture and cells and their waste products are removed. Bacteria may be maintained in the logarithmic phase of growth (steady state or balanced growth) by devices such as chemostats and turbidostats, that maintain and regulate the "open culture" vessel.

QUANTITATIVE MEASUREMENT OF BACTERIAL GROWTH: A number of parameters are used to measure cell growth and/or division, and a number of techniques can be used to measure each parameter. Cells can be counted directly while under a microscope or in an electronic particle counter. Both viable and nonviable organisms are so tallied. Most commonly, viable cell numbers are determined by colony count or "membrane-filter count."

Cell mass is measured directly as dry weight or by nitrogen content and indirectly by turbidometric measurement (optical density), using a spectrophotometer. Cell activities, like acid production, can be related to population size.

In basic and applied research, colony counts, direct microscopic counts, and turbidometric measurements are most often used. But in any endeavor one should know not only what organism(s) one is dealing with, but also the number of organisms and their phase of growth.

Programmed Self-Test

Do not begin this self-test before reading the corresponding chapter in the text.

REPRODUCTION (Text pages 118 to 121)

Most bacteria multiply by _____.

Streptomyces produce many reproductive _____ per organism.

One cell undergoing binary fission yields _____ cells.

binary (transverse) fission

spores

GROWTH (Text pages 121 to 127)

The time interval required for the cell to divide—or for the population to double—is known as the _____.

two

Escherichia coli may divide as often as every _____ minutes.	generation time
The generation time is strongly dependent on _____ _____ and on _____.	15 to 20
The four phases of growth in batch culture are _____, _____, _____, and _____.	nutrients in the medium; physical conditions
During the lag phase, bacterial _____ is usually still occurring.	lag; log; stationary; decline
Cell deaths equal cell divisions during the _____ _____.	metabolism
During the _____ phase of growth, cells divide steadily at a constant rate.	stationary phase
The stationary phase results from _____ and, less often, from _____.	logarithmic
During _____ "all" cells divide simultaneously.	nutrient exhaustion; production of toxic products
Cells are most likely to be in steady state or in balanced growth during the _____ phase.	synchronous growth
Two growth devices that maintain steady state are the _____ and _____.	logarithmic
The turbidostat is regulated by a _____.	turbidostat; chemostat

QUANTITATIVE MEASUREMENT OF BACTERIAL GROWTH (Text pages 127 to 133)

Bacteria can be counted easily and accurately (while under the microscope) with the _____ _____.	photoelectric eye
One organism multiplying in solid medium theoretically gives rise to one _____.	Petroff-Hausser counting chamber

Plate counts tend to be most accurate when the number of colonies developing on the plate falls in the range of _____.	colony
Viable plate count data are reported as _____.	30 to 300
A culture of about _____ to _____ cells per milliliter appears turbid to the naked eye.	cfu
Instruments that are used to measure turbidity of cell cultures are _____ and _____.	10^7; 10^8
Bacteria average about _____ percent nitrogen on a dry weight basis.	spectrophotometers; colorimeters
The most direct and reliable method for quantitative measurement of a mass of cells is _____.	14
To routinely relate indirect measurements of growth (turbidity) to a direct method (weight of the cell crop), one should obtain a _____.	dry weight
	standard curve

Multiple-Choice Test

Underline the correct answer.

1. One bacterium undergoes binary fission three times. None die. How many bacteria are there altogether? (a) 3; (b) 4; (c) 8; (d) 15.

2. The number of bacteria in the smallest squares of a Petroff-Hausser counting chamber averages 10. No dilutions were made. How many bacteria per milliliter were in the original culture? (a) 10; (b) 2×10^7; (c) 10^8; (d) 2×10^8.

3. Which genera of bacteria reproduces by budding? (a) *Nocardia*; (b) *Escherichia*; (c) *Streptomyces*; (d) *Hyphomicrobium*.

4. When almost all of the bacteria in a culture divide simultaneously, they are: (a) growing synchronously; (b) in the logarithmic phase of growth; (c) in balanced growth; (d) all of the above are correct.

5. Continuous cultivation of bacteria is achieved in a: (a) petri plate; (b) chemostat; (c) closed flask; (d) Petroff-Hausser counting chamber.

6. In which of the following cases would the lag phase of a population of bacteria be the shortest (i.e., approach log phase most rapidly) or nonexistent; (a) *E. coli* in the logarithmic phase of growth (in nutrient broth) is transferred to a fresh flask of the same medium; (b) *E. coli* in the logarithmic phase of growth in medium containing glucose as the sole source of carbon is transferred to fresh medium containing lactose as the sole source of carbon; (c) *E. coli* in the late stationary phase of growth (in nutrient broth) is transferred to a flask of fresh nutrient broth.

7. In the latter stages of the lag phase of growth (in a broth culture), bacteria: (a) rapidly divide; (b) are usually killed by excessive waste products; (c) grow larger (longer); (d) stop metabolizing.

8. In the exponential phase of growth, the number of bacteria in the culture increases from ten thousand (10^4)/ml to a billion (10^9)/ml in 1,000 min at 37°C. What is the generation time (time between cell divisions)? (a) 36 min; (b) 40 min; (c) 1 h; (d) 4 h.

9. You are measuring the number of bacteria in a flask during the stationary phase of growth. When you count them in a Petroff-Hausser chamber under the microscope, you find 10^8 cells per milliliter. At the same time you make appropriate dilutions and make a plate count. When the colonies grow, you find that there were only 10^7 cells per milliliter. You assume that: (a) you had poor technique; (b) you found that some of the bacteria in the culture were nonviable; (c) you are not dissatisfied with the discrepancy because you know that some cells divide on an agar plate, forming two colonies per cell; (d) you found that 10 million cells had two nuclei.

10. Dilution problem: 10 ml of media from a flask containing bacteria is placed in 90 ml of saline, and 1 ml of this saline dilution is placed in a 9-ml saline dilution blank. One-tenth (0.1) ml of this dilution is in turn placed in 9.9 ml of the third saline dilution tube. One-tenth ml of this suspension is then spread onto an agar plate. After 48 h, 150 colonies are apparent on the agar plate. How many bacteria per milliliter are in the original culture flask? (a) 150; (b) 1.5 x 10^5; (c) 1.5 x 10^7; (d) 5 x 10^8.

11. *Escherichia* is inoculated into a flask containing appropriate medium. During the exponential phase of growth, the number of bacteria in the culture is found to increase from one hundred (10^2)/ml to one billion (10^9)/ml in 23 h and 20 min. What is the generation time (time between cell division)? (a) 30 min; (b) 60 min; (c) 90 min; (d) 400 min; (e) 3-1/3 h.

MATCHING: These questions refer to the eubacterial growth curve. Match the phase of growth with its definition, cause, or attribute. Use each answer once.

12. a b c d Late lag   (a) active binary fission; few cell deaths
13. a b c d Log   (b) active cell growth; very few cell divisions
14. a b c d Stationary   (c) active binary fission; many cell deaths
15. a b c d Decline   (d) culture bathed in its own waste products

Answers: 1. (c); 2. (d); 3. (d); 4. (d); 5. (b); 6. (a); 7. (c); 8. (c); 9. (b); 10. (c); 11. (b); 12. (b); 13. (a); 14. (c); 15. (d).

Chapter 8

Pure Cultures and Cultural Characteristics

INTRODUCTION: When organisms grow on a laboratory medium, they are referred to as a *culture*. This chapter details how pure (one-species) cultures may be obtained and how they can be studied. Pure-culture techniques are used in every microbiology laboratory and have shaped the development of microbiology as a science. A knowledge of these techniques, therefore, is absolutely essential to anyone working with microorganisms.

Expanded Outline

I. Natural Microbial Populations (Mixed Cultures). Mixed populations of microorganisms are everywhere.

II. Pure Cultures. Microorganisms have been studied in pure culture, which consists of populations of cells all derived from a single parent cell.
    A. Methods of isolating pure cultures.
        1. Streak-plate, spread-plate, and pour-plate techniques — organisms spaced in and/or on agar so that an isolated colony can develop from one cell.
        2. Enrichment culture techniques — specially designed cultural and/or physical environment which favors growth of sought bacteria over other types.
        3. Serial-dilution technique — if the organism sought in mixed culture is present in greater numbers than other types, the unwanted organisms can be diluted out.
        4. Single-cell isolation technique — micromanipulators allow skilled operators to pick out one cell from others.

III. Maintenance and Preservation of Pure Cultures. Bank of pure cultures required in teaching, research, industry, and health fields.
    A. Methods of preservation — some organisms are better preserved by one technique than by another.
        1. Periodic transfer to fresh media — some heterotrophic bacteria remain viable for weeks on slants of nutrient agar. Different optima for various organisms are illustrated in Table 8-1.

Table 8-1. Procedure for the Preservation of Some Bacteria

BACTERIA	MEDIUM	TRANSFER TIME	INCUBATION TEMP., °C	STORAGE TEMP., °C
Neisseria spp. (saprophytic)	Cystine trypticase agar	1 month	35	35
Bacillus spp.	Nutrient agar	12 months and longer	28	10
Pseudomonas spp.	Nutrient agar	3 months	28	10
Clostridium spp.	Cooked meat medium	6 months and longer	28	Room
Mycobacterium spp. (saprophytic)	Glycerol agar	4 months	30	10

      2.   Overlaying cultures with mineral oil — certain species remain viable much longer (years) if the slants are covered with oil.

      3.   Lyophilization (rapid freeze-drying) — freeze-dried cultures are stored in small evacuated vessels; they may remain viable for decades.

      4.   Very low temperature storage — in liquid nitrogen (–196°C). Cells frozen in glycerol or dimethyl sulfoxide.

   B.   National culture collections. Over 500,000 isolates are stored worldwide in one or more headquarters. The American Type Culture Collection (Rockville, Md.) houses one of the largest assortments of microbes (bacteria, viruses, etc.).

IV.   Cultural Characteristics. The appearance of colonies on solid media and growth patterns in broths can be used to facilitate identification.

   A.   Agar plate colonies.

      1.   Size — pinpoint to many millimeters in diameter. Some spread confluently.

      2.   Margin or edge — evenly circular to numerous projections.

      3.   Elevation — flat to varying degrees of convex structure.

      4.   Chromogenesis or pigmentation — unpigmented or one of many hues.

      5.   Optical features — opaque, translucent, or opalescent.

   B.   Agar-streak (slant) growth — amount (scant to abundant), consistency (dry to viscous), and the above factors are considered.

   C.   Growth in nutrient broth.

      1.   Amount — scanty, moderate, abundant.

      2.   Distribution — uniform (evenly turbid), surface film (pellicle), sediment.

      3.   Odor — putrid, fruity, aromatic, negligible.

   D.   Growth in gelatin stabs.

      1.   Growth (no liquefaction) confined to or spread away from streak.

      2.   Liquefaction.

Summary

A pure culture consists of populations of cells derived from a single percent cell. Pure cultures may be obtained by isolating colonies in and/or on agar, by diluting out less numerous, unwanted varieties, by providing an environment specially designed to foster the growth of one kind of organism (enrichment culture technique), or by micromanipulation. Once obtained, pure cultures may be maintained on agar slants, or for longer periods of time on agar slants covered with oil, or for the longest periods of time in lyophiles or at very low temperatures (-196°C). Hundreds of thousands of microbial isolates are stored by these methods in thousands of centers throughout the world.

Pure cultures may be identified, in part, by their unique cultural characteristics. These include colony size, shape, color, and texture. However, even these characteristics may vary for a single species, depending on the nutrients furnished and the physical conditions of incubation.

Programmed Self-Test

Do not begin this self-test before reading the corresponding chapter in the text.

NATURAL POPULATIONS (MIXED CULTURES), AND PURE CULTURES (Text pages 135 to 144)

A pure culture consists of a population of cells which are _____.	
In the pour plate technique, medium is inoculated while it is at _____°C.	all derived from a single parent cell
The enrichment cultures technique was introduced by _____ and _____ between 1890 and 1900.	45
Special equipment, the _____ , can be used in conjunction with a microscope to pick a single organism from a hanging-drop preparation.	Beijerincki; Winogradsky
Pseudomonas spp. on nutrient agar at 10°C should be transferred to fresh media once every _____ .	micromanipulator
Some species have been preserved on slants overlayed with mineral oil for a period of _____ .	3 months
Preservation of cultures in a vacuum by rapid freeze-drying is called _____ .	15 to 20 years
Bacteria can be preserved at -196°C when frozen along with a protective agent, such as _____ or _____ .	lyophilization

The first known culture collection, the Krol Collection, was established in Prague around _____ .	glycerol; dimethyl sulfoxide

CULTURAL CHARACTERISTICS (Text pages 144 to 147)

Species of _____ and _____ can spread across the entire agar surface of a petri plate.	1900
Agar plate colonies are characterized according to size, margin, elevation, pigmentation, and _____ .	*Pseudomonas; Proteus*
Growth in nutrient broth can be characterized by amount, distribution, and _____ .	optical features
Serratia marcescens forms a _____ pigment, while *Micrococcus flavens* forms one that is _____ .	odor
Pellicle growth in broth and colonies that are irregular, raised, granular, and very brittle are characteristic of _____ .	red; yellow
	Mycobacterium

Multiple-Choice Test

Underline the correct answer.

1. If a culture is *Proteus vulgaris* and a gram stain shows gram-positive cocci, you would suspect: (a) mutation; (b) temporary modification of phenotype; (c) contamination; (d) recombination.

2. You have found that your isolette degrades oil and, therefore, can simultaneously help save our waterways and make you wealthy. How do you preserve this culture? (a) Make several broth cultures and refrigerate them; (b) Make broth cultures and freeze them; (c) streak the organism on petri plates and place these in a safety-deposit box; (d) on slants and in lyophiles.

3. Which of the following is an example of the enrichment culture technique? (a) A stool sample from a patient with dysentery is plated on salmonella-shigella agar; (b) the gram stain; (c) an organism that degrades potassium cyanide (KCN) is isolated from a synthetic medium containing KCN as a sole carbon source; (d) blood agar is employed to isolate *E. coli* from a river.

4. Cells may be best preserved at -196°C in: (a) water; (b) agar; (c) glycerol; (d) nutrient broth.

5. Lyophilization is a process of: (a) sterilization; (b) purification; (c) rapid freeze-drying; (d) low-temperature storage.

Answers: 1. (c);   2. (d);   3. (c);   4. (c);   5. (c).

Chapter 9

Enzymes and
Their Regulation

INTRODUCTION: From the simplest of compounds many kinds of cells synthesize some of the largest and most complex molecules known. Conversely, cells must continuously degrade larger compounds and derive the energy obtained when chemical bonds are broken. Many of these re-actions either do not occur in inanimate nature or, if they do, require or produce enough heat to kill a living cell. The organic catalysts that mediate these reactions at low temperatures are called *enzymes*; and if DNA is the mind of life and the cell membrane is the heart of life, then certainly enzymes are the hands of life. The subjects introduced in this chapter are complex and not even fully understood by enzymologists and geneticists; but at least you can gain a working knowledge of the structures, modes of action, and formation of enzymes.

Expanded Outline and Summary

I. Some Characteristics of Enzymes — organic catalysts (which in small amounts speed up chemical reactions without themselves being altered after the reaction) are produced by living cells.
   A. Intracellular enzymes (endoenzymes) — function in cell.
   B. Extracellular enzymes (exoenzymes) — function outside of cell.

II. Chemical and Physical Properties of Enzymes.
   A. Components.
      1. Holoenzyme — complete active structure composed of apoenzyme and coenzyme.
      2. Apoenzyme — high-molecular-weight protein.
      3. Coenzyme — low-molecular-weight organic molecule.
      4. Cofactor — inorganic (metal ion, e.g., Mn^{2+}, Fe^{2+}, Zn^{2+}) component necessary for activity of some enzymes.
   B. Size — large proteins. Molecular weights from 10,000 to 1 million. Enzymes strikingly larger than substances (substrates) they act upon.
   C. Activity — single molecule of enzyme may change 10,000 to 1 million molecules of substrate per minute.

  D. Stability — minor environmental alterations may inactivate enzymes. Thus, they are relatively unstable and represent a vulnerable point of attack in controlling bacteria.

  E. Specificity — high. One kind of enzyme reacts with only a single compound or class of compounds.

III. Nomenclature of Enzymes. Enzymes are named and classified according to precise rules set by the International Union of Biochemistry. Some enzymes also have common names.

IV. The Nature of Enzyme Reactions.

$$E + S \leftrightarrow ES \leftrightarrow EZ \leftrightarrow EP \leftrightarrow E + P$$

where

        E = enzyme
        S = substrate
      ES = enzyme-substrate complex
      EZ = transition-state complex
      EP = enzyme-product complex
        P = product

V. Mechanism of Enzyme Action. Theory: Chemical (electronic) affinity of substrate(s) for certain areas on enzyme surface (active sites). Distortion in substrate molecule(s). Chemical change ensues. Changed molecules no longer have affinity for enzyme and are released.

VI. Conditions Affecting Enzyme Activity. Enzyme concentrations, substrate concentration, pH, temperature.

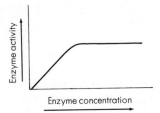

Figure 9-3. Effect of enzyme concentration on rate of activity.

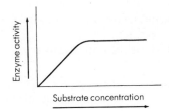

Figure 9-4. Effect of substrate concentration on rate of enzyme activity.

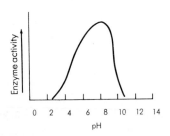

Figure 9-5. Effect of pH on enzyme activity.

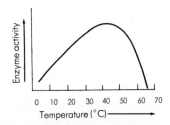

Figure 9-6. Effect of temperature on enzyme activity. In this example, enzyme destruction begins at approximately 55°C.

VII.   Inhibition of Enzyme Action.
   A.   Nonreversible — usually involves the modification or destruction of one or more functional groups of the enzyme (e.g., denaturation by heat).
   B.   Reversible.
      1.   Competitive — can be reversed by increasing substrate concentration (e.g., succinic acid and malonic acid; para-aminobenzoic acid and sulfanilamide).
      2.   Noncompetitive — cannot be reversed by increasing substrate concentration (e.g., cyanide, which "ties up iron").

VIII.   Conditions Affecting Enzyme Formation. Animal cells in a constant environment produce a relatively constant supply of enzymes. Bacteria, subject to changing environments, regulate production of some enzymes, producing sufficient quantities of the enzymes required to meet particular sets of circumstances and fewer amounts of those enzymes that are not needed at a particular time. Regulation of enzyme production enables bacteria to conserve valuable and limited energy, as those proteins that are required for survival are produced in larger quantities, while those proteins not required are produced in lesser quantities.
   A.   Constitutive enzymes — "always" produced by cell, no matter what environment the cell is in.
   B.   Adaptive (induced) enzymes — intracellular quantities vary, depending on dictates of environment (mainly nutrients).

IX.   Methods for the Detection and Measurement of Enzyme Activity. Experimental protocols require excess cofactors, coenzymes, and substrate as well as optimum pH and temperature so that the initial reaction rate is proportional to enzyme activity alone. The following are analytical methods for determining disappearance of substrate (S) or appearance of reaction products (P).
   A.   Spectrophotometric — some compounds (S and/or P) may be identified and their concentration measured by their absorption of light at a certain wavelength.
   B.   Radioisotopic — substrate is labeled (radioactively) and exposed to enzyme; some label may wind up in products.
   C.   Chromatographic — separation, identification, and often concentration measurement of compounds (S and/or P).

X.   Enzyme Preparations. Enzyme preparations used above may be obtained as follows:
   A.   Growing-culture technique — see how growing cells use substrates and produce products.
   B.   Resting-cell technique — harvested, washed cells are placed in special apparatus with reaction mixture. S and/or P assayed.
   C.   Cell-free enzyme technique — cell lysis, extraction, and purification of enzymes (to a greater or a lesser extent).

XI.   Regulation of Enzyme Activity. Previously (part VIII) it was noted that certain cells may or may not produce relatively large quantities of enzymes depending on the absence or presence of certain metabolites. Additionally, certain enzymes may function only when certain metabolites are, or are not, present. This section is involved with the kinds and mechanisms of enzyme regulation.
   A.   Direct control of catalysis (enzyme activity).
      1.   Control of catalytic mechanism itself. Regulation in cell by concentrations of substrates, products, cofactors, etc. Also spatial separations of enzyme systems within cell.

2. Coupling with other processes. Regulation by ligands (molecules capable of binding to an enzyme) which do not participate in the catalytic process itself.
   a. Types of coupled enzyme regulation.
      i. Precursor activation — first metabolite of pathway is regulatory ligand that activates last enzyme in sequence of reactions.
      ii. Polymerization-depolymerization (association-dissociation) reactions.
      iii. Energy-link control — regulatory ligands are nucleotides.
      iv. Hormone control — in eucaryotes only. Regulatory ligand is a hormone.
      v. Activating enzymes — substrates are other enzymes.
      vi. Feedback inhibition — regulatory ligand is end product of metabolic pathway that can shut off its own synthesis by inhibiting the activity of one of the early enzymes in its own biosynthetic pathway.
   b. Properties of regulatory enzymes. Not all enzymes are regulatory enzymes that control the activity of multienzyme systems. Regulatory enzymes are subject to the action of effectors, modifiers, or modulators which combine with enzymes and alter (increase or decrease) their affinity for substrates.
      i. Homotropic regulatory enzyme — substrate also modulator. Contains two or more binding sites for substrate, at least one of which is catalytic.
      ii. Heterotropic regulatory enzyme — modulator molecule different from substrate and separate binding site for modulator (allosteric enzyme).
      iii. Homotropic-heterotropic regulatory enzyme — modified by the substrate and one or more modulators that are not substrates.
B. Genetic control of catalysis (enzyme induction and repression). At the level of transcription (synthesis of mRNA template). If particular mRNA is not synthesized, specified proteins (often enzymes) are not produced and catalysis cannot occur.
   1. Definition of terms.
      a. Structural genes — specify proteins (enzymes).
      b. Regulator genes — control rate of protein synthesis.
      c. Operon — genetic unit consisting of regulator and structural genes.
      d. Inducer — often a substrate that stimulates transcription of the structural genes of an operon.
      e. Corepressors — combine with *repressor* to form *active complex* that combines with operator gene to inhibit transcription of the structural genes in the operon.
      f. Repressor — protein product of regulatory gene. Can function as in e above or can combine with inducer to form *inactive complex* which does not inhibit transcription.
   2. Example: The *lac* operon.
      i. β-Galactosidase (hydrolyzes lactose to glucose and galactose). Gene *z*.
      ii. β-Galactoside permease (transports lactose into cell). Gene *y*.
      iii. Thiogalactoside transacetylase (function unknown). Gene *a*.
      a. Regulator genes.
         i. *i* — repressor (code for repressor protein that binds to DNA at the *O* gene, thus preventing transcription).
         ii. *p* — promoter (site on DNA where RNA polymerase initiates transcription).
         iii. *o* — operator (segment of DNA that binds repressor).

b. Control.
  i. Negative — mediated by *lac* repressor. Inducers (e.g., lactose) bind to repressor and reduce affinity for the *O* operator.
  ii. Positive (catabolite repression). Expression of operon repressed by more efficient source of carbon (e.g., glucose). Glucose decreases amount of cyclic AMP which in higher concentrations activates CAP (protein), which in turn activates transcription of *lac* mRNA by RNA polymerase at promoter site.

Programmed Self-Test

Do not begin this self-test before reading the corresponding chapter in the text.

SOME CHARACTERISTICS OF ENZYMES (Text pages 150 to 153)

The word enzyme was coined in 1878 by Kühne from a Greek term meaning _____ .	
Liebig maintained that fermentations were caused by chemical substances not associated with _____ .	"in yeast"
_____ held that the fermentation process was inseparable from living cells.	living cells
In 1897, _____ showed that neither Liebig nor Pasteur was strictly wrong.	Pasteur
Substances which, in small amounts and without being altered, speed up chemical reactions are called _____ .	Büchner
Biochemical catalysts are called _____ .	catalysts
Enzymes functioning within the cell are called _____ or _____ .	enzymes
Extracellular enzymes are also called _____ .	intracellular enzymes; endoenzymes
Extracellular enzymes act mainly on _____ to allow them to enter the cell.	exoenzymes
The apoenzyme is a _____ .	nutrients

A coenzyme is a _____ -molecular-weight _____ molecule.	protein
Some enzymes require _____ for activation.	low; organic
The molecular weights of enzymes range from about _____ to _____ .	metals
Catalase splits hydrogen peroxide into _____ and _____ .	10,000; 1 million
A single enzyme molecule can affect the change of a maximum of _____ molecules of substrate per minute.	water; oxygen
The two most striking characteristics of enzymes are (1) their high catalytic efficiency and (2) their high degree of _____ .	1 million

NOMENCLATURE OF ENZYMES AND THE NATURE OF ENZYME REACTIONS (Text pages 153 to 156)

The names of single enzymes generally end in _____ .	specificity for substrates
Enzymes that occur in different structural forms but possess identical catalytic properties are called _____ .	*ase*
"ES" refers to an _____ .	isozymes *or* isoenzymes
When the concentration of the product of a reaction is increased in relation to the substrate, the reaction will gradually be _____ .	enzyme-substrate complex
The activation of the substrate molecule takes place because of high _____ affinity of the substrate for certain areas of the enzyme surface.	inhibited *or* reversed
Reactive areas of the enzyme surface are called _____ .	chemical (electronic)
In an enzyme, relatively few _____ are directly involved in the catalytic process.	active sites

CONDITIONS AFFECTING ENZYME ACTIVITY AND INHIBITION OF ENZYME ACTION
(Text pages 156 to 159)

High temperatures generally _____ enzymes.	amino acids
Low temperatures generally _____ enzymes.	destroy (denature)
Competitive inhibition can be reversed by increasing the _____ concentration.	do not destroy
A competitive inhibitor of the enzyme that catalyzes succinic acid to fumaric acid is _____ .	substrate
Sulfonamides are structurally similar to the folic acid precursor _____ .	malonic acid
Cyanide is a strong inhibitor of _____ - containing enzymes.	p-aminobenzoic acid
Cyanide inhibition of iron-containing enzymes is an example of _____ inhibition.	iron

CONDITIONS AFFECTING ENZYME FORMATION (Text pages 159 to 160)

Enzymes that are always produced by the cell independent of the composition of the medium in which it is grown are called _____ .	noncompetitive
The preferred term for adaptive enzyme is now _____ .	constitutive enzymes
The substance responsible for inducing the formation of an enzyme is often the _____ , which in this case is called the _____ .	induced enzyme

METHODS FOR THE DETECTION AND MEASUREMENT OF ENZYME ACTIVITY. ENZYME PREPARATIONS. (Text pages 160 to 163)

In measuring enzyme activity, the substrate concentration should be _____ .	substrate; inducer

Three methods of assaying for substrate and enzyme product concentrations are _____ , _____ , and _____ .

above saturation level

Enzymes in _____ , in _____ , and in _____ may be studied.

spectrophometric; radioisotopic; chromatographic

The _____ technique is used routinely for the characterization of the enzymatic activities of microorganisms.

growing cells; resting cells; cell-free extracts

REGULATION OF ENZYME ACTIVITY (Text pages 163 to 167)

In bacteria, it appears that all major metabolic pathways have the capacity for _____ .

growing-culture

Genetic control of enzyme synthesis includes both _____ and _____ .

self-regulation

In precursor activation, the _____ of a pathway is the regulatory ligand.

induction; repression

In feedback inhibition, the regulatory ligand is the _____ of a metabolic pathway.

first metabolite

Heterotropic regulatory enzymes are modified by _____ .

end product

The presence of a _____ leads to increased affinity of the regulatory enzyme for substrate.

a modulator other than the substrate

Enzymes with two different active sites, one for substrates and one for activators, are called _____ .

positive effector (activator)

Transcriptional control of the rate of enzyme synthesis is directed by _____ .

allosteric

Corepressors function by combining with the _____ to form an active complex which combines with _____ to prevent mRNA synthesis.

regulator genes

When inducers, such as lactose, are added to a culture of $E.$ $coli$, there is a _____ in the rate of synthesis of β-galactosidase.

repressor; the operator gene

β-galactosidase hydrolyzes lactose to _____ and _____ .	1,000-fold increase
Structural gene _____ codes for galactoside permease.	glucose; galactose
Regulator gene *i* codes for a _____ .	y
The promotor gene *p* is the site on DNA where _____ .	repressor protein
_____ bind to the operator (*O*) gene.	the RNA polymerase binds
Genes *z, y,* and *a* operate as a single unit of transcription which is initiated at _____ .	Repressor proteins
Positive control of the lactose operon is exerted by the phenomenon of _____ .	*p*
In catabolite repression, glucose results in a decreased concentration of _____ , which in sufficient quantities activates the _____ , which in turn activates _____ of *lac* mRNA by RNA polymerase at the promoter site.	catabolite repression
	cyclic AMP; CAP; transcription

Multiple-Choice Test

Underline the correct answer.

1. Enzymes that function within the cell are called: (a) endoenzymes; (b) exoenzymes; (c) co-enzymes; (d) apoenzymes.

2. Boiling _____ most enzymes. (a) Reversibly inactivates; (b) competitively inhibits; (c) has no effect on; (d) denatures.

3. Enzymes that are always produced by the cell, independent of the composition of the medium in which the cell is grown, are called: (a) induced enzymes; (b) constitutive enzymes; (c) adaptive enzymes; (d) holoenzymes.

4. Spectrophotometers measure: (a) radioactivity; (b) molecular weights of enzymes; (c) absorbance of certain wavelengths of light by certain compounds; (d) the number of active sites

5. Corepressors function by combining with the repressor to form an active complex which combines with the _____ to prevent mRNA synthesis. (a) Operator gene; (b) promoter gene; (c) *z* gene; (d) catabolite gene activator protein (CAP).

6. Catabolite repression is: (a) synonymous with feedback inhibition; (b) mediated by intracellular levels of lactose; (c) in part regulated by hormonal levels in procaryotic cells; (d) in part regulated by intracellular levels of cyclic AMP.

7. When a repressor protein combines with an inducer: (a) mRNA synthesis is inhibited; (b) the resulting complex is inactive; (c) lactose is not metabolized (in the example of the *lac* operon); (d) the complex then has a strong affinity for the operator.

8. "The regulatory ligand is the end product of a metabolic pathway which can shut off its own synthesis by inhibiting the activity of one of the early enzymes in its own biosynthetic pathway." This is the mechanism of: (a) precursor activation; (b) energy-link control; (c) activating enzymes; (d) feedback inhibition.

9. The specificity of an enzyme is dependent on the composition of its protein. Proteins are composed of: (a) carbohydrates; (b) vitamins; (c) amino acids; (d) nucleic acids.

10. A competitive inhibitor of enzymes catalyzing reactions of succinic acid is: (a) sulfanilamide; (b) cyanide; (c) lead; (d) malonic acid.

11. A nonreversible enzyme inhibitor: (a) competes with the substrate for an active site on an enzyme; (b) "destroys" the substrate; (c) destroys enzyme activity; (d) forces the Michaelis-Menton reaction to proceed from left to right only.

12. Physically and chemically, the living cell is: (a) a closed system; (b) an open system; (c) in a maximum state or entropy; (d) devoid of energy-extracting mechanisms; (e) pure energy.

13. According to Jacob's and Monad's operon concept of enzyme induction (and, by extrapolation, repression), controls over enzyme synthesis operate at the level of: (a) DNA synthesis; (b) mRNA synthesis; (c) protein synthesis on a ribosome; (d) answers a, b, and c are all correct.

14. According to the model of the operon, *E. coli* makes the enzymes necessary to utilize lactose as a carbon source: (a) only when the bacteria are exposed to lactose; (b) all the time; (c) only when the bacteria are not exposed to lactose; (d) when under observation by Jacob and Monad.

15. Apoenzymes are composed of several hundred: (a) proteins; (b) carbohydrates; (c) anabolites; (d) amino acids.

16. Which of the following is a coenzyme? (a) PABA; (b) ATP; (c) thiamine (vitamin B_1); (d) penicillinase.

17. Cyanide is poisonous to mammals and bacteria because, among other things, it: (a) competes with substrates for active sites on enzymes; (b) breaks hydrogen bonds of enzymes, thereby denaturing them and so inactivating them; (c) drops the pH low enough to inactivate enzymes; (d) breaks the chelate of iron-containing enzymes like catalase, thereby inactivating them.

Answers: 1. (a); 2. (d); 3. (b); 4. (c); 5. (a); 6. (d); 7. (b); 8. (d); 9. (c); 10. (d); 11. (c);
        12. (b); 13. (b); 14. (a); 15. (d); 16. (c); 17. (d).

Chapter 10

Bacterial Metabolism:
Energy Production

INTRODUCTION: Like other forms of life, and often utilizing similar biochemical pathways, bacteria derive the energy necessary to sustain their existence by converting some compounds to other compounds. Energy is required for so many vital processes that nondormant cells must continuously produce it or die. In this chapter the various means (e.g., aerobic, anaerobic, light-dependent) by which various bacteria derive energy are discussed.

Expanded Outline

I. Fundamental Principles of Energetics
    A. Free-energy change (ΔG). Expressed in calories (cal). The amount of energy liberated or taken up during the course of a reaction
        1. Exergonic reaction — release of energy ($-\Delta G$)
        2. Endergonic reaction — requires energy ($+\Delta G$)
    B. Coupled reactions. Energy released from exergonic reactions is used to drive endergonic reactions via a common reactant
        1. Common reactant — usually high-energy-transfer compound (e.g., ATP)
    C. Oxidation-reduction reactions. Probably most common reaction involved in energy production
        1. Terms
            a. Oxidation — loss of electrons
            b. Dehydrogenations — oxidations involving the loss of hydrogen atoms
            c. Reduction — gain of electrons
            d. Oxidizing agent (oxidant) — absorbs electrons and becomes reduced
               (e.g., $Fe^{3+} + e^- \rightarrow Fe^{2+}$)
            e. Reducing agent (reductant) — donates electrons and becomes oxidized
        2. Oxidation-reduction (O/R) systems
            a. Standard reduction potential or electromotive potential (E_0'). The more positive the E_0', the greater the oxidizing ability of the compound (e.g., the greater its ability to donate electrons).

b. Energy release — comes from one O/R system reacting with another. If the E_0' difference from one O/R system to another is sufficiently large, ADP may be converted to the higher-energy compound ATP.

II. Energy Production by Aerobic Respiration — The Cytochrome System (also known as the respiratory chain or electron-transport system).
A. Overall reaction. Sequence of oxidation reactions that transfers electrons from one compound to another (sometimes releasing enough energy to generate ATP). The final electron acceptor is O_2, which is converted to H_2O.
B. Compounds of the cytochrome system
   1. Nicotinamide-adenine-dinucleotide (NAD) and nicotinamide-adenine-dinucleotide-phosphate (NADP). Coenzymes to dehydrogenases. Vitamin niacin is precursor in NAD biosynthesis.
      a. Reduced form: NADH (NADPH)
      b. Oxidized form: NAD (NADP)
   2. Flavin-adenine-dinucleotide (FAD) and flavin-mononucleotide (FMN). Coenzymes to dehydrogenases. Flavoproteins are partly composed of FAD or FMN, and part of this structure is the vitamin riboflavin.
      a. Reduced from: $FADH_2$ ($FMNH_2$)
      b. Oxidized form: FAD (FMN)
   3. Coenzyme Q (ubiquinone). Fat-soluble coenzyme that functions as acceptor of e^- from flavin-linked dehydrogenases.
   4. Cytochromes. Contain single iron atom which is responsible for the acceptance and donation of electrons. On the basis of their absorption spectra they are divided into cytochromes *b, c, c, a,* and a_3. Each has a different function in the electron-transport chain.
C. Sequence of oxidation — see text Fig. 10-2.
D. Sources of electrons for the respiratory chain
   1. Heterotrophic bacteria — examples of how glucose indirectly contributes electrons to the respiratory chain
      a. Glycolysis — glucose → 2 pyruvic acid molecules (See Figs. 10-A, 10-8, 10-B, 10-2 in Summary.)
      b. Tricarboxylic acid cycle (TCA; Krebs cycle) — glucose + $6O_2$ → $6CO_2$ + $6H_2O$ (See Figs. 10-8, 10-2 in Summary.)
      c. Pentose cycle — alternative pathway of glycolysis (See text Fig. 10-5.)
      d. CO_2 fixation — unrelated to autotrophic CO_2 fixation. Provides compounds to be used in Krebs cycle. There are three variations of CO_2 fixation that convert either pyruvate or phosphoenolpyruvate (PEP) to oxaloacetate.
      e. Glyoxylate cycle — modification or "bypass" of Krebs cycle. 2 acetyl-CoA → succinate + 2H + 2CoA
      f. Lipid metabolism — glycerol converted and then catabolized via carbohydrate catabolic pathways; fatty acids are degraded to two-carbon compounds which can enter the TCA cycle.
      g. Catabolism of proteins — extracellular proteases hydrolyze proteins to peptides, which are taken up by the cell and catabolized by one of many pathways, depending on strain of organism and type of amino acid.

2. Chemoautotrophic bacteria. CO_2 fixed to glyceraldehyde 3-P, which requires lots of energy derived from the oxidations of inorganic compounds. NAD usually converted to NADH by consumption of ATP. Because these processes are energetically inefficient, chemoautotrophic bacteria, while the least fastidious, grow more slowly than other metabolic types of bacteria.

III. Energy Production by Anaerobic Dissimilation. Oxygen not the final electron acceptor.
   A. Anaerobic respiration — inorganic compound other than oxygen is final electron acceptor. The following are two examples:
      1. Nitrate final electron acceptor — enzyme, *respiratory nitrate reductase*, catalyzes the reaction, coupling reduction of nitrate with the oxidation of a cytochrome:
      $$C_6H_{12}O_6 + 12NO_3^- \rightarrow 6CO_2 + 6H_2O + 12NO_2$$
      2. Sulfate final electron acceptor — cytochrome C_3 (of *Desulfovibrio*) is oxidized while sulfate is reduced, probably resulting in the production of ATP:
      $$2 \text{ Lactate} + SO_4{}^{2-} + 4H^+ \rightarrow 2 \text{ acetate} + 2CO_2 + S^2 + 2H_2O$$
   B. Fermentation – does not involve respiratory chain or cytochrome
      1. Glycolysis — see Figs. 10-A and 10-8: The Embden-Meyerhof pathway and by-products. Cells consume two molecules of ATP and generate four molecules of ATP.
      2. Strickland reaction — pairs of amino acids are used, one becoming oxidized, the other reduced.

IV. Energy Production by Photosynthesis. Green plants and some bacteria reduce CO_2 to metabolically useful carbohydrate. This process requires a great deal of energy provided by trapped sunlight: $2H_2A + CO_2 \xrightarrow{\text{light}} (CH_2O) + 2A + H_2O$, where A is oxygen in the case of plants and often S in the case of bacteria. There are two main processes for converting light energy into chemical energy.
   A. Cyclic photophosphorylation — bacteriochlorophyll is excited by light, becomes positively charged, traps electrons, and passes them as shown:

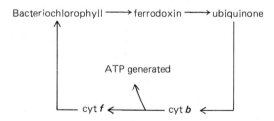

   B. Noncyclic photophosphorylation — occurs in plants and algae.
      1. Light-pigment system I — like bacterial pigments.
      2. System II — electron is transferred from hydroxyl ion of water and subsequently produces ATP via the cytochrome system. The electron reduces NADP with the production of another ATP.

Summary

Bacteria, as a group, are metabolically as well as morphologically diverse. Various species derive energy by aerobic, anaerobic, and/or light-dependent pathways. Energy released from exergonic reactions is used to drive endergonic reactions via a common reactant which is often ATP. After reading the text and this corresponding expanded outline, you should now be familiar with some of the diverse mechanisms that enable cells to produce chemical energy. Therefore, to impart a greater appreciation of some of the nuances, this summary will be limited to a single example which can be covered in greater depth. Many aerobes can convert glucose to carbon dioxide, water, and energy via the Embden-Meyerhof and Krebs cycles, in conjunction with the cytochrome system. In the Embden-Meyerhof pathway (Fig. 10-A) glucose is, in three sequential reactions, converted to fructose-1, 6-diphosphate. This requires the "expenditure" of 2 ATPs. However, fructose-1, 6-phosphate can be cleaved into two three-carbon molecules, both of which are converted, in a sequence of reactions, to pyruvic acid, thus producing 4 ATPs. Therefore, there is a net gain of 2 ATPs and 2 NADHs. Each reaction is mediated by a specific enzyme, without which glucose could not be so utilized.

Pyruvate can be converted to acetyl-CoA (Fig. 10-8) with the aid of coenzyme A, the energy from TTP, and the concomitant reduction of NAD.

In the Krebs cycle, acetyl-CoA is joined to oxaloacetic acid to form the six-carbon citric acid (Fig. 10-B). In seven distinct, enzyme-mediated reactions, $2CO_2$s are removed, 3 NADs are reduced, and oxaloacetic acid is again a product. This oxaloacetic acid is then available to be joined to another molecule of active acetate. In this way all the carbons from glucose can be converted to CO_2, and potential energy is thereby gained from the formation of high-energy bonds (in ATPs and GTPs) and the reductions of NADs and FADs.

However, without a cytochrome system and the electron acceptor O_2, NADH + FADH could not be reoxidized. Without NAD and FAD to accept H (electrons) from isocitric acid, a-ketoglutaric acid, and malic acid, the Krebs reactions could not occur. Oxidation of NADH and FADH is accomplished by the electron-transport chain (Fig. 10-2). When NAD passes electrons to FAD, when cyt b passes electrons to cyt c, and when cyt a passes electrons to cyt a_3, enough energy is released to enable ADPs to form high-energy bonds and thereby be converted to ATP. Finally, oxygen accepts the electrons and is converted to water.

To cite one simplistic analogy, when the bonds of glucose are broken, energy is released. If all the energy were released suddenly as heat, like the breaking of bonds of petroleum in the case of an automobile, than the cell would die, for the energy would not be channeled *efficiently* to drive anabolic reactions, but would instead cause thermal damage. But cells chemically capture energy in a much more efficient and controlled manner than any machine. The electron-transport chain, in this analogy, resembles a waterfall. NADH has a great deal of potential energy, and if it passed electrons downhill, directly to O_2, then the system would resemble a giant waterfall that would drive a turbine (make ATPs), but so much energy would be released suddenly that a great deal of it would be wasted heat. Instead, the electron-transport chain resembles a series of smaller waterfalls. As the electrons flow "downhill" from NAD(P) to cyt_3, three (perhaps fewer in procaryotes) of the drops are sufficiently great to produce enough energy to form an ATP from ADP and inorganic phosphate. These ATPs can then deliver their stored energy when and where required.

The Embden-Meyerhof and the Krebs cycles represent but two of thousands of known biochemical pathways. Just as these pathways "connect" when oxygen is present, so all the metabolic reactions are interrelated.

The two main purposes of metabolism are the building of a chemical compounds and the production of energy: energy used for mechanical work (motion), chemical work (anabolism), osmotic work, etc. A continuous flow of this energy is vital to the highly organized open system that we call life. Take away this energy supply and the most highly organized systems in the universe (cells) will quickly drift toward entropy (death).

Here is a summary of energy considerations involving the Embden-Meyerhof, Krebs, and oxidative phosphorylation pathways (per 1 mole of glucose oxidized completely to $CO_2 + H_2O$).

EMBDEN-MYERHOF PATHWAY

$-2ATP + 4ATP \longrightarrow$	2ATP
2 NADH (when O_2 is present) $\longrightarrow$ oxidative phosphorylation $\longrightarrow$	6ATP
	8ATP

LINK

---

2 pyruvate $\longrightarrow$ 2 acetyl-CoA + 2NADH $\longrightarrow$ oxidative phosphorylation	6ATP

KREBS

---

2 isocitrate $\longrightarrow$ 28-ketoglutarate + $2CO_2$ + 2NADH $\longrightarrow$ oxidative phosphorylation $\longrightarrow$	6ATP
2 α-ketoglutarate $\longrightarrow$ 2 succinyl-CoA + $2CO_2$ + 2NADH $\longrightarrow$ oxidative phosphorylation $\longrightarrow$	6ATP
2 succinyl CoA $\longrightarrow$ 2 succinate + 2GTP	= 2ATP
2 succinate $\longrightarrow$ 2 fumarate + 2FAD $\longrightarrow$ oxidative phosphorylation $\longrightarrow$	4ATP
2 malate $\longrightarrow$ 2 oxaloacetate $\longrightarrow$ 2NADH $\longrightarrow$ oxidative phosphorylation $\longrightarrow$	6ATP
	24ATP

TOTAL

EM: 8ATP, Link: 6ATP, Krebs: 24ATP = 38ATP

Thus, for each mole of glucose (180 g) consumed, by humans and perhaps by certain bacteria, about 320 large calories are produced (enough to raise 10 l of water 32°C) provided there is ample oxygen and all the glucose is fully oxidized. The efficiency of this release of chemical bond energy is about 45 percent.

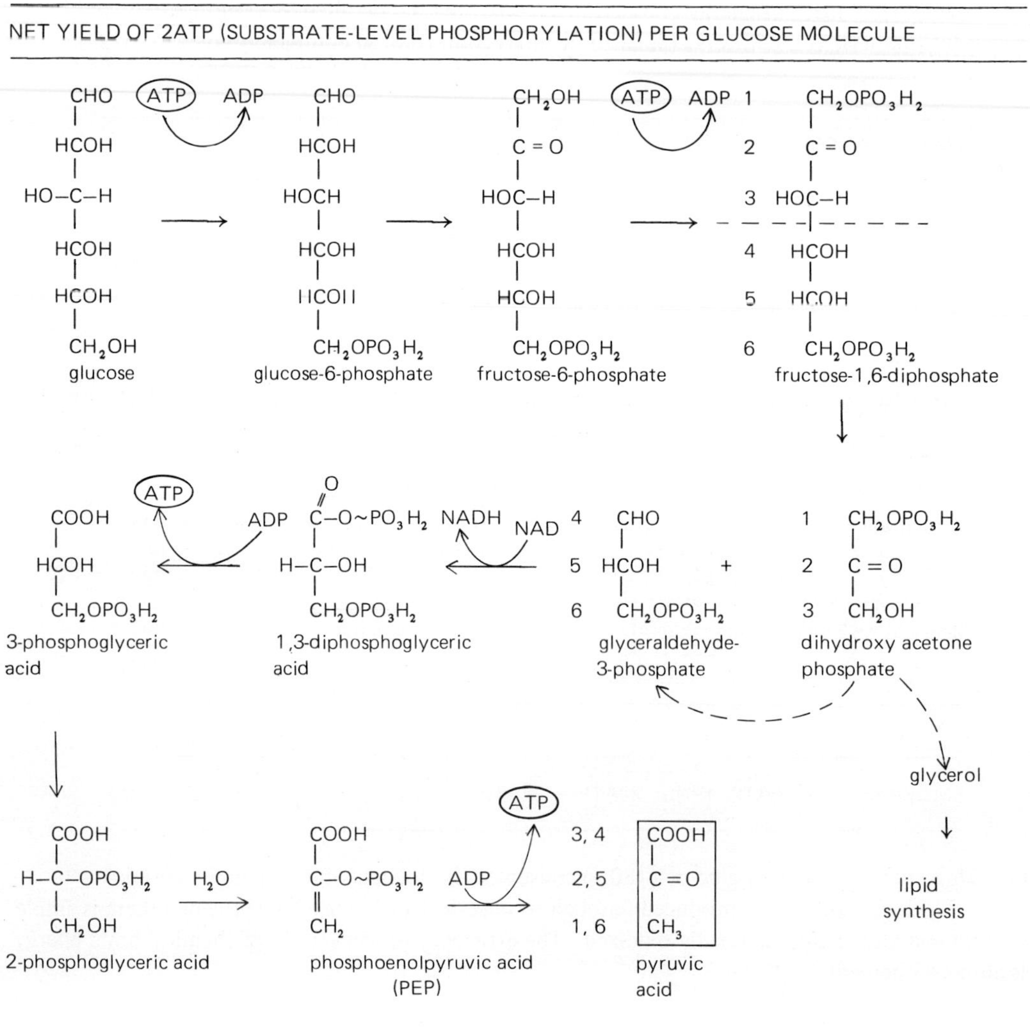
NET YIELD OF 2ATP (SUBSTRATE-LEVEL PHOSPHORYLATION) PER GLUCOSE MOLECULE
ATP
ADP
glucose
glucose-6-phosphate
fructose-6-phosphate
fructose-1,6-diphosphate
glyceraldehyde-3-phosphate
dihydroxy acetone phosphate
NADH
NAD
1,3-diphosphoglyceric acid
3-phosphoglyceric acid
2-phosphoglyceric acid
H₂O
phosphoenolpyruvic acid (PEP)
pyruvic acid
glycerol
lipid synthesis

Figure 10-A. Embden-Meyerhof Pathway (glycolysis) (Note that this pathway as represented here includes the chemical formulas of the compounds involved. Cf. text Fig. 10-3.)

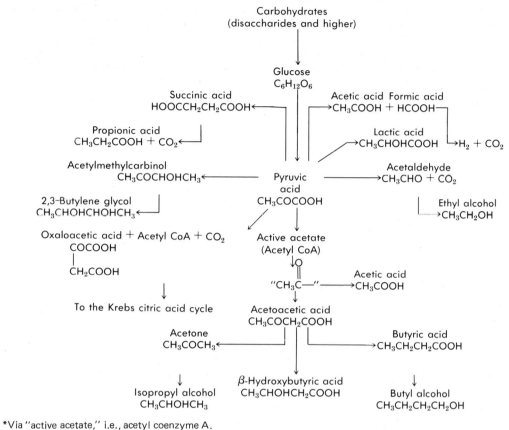

*Via "active acetate," i.e., acetyl coenzyme A.

Figure 10-8. Pyruvic acid as the "hub" of bacterial fermentation pathways.

Functions: 1. Interconnection of carbohydrate, lipid, and amino acid metabolism.
2. Supply of carbon "skeletons" for biosynthesis, ATP formation via electron-transport system.
3. Source of electrons for the respiratory chain.

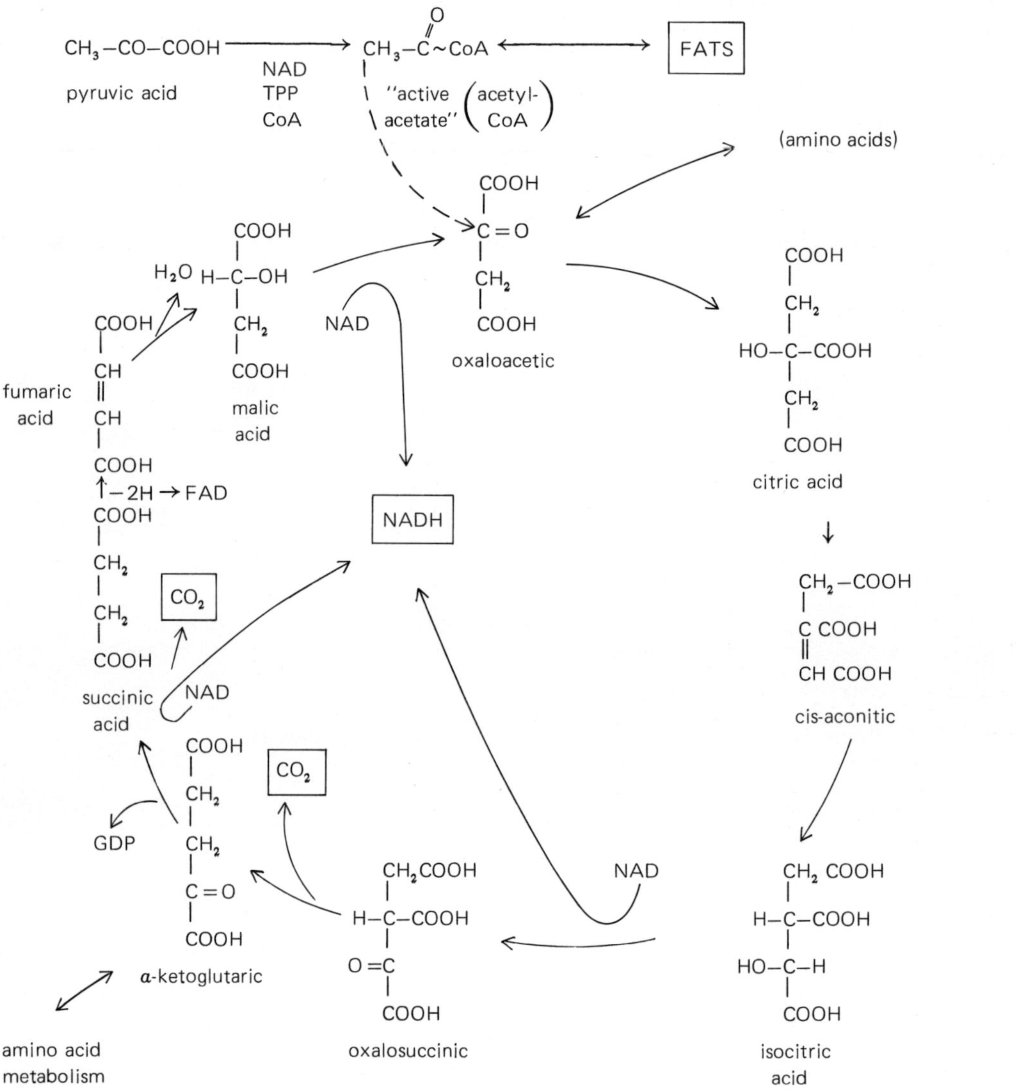

Figure 10-B. The citric acid cycle (Krebs).

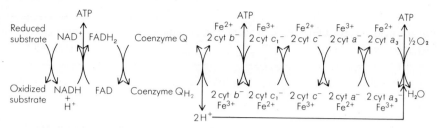

Figure 10-2. The respiratory chain.

Programmed Self-Test

Do not begin this self-test before reading the corresponding chapter in the text.

FUNDAMENTAL PRINCIPLES OF ENERGETICS (Text pages 170 to 174)

The amount of energy liberated or taken up during the course of a reaction is referred to as the _____ .	
If ΔG of a chemical reaction has a negative value, the reaction _____ and is termed _____ .	free-energy change (ΔG)
Using *standard concentration,* the concentration of all reactants is _____ in the steady state.	releases energy; exergonic
Under conditions of standard concentration, the free energy change (ΔG) of a reaction is referred to by the special term _____ .	$1.0\,M$
A common reactant (Y) coupling an endergonic reaction with an exergonic reaction is referred to as an _____ or _____ compound.	$\Delta G°$
Of the high-energy-transfer compounds found in bacteria, _____ is considered the most important.	energy-rich; energy-transfer
Energy is released from ATP by _____ .	ATP
When ATP is hydrolyzed within the cell, the free energy may be as high as _____ .	hydrolysis
Oxidation is the _____ of electrons.	−12.5 kcal
An oxidizing agent (oxidant) _____ electrons and will, therefore, become _____ .	loss

When fumaric acid absorbs two hydrogen atoms (which contain electrons), it becomes reduced to _____ .

absorbs; reduced

The ferrous ion is a _____ agent; it _____ electrons and becomes oxidized to a _____ ion.

succinic acid

Energy production by bacteria may be roughly divided into three categories: _____ , _____ , and _____ .

reducing; donates; ferric

ENERGY PRODUCTION BY AEROBIC RESPIRATION – THE CYTOCHROME SYSTEM (Text pages 174 to 181)

The respiratory chain is also known as the _____ or _____ .

aerobic; anaerobic; light-dependent

Enzymes which remove electrons and hydrogen ions from reduced substrates are referred to as _____ .

cytochrome system; electron-transport system

Coenzyme Q is also called _____.

dehydrogenases

Cytochromes can be classified into three main groups based on differences in _____ .

ubiquinone

The respiratory chain of bacteria is physically associated with _____.

absorption spectra

In glycolysis, glucose is eventually converted into _____ .

the cell membrane

The tricarboxylic acid cycle is also called the _____.

pyruvic acid

In bacteria, _____ is often the end product of heterotrophic CO_2 fixation.

Krebs cycle

The special enzymatic mechanisms by which TCA-cycle intermediates are replenished are termed _____ reactions.

oxaloacetate

ENERGY PRODUCTION BY ANAEROBIC DISSIMILATION (Text pages 181 to 185)

Spirillum itersonii can substitute _____for oxygen as the final electron acceptor in a respiratory chain.

anapterotic

Anaerobic mechanisms of energy production which do not involve a respiratory chain or cytochromes are called _____ .

nitrate

Some clostridia have special enzymes that enable them to ferment pairs of _____ in a reaction known as the

_____ .

fermentation

ENERGY PRODUCTION BY PHOTOSYNTHESIS (Text pages 185 to 187)

In order for CO_2 to be reduced to carbohydrate, an abundance of two important factors, _____ and _____ , is necessary.

amino acids;
 Strickland reaction

Instead of consuming water during photosynthesis, bacteria may instead use _____ .

ATP; a chemical
 reductant

Excited bacteriochlorophyll is a strong _____ agent.

H_2S

The form of photosynthesis that occurs in bacteria is usually

_____ .

oxidizing

In noncyclic photophosphorylation, the electron is *not* recycled to chlorophyll but is channeled to reduce _____ .

cyclic phosphorylation

NADP

Multiple-Choice Test

Underline the correct answer.

1. In the anaerobic energy-extracting mechanism, called fermentation, the final electron acceptor is: (a) oxygen; (b) carbon dioxide; (c) an organic compound; (d) a catabolic enzyme.

2. A possible end product of the Krebs cycle is: (a) DNA; (b) RNA; (c) CO_2; (d) O_2; (e) lactic acid.

3. Organisms that only derive energy by splitting the chemical bonds of molecules with more than one carbon atom are called: (a) autotrophs; (b) phototrophs; (c) bacteria; (d) heterotrophs.

4. In cells, energy is stored: (a) as heat; (b) as sunlight; (c) in NO_3; (d) in ATP; (e) in AMP.

5. During the process of microbial fermentation, which one of these *cannot* be the only end product(s)? (a) Carbon dioxide and water; (b) acetyl methyl carbonyl; (c) organic acids; (d) organic acid and inorganic gas; (e) alcohols and gas.

Answers: 1. (c); 2. (c); 3. (d); 4. (e); 5. (a).

Catabolic Pathway Comprehension Test

I. Embden-Meyerhof (EM). Questions 1 to 5 refer to the diagram below.

1. Place a circle around, and label "A", the arrows of those steps that consume energy (e.g., $\overset{A}{\longrightarrow}$).

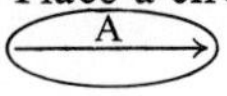

2. Likewise label those steps that release "usable" energy "B".

3. Similarly, label the step that involves a substrate-level phosphorylation "C".

4. What is the net gain of ATP molecules from the anaerobic conversion of glucose to pyruvic acid?

5. Which of the following molecules contains the most potential energy? (a) Glucose; (b) glucose-6-phosphate, (c) fructose-1,6-diphosphate; (d) pyruvic acid.

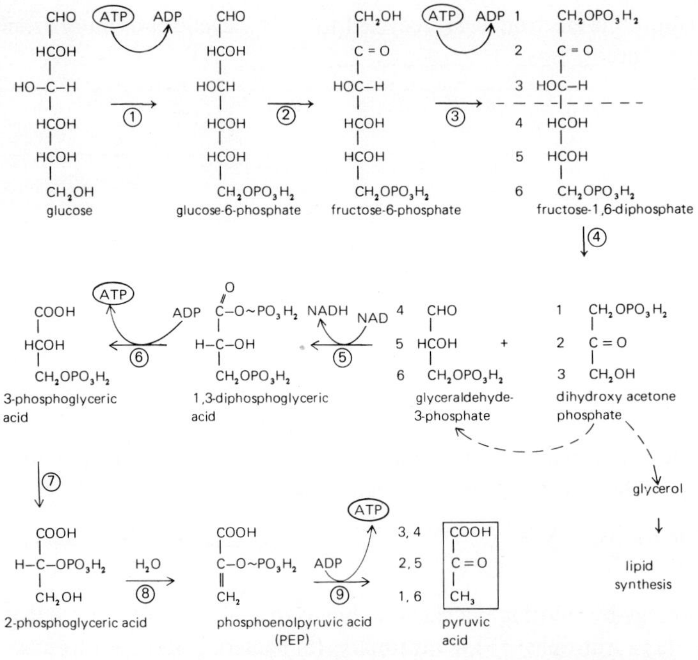

Answers: 1. 1, 3; 2. 6, 9 (and 5 in the presence of oxygen); 3. 5; 4. 2; 5. (c).

II. Krebs cycle. Questions 6 to 10 refer to the diagram below.

6. As in question 1, circle and label "A" the compound that will yield 3 ATPs in eucaryotes in the presence of oxygen.

7. Likewise, label with a "B" the compound that releases enough energy to "synthesize" 2 ATPs during oxidative phosphorylation.

8. What is the net number of ATPs made when glucose is converted to CO_2 and H_2O via the EM, Krebs, and cytochrome systems?

9. Oxaloacetic acid is generated in the: (a) EM pathway; (b) Krebs cycle; (c) cytochrome system; (d) course of amino acid synthesis.

10. Citric to isocitric acid involves the loss and gain of: (a) H_2O; (b) CO_2; (c) CoA; (d) COOH; (e) CH_2.

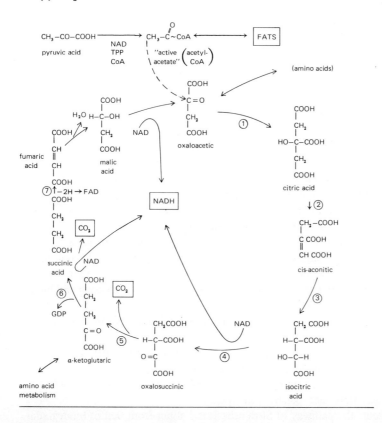

Answers: 6. NADH; 7. FADH; 8. 38; 9. (b); 10. (a).

Chapter 11

Bacterial Metabolism: Energy Utilization and Biosynthesis

INTRODUCTION: The production of energy (formation of molecules such as ATP) is necessary for vital processes such as motility, active nutrient transport, biosynthesis of macromolecules, and the fixation of carbon dioxide by autotrophic bacteria. In this chapter selected examples of such energy-requiring processes are discussed.

Expanded Outline and Summary

I. Expenditure of Energy.
  A. Heat production.
    1. ATPase may dissipate excess ATP, thus aiding in the regulation of energy metabolism.
    2. Inefficiency of biochemical reactions: Not all energy released from catabolism is captured in high-energy compounds; some is released as heat.
  B. Motility—involves the transformation of chemical energy into mechanical energy. ATP is believed to yield the required chemical energy.
  C. Transport of nutrients by bacteria.
    1. Transport processes not requiring metabolic energy.
      a. Simple or passive diffusion, e.g., water and some lipid-soluble molecules.
      b. Facilitated diffusion—Solute combines reversibly with specific carrier molecule in the membrane (called permease or porter), and carrier-solute complex oscillates between the inner and outer surfaces of the membrane, releasing and binding the solute on either side.
    2. Transport processes requiring metabolic energy (see text pages 193 to 194 for mechanisms).
      a. Group translocation—certain sugars and nucleic acids, among other compounds, are transported into the cell by this mechanism.
      b. Active transport—mechanism by which most solutes are taken into the cell.
  D. Biosynthesis of macromolecules (general principles).
    1. For each molecule the pathway of biosynthesis is distinct from that of biodegradation; thus, stable macromolecules may exist.

2. Energy-requiring biosynthetic processes are always coupled to energy-yielding reactions, the sums of which are exergonic and irreversible in the direction of biosynthesis.

3. Biosynthetic pathways are controlled independent of corresponding biodegradative pathways.

Note: These three factors enable cells to synthesize and retain quantities of macromolecules necessary to sustain life.

II. The structure and Biosynthesis of DNA (deoxyribonucleic acid).
   A. Structure of DNA.

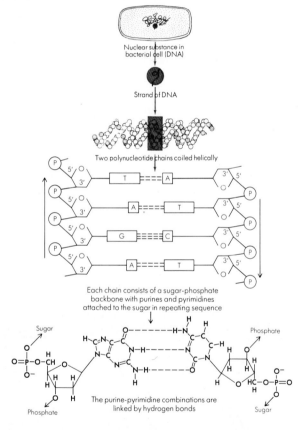

Figure 11-4. DNA molecular configuration and chemical structure as viewed in progressively greater detail.

1. The double helix—long, narrow molecule composed of two strands, wound around one another. Each strand has opposite polarity, one being terminated by 3'-OH, the other by 5'-$OPO_3{}^{2-}$.

2. Components of DNA.
   a. Bases.
      i. Purines—adenine, guanine.
      ii. Pyrimidines—cytosine, thymine.

        b. Sugar—deoxyribose (five-carbon).

        c. Phosphoric acid group.

   3. Arrangement of the components in DNA.

        a. Nucleoside—base + sugar.

        b. Nucleotide—nucleoside + phosphate.

        c. Polynucleotide—strand of DNA composed of chain of nucleotides linked together by phosphodiester bonds. Sugars, which form the "backbone" of the molecule, are connected by outward-projecting phosphodiester bonds; the bases project inward.

        d. Double helix—consists of a series of complementary base pairs (i.e., a base on one strand linked to a *complementary* base on the opposite strand). In DNA there occur only two types of complementary base pairs:

           i. adenine on one polynucleotide strand is linked to thymine on the opposite polynucleotide strand by two hydrogen bonds.

           ii. guanine on one polynucleotide strand is linked to cytosine on the other polynucleotide strand by *three* hydrogen bonds.

  B. Biosynthesis of nucleotides—involves numerous enzymatically catalyzed reactions, some requiring energy from ATP. A nucleotide pool must be present before DNA can be synthesized.

  C. Synthesis of DNA from nucleotides.

   1. Pool of nucleotide triphosphates (activated forms of nucleotides) are synthesized.

   2. The two strands in the double helix are nicked ("cut") at a particular point where the synthesis of new DNA is to begin.

   3. The two strands denature (separate) at the nick.

   4. Each single strand acts as a template for the assembly of a new, complementary, strand.

   5. In this way, two *double*-stranded daughter DNA molecules, each consisting of one parental strand and one newly synthesized strand, are formed.

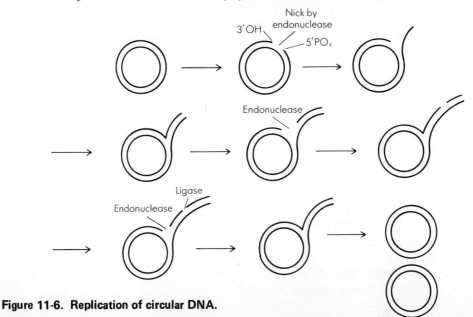

Figure 11-6. Replication of circular DNA.

III. Biosynthesis of Proteins (another example of the biosynthesis of an informational macro-
molecule).
   A. The nature of proteins.
       1. Functions.
           a. Structural (e.g., flagella).
           b. Enzymatic.
       2. Composition—may contain from a hundred or so to many thousands of amino
           acids, of which there are about 20 different kinds, joined together by peptide bonds.
       3. Diversity—there are thousands of different proteins in a bacterial cell, and each dif-
           fers from all the others in its sequence of amino acids. The sequence of amino acids
           is ultimately determined by the sequence of bases in the genetic code.
   B. The genetic code.
       1. Triplet—three bases constitute a "word," specifying either an amino acid or the
           termination of protein synthesis. "Reading" moves sequentially from one triplet
           to the next without pause.
           a. Nonsense triplet—one of the three "words" terminating protein synthesis.
       2. Redundancy or degeneracy—the same amino acid may be specified by more than
           one "word" (there may be 0, 1, 2, or 3 synonyms depending on the specified amino
           acid). In such cases, the genetic code is said to be *degenerate*.
       3. Universality—identical triplets specify identical amino acids regardless of the life
           form.
   C. Transcription—synthesis of messenger RNA (mRNA) complementary to one of the two
       strands of the DNA template.
       1. mRNA—like DNA except that it is single-stranded and, like other RNA molecules,
           contains ribose in place of deoxyribose and uracil in place of thymine. If the se-
           quence of bases in the DNA strand is:

   | adenine | cytosine | guanine | guanine | thymine | thymine |

   the complementary sequence of bases in mRNA would be

   | uracil | guanine | cytosine | cytosine | adenine | adenine |

       2. Process—the two DNA strands separate, and one of them serves as the template for
           the synthesis of a complementary strand of RNA by a DNA-dependent RNA poly-
           merase.

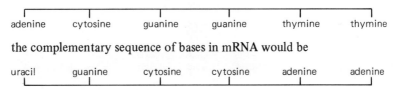

   D. Translation—process in which the genetic information present in a mRNA molecule
       directs the order of the specific amino acids during protein synthesis.
       1. Molecules and structures involved.
           a. mRNA—See above. Triplets termed codons.
           b. Transfer RNA (tRNA)—Single-stranded molecule containing 76 to 79 nucelotides.
               Has "cloverleaf" conformation because some portions of its base sequence are

complementary to other portions, so that some base pairing occurs. Three un-
paired bases form an anticodon triplet. An amino acid can be linked to the
ribose-phosphate of the terminal adenylic acid. Activation—Specific enzymes
(aminoacyl-tRNA synthetases) link specific activated amino acids to specific
tRNAs. Thus, a specific tRNA with a specific anticodon carries a specific amino
acid (one of the 20 kinds).

c. Ribosomes—composed of rRNA and protein. Intact bacterial ribosomes (70S)
consist of a larger 50S subunit and a smaller 30S subunit. Ribosomes are the
sites of protein synthesis. When bound on the ribosome, codons of mRNA at-
tract complementary anticodons of various tRNA molecules, so that amino
acids attached to the tRNA become linked by peptide bonds in a specific sequence determined by the mRNA. Ribosomes greatly enhance codon- (and
proper codon-) anticodon binding and recognition.

2. Assembly of the protein chain (refer to Fig. 11-9).
a. Ribosome rolls to codon (GCA), which receives the incoming aminoacyl-tRNA
(ala-tRNA). Binding of specific tRNA to mRNA also requires GTP and T factor
(protein).
b. Peptidyl transferase catalyzes the formation of the peptide bond between the
growing peptide chain and the additional amino acid.

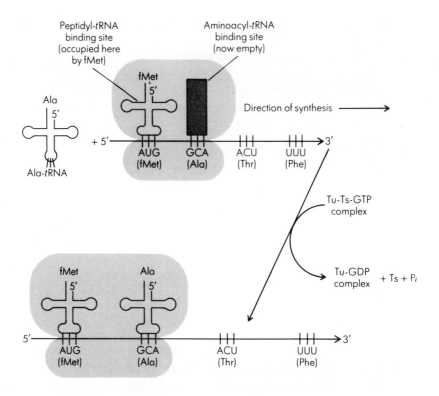

Figure 11-9. Diagram of protein-chain assembly at a ribosome.

Figure 11-9. *(Continued.)*

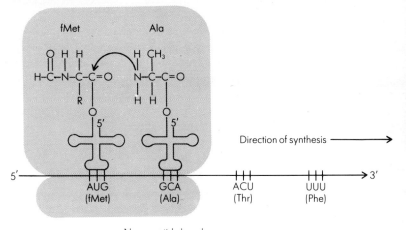

B

New peptide bond

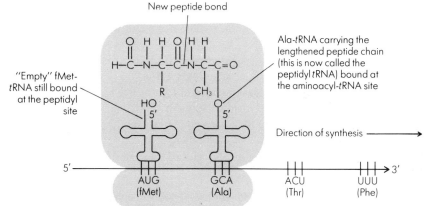

C

D

    c. Once tRNA has donated its peptide chain to the next aminoacyl-tRNA, it leaves
        the site to become reactivated. This occurs as part of the *translocation reaction*
        where "peptidyl-tRNA is physically shifted from the aminoacyl site to the pep-
        tidyl site, thus bumping the empty tRNA from the peptidyl site." Simultane-
        ously mRNA moves along the ribosome by one codon.
    d. This peptide elongation step occurs repetitively until the protein is synthesized
        and/or termination occurs:

                                            mRNA

IV.   The Structure and Biosynthesis of a Cell-Wall Peptidoglycan.
    A.   Composition—varies from one species to another but is generally composed of:
        1. Acetylglucosamine (AGA).
        2. Acetylmuramic acid (AMA).
        3. Peptide consisting of four or five amino acids.
    B.   Structure—rigid component consisting of alternating units of AGA and AMA with
        short peptide chains projecting from the AMA units. Many of the peptide chains are
        cross-linked to each other.
    C.   Synthesis of peptidoglycan. See Fig. 11-12 and text pages 206 to 207 for summary of
        reactions.

V.   Fixation of Carbon Dioxide by Autotrophic Bacteria. These are highly endergonic reduc-
    tion processes requiring electron donors such as NADH or reduced ferredoxin. In the re-
    ductive pentose cycle (Calvin-Bassham cycle), a two-carbon compound is converted to a
    three-carbon sugar. See Fig. 11-13.

Programmed Self-Test

Do not begin this self-test before reading the corresponding chapter in the text.

EXPENDITURE OF ENERGY (Text pages 190 to 194)

Presumably, the activity of the enzyme _____ is mainly
responsible for bacterial heat production.

Except for water and some lipid-soluble molecules, few compounds   ATPase
can enter the cell by _____ diffusion.

In *facilitated diffusion*, membrane "carrier" molecules are known   simple (passive)
as _____ .

During group translocation, sugars are taken into cells in the form sugar-_____.	permeases *or* porters
Energy-requiring _____ processes are obligatorily coupled to the energy-yielding breakdown of ATP so that the overall coupled reaction is exergonic and thus irreversible.	phosphates

THE STRUCTURE AND BIOSYNTHESIS OF DNA (Text pages 194 to 198)

Two kinds of purine are _____ and_____.	biosynthetic
Two kinds of pyrimidine are _____ and _____.	adenine; guanine
In double-stranded DNA, adenine is paired with _____.	cytosine; thymine
A nucleotide is composed of a _____, a _____ _____, and a _____ group.	thymine
Weak bonds known as _____ form a link between a base on one strand of DNA and an opposing base on the other strand of DNA.	base; five-carbon sugar; phosphoric acid (or phosphate)

BIOSYNTHESIS OF PROTEINS (Text pages 198 to 205)

The building blocks of proteins are _____.	hydrogen bonds
In proteins amino acids are joined by _____.	amino acids
Protein synthesis occurs on _____.	peptide linkages
The transcription of DNA results in the synthesis of _____.	ribosomes
In RNA the sugar is _____.	mRNA
The genetic code is called _____ because the same amino acid may be coded for by more than one kind of codon.	ribose
The process in which the genetic information present in mRNA molecules directs the order of the specific amino acids during protein synthesis is called _____.	degenerate

To the ribose of the terminal nucleotide of tRNA, a specific _____ can be enzymatically linked.	translation
Ribosomes are composed of _____ and _____.	amino acid
Ribosomes of bacteria are composed of two subunits; one _____S, the other _____S.	rRNA; proteins
The enzyme _____ catalyzes the formation of the peptide bond between the growing peptide chain and the new amino acid to be added.	50; 30
The translocation reaction requires energy, which is obtained from the hydrolysis of _____.	peptidyl transferase
A molecule of mRNA to which several ribosomes are attached is referred to as a _____.	GTP

THE STRUCTURE AND BIOSYNTHESIS OF CELL-WALL PEPTIDOGLYCAN; FIXATION OF CARBON DIOXIDE BY AUTOTROPHIC BACTERIA (Text pages 205 to 208)

Peptidoglycans are very large polymers composed of three kinds of building blocks, _____, _____, and _____.	polysome
Several amino acids in the peptide of peptidoglycan are in the ____ configuration, which is uncommon in nature.	acetylglucosamine; acetylmuramic acid; peptide
In peptidoglycan, short peptide chains project from the _____ component.	*D*
The reductive pentose cycle is also referred to as the _____ _____ cycle.	acetylmuramic acid
Besides being highly endergonic, carbon dioxide fixation is a _____ process.	Calvin-Bassham
The organic end product of the reductive pentose cycle is _____.	reduction
	glucose

Multiple-Choice Test

Underline the correct answer.

1. Group translocation transport *differs* from active transport in that during the process of group translocation: (a) energy is required; (b) the solute is chemically modified; (c) energy is not required; (d) water and some lipid-soluble molecules enter the cell, while in active transport sugars enter the cell.

2. Anticodons are found in: (a) DNA; (b) mRNA; (c) tRNA; (d) ribosomes.

3. ATP is a: (a) base; (b) nucleotide; (c) nucleoside; (d) high-energy-containing protein.

4. Which life processes require energy? Choose the three correct answers. (a) Anabolic; (b) catabolic; (c) diffusion; (d) active transport of nutrients across a membrane; (e) DNA replication.

5. How many amino acids can a sequence of 9 bases (on mRNA) code for? (a) 1; (b) 3; (c) 9; (d) 27.

6. Hydrogen bonds are: (a) strong, and thus DNA does not shear; (b) strong, preventing DNA from denaturation; (c) weak, enabling DNA replication and transcription to occur; (d) weak, enabling catalase to convert hydrogen peroxide into water and oxygen.

7. In the DNA double helix, the paired bases adenine and thymine are bonded to one another by: (a) two hydrogen bonds; (b) three hydrogen bonds; (c) the phosphodiester bonds; (d) peptide bonds.

8. In the DNA double helix, a purine pairs with: (a) another purine; (b) a pyrimidine; (c) adenine or guanine; (d) the phosphodiester bond.

9. In a DNA molecule (procaryotic chromosome), there are: (a) just about the same number of adenine bases as there are thymine bases; (b) more adenine bases than thymine bases; (c) more thymine bases than adenine bases; (d) a number of adenine and thymine bases varying with the organism (i.e., insufficient information to determine answer).

10. A polysome consists of: (a) ribosomes complexed with mRNA; (b) ribosomes complexed with DNA; (c) tRNA, mRNA, protein complex; (d) the complex of a 30S and 50S subunit which makes a ribosome.

11. Which one of the following bases is not found in DNA? (a) A; (b) T; (c) G; (d) C; (e) U.

12. Which of the following molecules has the fewest nucleotides; (a) DNA; (b) mRNA; (c) rRNA; (d) tRNA.

13. Ochre (UAA), amber (UAG), and azure (UGA) are nonsense codons that specify: (a) nothing; (b) the amino acid phenyl alanine; (c) termination of protein synthesis; (d) termination of DNA synthesis.

14. The anticodon is ACU. What is the code (triplet word) on the active (transcribing) DNA strand? (a) UGA; (b) TGA; (c) ACT; (d) ACU.

15. The same enzyme is used to replicate DNA as is used to transcribe mRNA. (a) True; (b) false; (c) not known for sure.

16. There are four letters in the genetic code. A codon comprises three letters. How many different codons are there? (a) One for each amino acid; (b) 12; (c) 48; (d) 64.

Answers: 1. (b); 2. (c); 3. (b); 4. (a), (d), (e); 5. (b); 6. (c); 7. (a); 8. (b); 9. (a); 10. (a); 11. (e); 12. (d); 13. (c); 14. (b); 15. (b); 16. (d).

Chapter 12

Modifications,
Mutations,
and Genetics

INTRODUCTION: In the preceding chapter it was shown that the genetic code is universal. Furthermore, microorganisms exhibit the same, or comparable, genetic properties as higher organisms. In fact, the genetics of animals and plants has been elucidated by microbial geneticists, working with their much more readily manipulated biosystems. By the same token, just as higher forms of life change and evolve, so do microorganisms. Because of rapid multiplication, the conservation of genetic material, and (rapidly expressed) genetic recombination, many microorganisms can undergo change more quickly than any other form of life. Therefore, whatever the investigation, no one should myopically view bacteria and viruses as static entities. For example, in the health field, attenuated vaccines and the epidemiology of influenza are based on the evolution of microbial species. This chapter explores some of the principles of genetic variability.

Expanded Outline and Summary

I. Variability and Inheritance Characteristics. The inherent characteristics of an organism, those governed by its genetic code, may be altered by genetic recombination (progeny with combinations of genes different from those present in parent cells) or by mutation. Both are relatively rare events in a microorganism. However, because microorganisms tend to be so numerous and to multiply so rapidly, genetic change is very apparent among populations of bacteria and viruses.
   A. Genotype—a term which refers to the entire array of genes possessed by the cell which remain relatively constant. Change of genotype involves a relatively permanent alteration of genes. The genotype represents the total potential capability of the cell.
   B. Phenotype—a term which refers to those genetic capabilities expressed by the cell under a given set of environmental conditions.

II. Phenotypic Changes. The properties of any species remain relatively constant, but some environmentally or growth-induced alterations may occur.
   A. Morphological modifications—these include cell size, cell shape, capsule production.

All are influenced by the composition of the growth medium, and may be governed by the growth cycle of the species.

B.   Cultural modifications—one example is *Serratia marcescens,* which produces a red pigment at room temperature ($\sim 20°C$) and no pigment at $37°C$.

C.   Modifications in physiological and biochemical characteristics.
1.   Rapidly multiplying cells are more susceptible to destruction by chemicals than are cells in the stationary phase of growth.
2.   Certain enzymes (e.g., β-galactosidase) may be copiously synthesized in one growth medium (or combination of environmental conditions) but not in another.

III.   Genotypic Changes.   Genes determine phenotypic characteristics, and mutations may lead to altered phenotypic characteristics.

A.   The gene and DNA.   The gene is defined as a sequence of nucleotide pairs in DNA molecules (i.e., chromosomes) which codes for a specific polypeptide chain.   In bacteria (about 3,800 genes) and many viruses (as few as 6 to 7 genes), the chromosome is a single circular molecule.

B.   Molecular mechanism of mutation.   A mutation is a change in the nucleotide sequence of DNA which usually results in the formation of an altered protein.   This protein may have a changed function, may have an impaired function, or may be nonfunctional.
1.   Types of mutations (two prominent types are discussed).
a.   Point mutation—the substitution of one nucleotide for another (base pair substitution).
i.   Effects.
A.   Missense mutation—codon in mRNA specifies an amino acid different from the one present in normal protein; the result is a less active or inactive protein.
B.   Nonsense mutation—formation of any protein-synthesis-terminating codons in mRNA so that translation of the genetic message is prematurely terminated; the result is the loss of the protein or the formation of a smaller, nonfunctional polypeptide or protein.
C.   Neutral mutation—change in a mRNA codon to a synonym (degeneracy) so that there is no change in the protein.
ii.   Types of point mutation.
A.   Transition—substitution of one purine for another purine or one pyrimidine for another pyrimidine.
B.   Transversion—replacement of a purine by a pyrimidine and vice versa.
b.   Frameshift mutation.   During protein synthesis, the reading of the genetic code starts from one end of the mRNA template and proceeds in consecutive blocks of three bases.   Therefore, frameshift mutations, caused by the addition or deletion of multiples of one or two bases, lead to completely nonfunctional genes, as numerous missense and nonsense mutations are generated.

C.   Occurrence of mutations.
1.   Spontaneous—mutations that occur during normal growth conditions.   Because DNA is a relatively stable molecule, spontaneous mutations are rare events, oc-

curring at rates of from 10^{-6} to 10^{-10}/bacterium/generation. Therefore, one of every 1 million or more cells is likely to be a mutant. Spontaneous mutations may be caused by biological imperfection and by low levels of x-rays, chemicals, etc., in the environment.

   2. Mutagen-induced (some examples).
       a. Nitrous acid—removes amino groups from nucleotides.
       b. Base analogs (e.g., 2-aminopurine or 5-bromouracil)—similar in structure to bases, these compounds may be incorporated into DNA during replication and induce errors during subsequent DNA replication.
   3. Mutation rate—defined as the average number of mutations per cell per division. Under conditions where mutant cells can be detected, using large populations, the mutation rate can be calculated if one knows:
       a. The number of mutations that arise.
       b. The number of generations that have occurred.
       c. The mean number of bacteria.
       d. The back (reverse) mutation rate.
  D. Types and selection of bacterial mutants.
   1. Types of some commonly encountered or induced mutants include those with:
       a. Increased tolerance to inhibitory agents such as antibiotics.
       b. Altered fermentation pattern or decreased capacity to produce some end product.
       c. A nutritional deficiency, i.e., those that require a more complex medium for growth (auxotroph) than the original culture from which they were derived (often prototroph).
       d. Altered colonial appearance.
       e. A chemical change in cell structure (antigenic or bacteriophage-resistant mutants).
       f. Changes in morphological features.
   2. Selection of bacterial mutants—mutants generally constitute a small percentage of the entire population, so the *penicillin technique* enriches for mutants, while the *replica plating technique* enables an investigator to quickly and accurately screen large numbers of potentially mutated cells.

IV. Bacterial Recombination. Bacteria are haploid organisms that are not differentiated into gametic and somatic cells. In bacteria that have displayed sexuality, cells fall into two categories: donors and recipients. Generally (and this uniquely applies to bacteria), only a fraction of the donor genome gets into the recipient cell. The recipient cell is thus a zygote that is incompletely diploid (merozygote). Genetic recombination is limited to the diploid portion of the chromosome, as a recombinant chromosome is formed from the DNA of two different organisms.

 V. Bacterial Recombination: Conjugation.
  A. Discovery by Lederberg and Tatum (opened the exciting era of microbial genetics).

E. coli auxotrophic* for genes a, b, and c (wildtype* D, E, and F)

mixed with

E. coli auxotrophic* for genes d, e, and f (wildtype A, B, and C)

$$\downarrow 1/10^6 - 1/10^7$$

Prototroph* (wildtypic) for: ABC DEF (grew on minimal medium containing only glucose and salts)

Triple auxotrophs were used to preclude the possibility of back mutation. Therefore, auxotroph production had to be the result of recombination.

B.   Conjugation can be mediated by *episomes*.

    1. Definition: "Small" length of circular double-stranded DNA (about 1/100 the size of a bacterial chromosome) that may be found in the cytoplasm or integrated in the chromosome itself.

    2. Some functional units (genes). Enough genetic material for about 40 total genes.

       a. Genes concerned with DNA replication → DNA polymerase?

       b. Pili (hollow protein tubules on the cell surface that can attach to the surfaces of other cells) → pili protein.

       c. Transfer → the episome and any other DNA attached to it (e.g., the chromosome).

    3. Episome replication.

       a. In cytoplasm—replicates approximately when chromosome replicates.

       b. Integrated into chromosome—with chromosome as part of the chromosome.

    4. Some types of episomes.

       a. Fertility factor (F).

       b. Lambda (λ)?

         i. Prophage—in chromosome.

         ii. Lytic state—in "cytoplasm."

C.   Conjugation may only occur between cells possessing the episome (F^+ or Hfr) and those without it (F^-).

D.   Conjugation between a bacterium (specifically *E. coli*) that has the F episome "in the cytoplasm" (out of the chromosome), designated F^+, and one that does not have an F episome, designated F^-. Note: Cells with the episome can only donate it, and only those cells without episomes are recipients.

$$F^+ \times F^- \rightarrow 2F^+$$

F^+ remains F^+—upon contact with F^-, F^+ makes a new episome, transfers *it*, and retains its own F episome. F^- cell becomes F^+ as it receives the eipsome.

---

*Definitions:

  Auxotroph: Strain of a microorganism which requires some nutrient not required by the original strain (prototroph) from which it was derived. (Therefore prototrophic: some nutrients not required.)

  Wildtype: Also original strain (prototroph) with the further proviso that the strain is assumed to be found in nature.

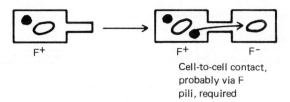

E. Conjugation between bacteria that have the F episome integrated in the chromosome (designated Hfr) and F⁻ cells.
1. Collision.
2. Conjugal bridge formed.
3. Unidirectional transfer of chromosome into recipient (F⁻). Circular chromosome breaks at the episome or proximally to it.
  a. Hfr synthesizes new chromosome (upon contact), under direction of F particle, and sends one strand of this new chromosome into the F⁻ cell.

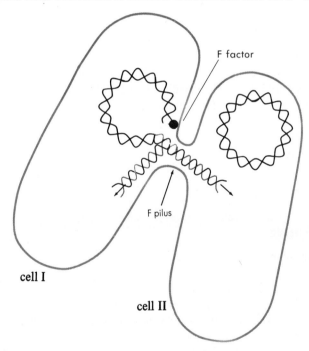

Figure 12-16. Suggested mechanism for DNA transfer during conjugation.

  b. 50 to 60 genes/min go from Hfr to F⁻ (90 to 100 min for transfer of entire chromosome).
  c. F particle (at rear of chromosome) usually does not enter recipient (conjugation lasts less than 90 min). Therefore, F⁻ cell remains F⁻.

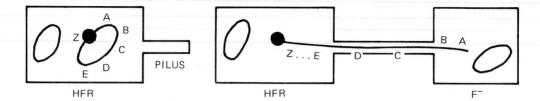

4. Homolgous lineup of donated and recipient chromosome.
5. Genetic exchange (crossover).
6. Separation of the two cells.
   a. Hfr remains unchanged.
   b. F⁻ stays F⁻ (unless conjugation occurs, and this is an extremely rare event, for the full 90 to 100 min) but may acquire genes from the donor.
F. Scope of conjugation (gram-negative rods).
   1. Enteric—*Escherichia, Salmonella* (typhoid fever), *Shigella* (dysentery), *Proteus.*
   2. Other—*Serratia, Pseudomonads, Vibrio* (cholera and dysentery), *Klebsiella* (pneumonia).
G. *Plasmids* (any extrachromosomal element).
   1. Definition—Another comparatively small molecule of DNA, which is like an episome in that one gene codes for pili protein, another codes for DNA replication, and a third is believed to mediate transfer of the plasmid itself *plus* any other *DNA* (genes) *joined* to *it.* The major difference between an episome and a plasmid is that the latter is not found integrated in the cell chromosome; it remains in the "cytoplasm."
   2. Examples:
      a. Resistance transfer factor (RTF) or R factor carries genes that confer resistance to specific antibiotics.
      b. Bacteriocin factors (in the case of *E. coli,* colicin or col factors) produce a protein that kills cells of the same species that do not possess the bacteriocin plasmid.

VI. Bacterial Recombination: Transformation.
   A. History and impact.
      1. Griffith (1928), working on the virulence factors of pneumococci, found that dead, capsulated (smooth, virulent) organisms enabled live, noncapsulated organisms (rough, avirulent) to produce a capsule and thereby become virulent.
      3. Avery, Macleod, McCarty (1944) proved that it was DNA that enabled one strain of pneumococci to impart a phenotypic property on another strain of pneumococci, thus providing evidence that DNA was indeed the "storehouse" of the genetic code.
   B. Mechanism of transformation.
      1. Naked (extracted) donor DNA contacts *competent* recipient cells.
      2. Competent recipient cells—those that can take up DNA fragments, probably by means of a DNA specific receptor ("permiase").
         a. Competence limited to only a few genera (e.g., *Bacillus, Haemophilus, Neisseria, Streptococci*), and only selected species within those genera.

    b. Genetic capability for competence is phenotypically expressed only during the late logarithmic growth phase.

  3. Once a DNA fragment (exogenote) has entered the recipient cell—as in conjugation—there is possible homologous base pairing, crossing over, and genetic recombination.

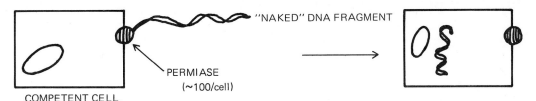

VII. **Bacterial Recombination-Transduction.** During conjugation, pili act as vectors (transmitters) of genes, while in transformation "permeases" act as vectors of naked DNA. In transduction, it is the bacteriophage that transmits genetic material. Keep in mind that although the mechanisms for introducing exogenote DNA into recipient cells vary among the three forms of bacterial recombination, once inside the recipient cell, exogenote DNA fragments are recombined with recipient DNA via like processes. This is true for conjugation, transduction, and transformation. After you read the later chapter on bacteriophage, the mechanisms of transduction should become still clearer.

  A. History. Transduction was discovered by Zinder and Lederberg (1952). U-tube experiments showed that although prototrophic and auxotrophic *Salmonella* could not make contact (ruling out conjugation), recombination still occurred in the presence of DNAase (ruling out transformation). Thus, another process must mediate sexual recombination.

  B. Process of transduction. Modified phages act as vectors of genes. A phage may infect a bacterium, and some of the virus progeny that emerge from the lysed cell may carry some bacterial genes instead of part or all of the viral genome. Such viruses are called *defective* because they can no longer reproduce. Instead when they reinfect another bacterium they inject some of the genes (exogenote) of their former host. Then genetic recombination can occur within the recipient cell. There are basically two types of bacteriophage life cycles: lytic and lysogenic. Generalized transduction may occur during the lytic cycle, while specialized transduction may occur during the lysogenic cycle.

  C. Specialized (restricted) transduction. The best-studied example is the action of the bacteriophage lambda (λ), which during the lysogenic cycle integrates its DNA into the *E. coli* chromosome close to the galactose genes (those controlling galactose fermentation). Viral DNA integrated into bacterial DNA is termed a *prophage*.

The λ prophage remains relatively dormant and is replicated when the *E. coli* DNA is replicated. When the *E. coli* divides, a chromosome, still containing λ DNA, is passed to the daughter cells. When λ is induced, or spontaneously enters the lytic cycle, the prophage is excised from the chromosome, which is repaired. Rarely, the excision enzymes "err" so that a part of the bacterial DNA (containing galactose genes) is excised along with some viral genome.

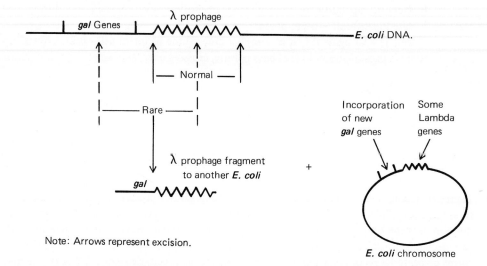

Note: Arrows represent excision.

When the *E. coli* is lysed during the lytic bacteriophage life cycle, a defective λ whose protein coat encloses an incomplete viral gene complement plus some *gal* genes, may escape and send *gal* genes (exogenote) into another *E. coli*. Genetic recombination for this single focus may then occur.

D. Generalized transduction. In the lytic cycle, a phage infects a bacterium, and eventually replicate copies of the protein coat normally enclose replicate copies of the viral genome. Thus, many viruses emerge to initiate the cycle anew. Rarely, however, the viral protein encloses *bacterial DNA* rather than viral genome and thus serves an an exogenote vector when it reinfects another bacterium. In generalized transduction, the transferred fragments of bacterial DNA are about the size of the virus genome and may contain scores to a thousand bacterial genes, depending on the size of the transducing virus. Unlike specialized transduction, where only specific genes are transferred, in generalized transduction it is normally possible to recombine any group of genes found on the bacterial chromosome.

VIII. Implications of Microbial Genetic Engineering.
A. Methods. Using certain enzymes, like DNA-restriction nucleases, unlike pieces of DNA can be joined in a test tube and made to function within cells. Such hybrid DNA molecules can replicate in cells.
B. Outcomes and uses. Whole new species can be created. Potentially any organism can be imbued with some of the properties of any other living organism. Some of the more obvious applications are:
1. Bacteria can be made to cheaply produce industrial products, including antibiotics.
2. New strains of bacteria may be created that can symbiotically fix nitrogen for plants (other than legumes), thus eliminating the need for frequent fertilization and greatly increasing the world's food supply.
3. Genetic disorders may be rectified by replacing defective genes with normal ones.
C. Potential hazards. When interfering with inheritance in this manner, outcomes are difficult to predict even under the most carefully controlled circumstances. Some obvious dangers are:

1. Antibiotic-resistant organisms may be created.
2. Lethal pathogens may be created.
3. The techniques, once fully developed, may be usurped for evil uses, such as germ warfare or the attempt to create a "master race."

Programmed Self-Test

Do not begin this self-test before reading the corresponding chapter in the text.

VARIABILITY AND INHERITANCE OF CHARACTERISTICS (Text pages 211 to 212)

Progeny cells arise with combinations of genes different from those present in parent cells. This is a definition of _____ _____.	
The entire array of genes possessed by the cell is called the _____.	genetic recombination
The array of properties expressed by a cell at a given time is called the _____.	genotype

PHENOTYPIC CHANGES (MODIFICATIONS) (Text pages 212 to 216)

A cell change imposed by the environment without genetic change is called phenotypic change or _____.	phenotype
When *Bacillus sphaericus* is grown in medium containing 2% peptone, entire population occurs as _____.	modification
Serratia produces a red pigment at _____ but not at _____.	vegetative cells
Enzyme induction is an example of a _____ change.	room temperature; 37°C

GENOTYPIC CHANGES (Text pages 216 to 226)

A gene alteration is termed a _____.	phenotypic

Viruses that infect bacteria are called _____.	mutation
DNA replication in which one polynucleotide chain acts as a template to direct the synthesis of a new chain complementary to itself is called _____.	bacteriophages
The chromosome of *E. coli* contains about _____ genes.	semiconservative
When one purine is substituted for another purine, the mutation is called a _____.	3,800
A mutation leading to the formation of a chain-terminating codon is called a _____ mutation.	transition
The deletion of a base from DNA is termed a _____ mutation.	nonsense
5-Bromouracil is very similar, in chemical structure, to the base thymine. 5-Bromouracil is, therefore, termed a _____.	frameshift
Mutants demonstrating a nutritional requirement beyond that of the parent type are called _____.	base analog
Penicillin acts only upon _____ cells.	auxotrophs

BACTERIAL RECOMBINATIONS; CONJUGATION (Text pages 226 to 234)

An incompletely diploid zygote is termed a _____.	growing
The F factor is one example of an _____.	merozygote
When *E. coli* has the F factor integrated into the chromosome, it is called _____.	episome
Can an F$^+$ cell be successfully mated with another F$^+$ cell?	Hfr
Extrachromosomal genetic elements are called _____.	No
Episomes are pieces of DNA about _____ times the size of the bacterial chromosome.	plasmids
R factors confer resistance to _____.	1/100
F$^+$ bacteria have _____ on the cell surface.	antibiotics

TRANSFORMATION (Text pages 234 to 235)

The phenomenon of transformation was first observed in 1928 by _____.	pili
When Griffith injected mice with both living rough pneumococci and heat-killed smooth pneumococci, _____ _____ were isolated from the dead mice.	Griffith
Transformable bacteria are said to be _____.	living smooth (capsulated) pneumococci
The few genera that can be transformed are competent mainly during the _____ phase of growth.	competent
Bacterial genera that can be transformed include *Haemophilus, Neisseria, Streptococcus, Rhizobium,* and_____.	late logarithmic
Competent cells differ from noncompetent cells in that they can take up the large molecular _____ fragments.	*Bacillus*

TRANSDUCTION (Text pages 236 to 237)

Viral genomes integrated into bacterial genomes are called _____.	DNA
Bacteria that carry prophages are called _____.	prophages
The case in which a (temperate) phage can transfer any gene on a bacterial chromosome is called _____.	lysogenic
In _____ transduction, phages transduce only those bacterial genes adjacent to the prophage in the bacterial chromosome.	generalized transduction
Lambda transduces genes controlling _____ fermentation.	specialized (restricted)
Defective phages are missing all or part of their _____.	galactose

THE IMPLICATIONS OF MICROBIAL GENETIC ENGINEERING (Text pages 238 to 239)

Enzymes called _____ generate DNA fragments with "sticky" ends, especially suitable for rejoining to other DNA molecules.	genome
For purposes of genetic engineering, *Klebsiella* may prove valuable because of a gene complement that enables it to_____.	DNA-restriction endonucleases
	fix nitrogen

Multiple-Choice Test

Underline the correct answer.

1. Bacteria are almost always: (a) haploid; (b) diploid; (c) polyploid; (d) heterozygous.

2. When a mutation is caused by the substitution of adenine with thymine, the mutation is called a: (a) transition; (b) transversion; (c) frameshift; (d) inversion.

3. When there is a change in the mRNA codon but no change in the corresponding amino acid because the mutant codon is a synonym for the original codon, the mutation is termed: (a) missense; (b) nonsense; (c) neutral; (d) frameshift.

Questions 4 to 6 refer to this statement: A given sequence of bases on a DNA molecule reads CAT CAT CAT . . . (repeating).

4. Which type of mutation would cause the following change in the code: CAC CAT CAT? (a) Deletion; (b) insertion; (c) point; (d) transversion.

5. What class of mutation would cause this change: CTC ATC ATC? (a) Deletion; (b) insertion; (c) point; (d) transversion; (e) transition.

6. Does a point mutation *always* lead to a phenotypic change in a given protein? (a) Yes; (b) no; (c) yes, but this may not affect the cell in any way.

7. The following abstract appeared preceding an article in an issue of the *J. Gen. Microbiol.* (73:403–407):

> Auxotrophic, phage-resistant and streptomycin-resistant mutants of *Caulobacter* were used to demonstrate genetic recombinations in this genus. Forty of a possible 170 mating pairs gave recombinant frequencies of from 100 to 1000 times greater than reversion frequencies for the markers used. Stability of the recombinants was demonstrated by successive cloning on both complete and minimal medium. Cell contact is apparently required for recombination since both cell types of a mating pair must be present for prototroph formation.

What kind of recombination is the author dealing with? (a) Conjugation; (b) transduction; (c) transformation; (d) the author is referring to no kind of recombination but is referring to mutational reversion.

Questions 8 and 9 refer to this statement: Two strains of *Salmonella* are placed in a U tube. The strain added to the left arm is auxotrophic for histidine; the strain added to the right arm is prototrophic.

8. When a filter with 0.5-μm pores (smaller than *Salmonella*) is placed between the two strains, separating them, genetic recombination still occurs. This rules out the process of: (a) conjugation; (b) transformation; (c) generalized transduction; (d) specialized transduction.

9. When DNAase is also added to the U-tube, recombination still occurs. This rules out the process of: (a) conjugation; (b) transformation; (c) generalized transduction; (d) specialized transduction.

10. Who performed the first experiment in which transformation was believed to have occurred? (a) Beedle; (b) Griffith; (c) Lederberg; (d) Adleberg.

11. Which of these statements *distinguishes* a plasmid from an episome? (a) One of its genes makes a DNA polymerase, so it is a replicon; (b) another "gene" facilitates DNA transfer through a pili; (c) it has never been isolated when integrated into the chromosome, so presumably it cannot integrate; (d) it consists of double-stranded DNA.

12. Which of the following is *not* characteristic of specialized transduction? (a) It occurs during the lytic cycle of a bacteriophage such as P_1; (b) the prophage state is a necessary prerequisite to the "err" formation of a defective temperate virion; (c) it usually involves the recombination of a single gene (i.e., galactose); (d) prophage induction results in some virus genes being left in the bacterial chromosome while a bacterial gene remains contiguous with the viral genome.

13. Which of the following types of mutations *most often* kills cells? (a) Point; (b) deletion of three bases from the chromosome; (c) deletion of four bases from the chromosome; (d) a change in a DNA triplet from AAA to AAG.

14. In all three processes of bacterial genetic recombination, there is a homologous lineup of donated and recipient chromosomes and a subsequent exchange of genetic markers. However, in (1) conjugation, (2) transformation, and (3) transduction, respectively, there are different DNA transfer mediating mechanisms. These are (match the above order): (a) (1) virus, (2) permease, (3) pili, respectively; (b) (1) permease, (2) virus, (3) pili, respectively; (c) (1) virus, (2) pili, (3) permease, respectively; (d) (1) pili, (2) permease, (3) virus, respectively.

15. A mutated strain of *E. coli* (e.g., one that can no longer synthesize the amino acid arginine) is called: (a) wildtype; (b) auxotrophic; (c) parental; (d) prototrophic.

16. Bacilli are exposed to ultraviolet irradiation. The survivors are inoculated into "minimal medium" which contains penicillin. Thus: (a) mutant cells die for lack of proper nutrients; (b) all cells (mutant and nonmutant) are killed by penicillin; (c) the bacilli grow a resistance transfer factor; (d) nonmutant cells grow and are killed by the penicillin, while mutant cells remain dormant and can be recovered upon transfer to a nutritionally complete medium without antibiotic.

17. Genera that are capable of being transformed are competent: (a) throughout their life cycles; (b) any time during the logarithmic phase of growth; (c) usually when they are in the middle to late logarithmic phase of growth; (d) only when they have the F factor.

18. Which of the following genera is *not* capable of conjugation? (a) *Staphylococcus;* (b) *Pseudomonas;* (c) *Vibrio;* (d) *Escherichia.*

Bacterial Genetic Recombination

Questions 19 to 23 refer to this diagram.

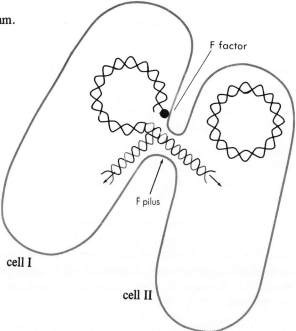

F factor

F pilus

cell I

cell II

19. The process depicted here is: (a) conjugation; (b) transformation; (c) generalized transduction; (d) specialized transduction.

20. Part of the chromosome is being transferred from: (a) the F$^-$ to the F$^+$ cell; (b) the F$^-$ to the Hfr cell; (c) the F$^+$ to the F$^-$ cell; (d) the Hfr to the F$^-$ cell.

21. Which cell has synthesized the pilus? (a) Cell I; (b) cell II; (c) cells I and II; (d) either cell I or cell II.

22. After conjugation is completed, it is *likely* that: (a) cell I will be F$^-$ and cell II, F$^+$; (b) cell I will be Hfr and cell II, Hfr; (c) cell I will be Hfr and cell II, F$^-$; (d) cell I will die and cell II will be F$^+$.

23. If cell type I completed conjugation, cell type I would probably: (a) die, having lost its chromosome; (b) die, because of the trauma of the conjugal process; (c) survive, having replicated its chromosome prior to DNA transfer; (d) survive, for a time, without a chromosome.

Answers: 1. (a); 2. (b); 3. (c); 4. (c); 5. (a); 6. (b); 7. (a); 8. (a); 9. (b); 10. (b); 11. (c); 12. (a); 13. (c); 14. (d); 15. (b); 16. (d); 17. (c); 18. (a); 19. (a); 20. (d); 21. (a); 22. (c); 23. (c).

Chapter 13

The World of Bacteria I: Kingdom Procaryotae

INTRODUCTION: Bacteria that have parasitic or commensalistic relationships with humans are most frequently studied in the greatest detail. Such bacteria are generally rapidly multiplying heterotrophs with relatively uncomplicated morphologies (cocci, rods, spirals) and simple life cycles consisting of growth followed by binary fission. However, these bacteria represent only one facet of procaryotes, for bacteria as a group are in many respects remarkably diverse in appearance, behavior, nutrition, and habitation. If there is a type of metabolism, there exists a bacterial species to carry it out; if some eucaryotic cells interact, so do some procaryotes; if there is an econiche that can support life, then it will support bacterial life.

This chapter introduces you to the kingdom of bacteria. It is hoped that the following inclusive table will serve as an *orienting reference* as you meet the species that may benefit or harm us, that may yield some secrets of biology, that may, indeed, make life possible on earth. Do not be awed by the many names and the numerous associated properties. Instead, try to obtain a general appreciation of the diversity of the procaryotes. When some of the various organisms are reintroduced to you in connection with their "roles," the familiarity that you attain now will lead to better comprehension later.

Expanded Outline and Orientation

The following table lists all the major groups of bacteria. The table is arranged to reflect a grouping established in the "Dictionary of Bacteria," *Bergey's Manual of Determinative Bacteriology.* If you wish to learn more about a particular group of bacteria in connection with laboratory work or later course topics, the table serves as a starting point that can lead you to the proper section in *Bergey's Manual* where much more detailed information is presented. The table should also help you become familiar with the procaryotes, for it condenses most of the material in Chapter 13. But such a table is dry, whereas the species themselves are not. Ideally the observation of each group of bacteria in the lab reinforces understanding and increases familiarity. Also, such a table represents bacteria as static, whereas actually they are interesting, dynamic creatures. Consider, for example, the life cycles of two groups of bacteria, *Hyphomicrobium* and *Myxobacterium.*

Bergey's Manual of Determinative Bacteriology **Kingdom Procaryotae**

PART	GROUP OF BACTERIA	SUBDIVISION(S)	EXAMPLE(S) OF GENERA	MORPHOLOGY (distinguishing characteristics)
1	Phototrophic bacteria	Families: Rhodospirillaceae	*Rhodopseudomonas*	Rods, some bud
	Order I. *Rhodospirillales*	Chromatiaceae Chlorobiaceae		Spheres, rods, spirals.
2	Gliding bacteria	Order I. Myxobacterales	*Stigmatella*	Glide; no rigid cell wall; produce slime; form fruiting bodies
		Order II. Cytophagales	*Flexibacter*	Glide; rods or long filaments; no fruiting bodies
3	Sheathed bacteria	Genera: *Sphaerotilus, Leptothrix, Streptothrix, Lieskeela,* and three others		Rods; flagellated; sheathed; often grow in long filaments
4	Budding and/or appendaged bacteria	Genera: *Gallionella* (and *Nevskia*),		Secreted appendages; bean-shaped; binary fission
		Hyphomicrobium,		Buds from apex of hyphae; motile stage
		Caulobacter		Stalk; binary fission
5	The spirochetes	Order: Spirochaetales	Comprises five genera	Slender, flexuous, helical, 3 to 500 μm long
6	Spiral and curved bacteria	Family: Spirillaceae	*Spirillum, Campylobacter*	Rigid, curved rods 0.5 to 60 μm long (some species S shaped)
7	Gram-negative aerobic rods and cocci	Pseudomonadaceae	*Pseudomonas; Xanthomonas*	Rods; polar flagellation
		Azotobacteraceae	*Azotobacter*	Pleomorphic rod-shaped to oval
		Rhizobiaceae	*Rhizobium*	Gram-negative rods; motile
		Methylomonadaceae	*Methylomonas* (rods), *Methylococcus* (cocci),	
		Halobacteriaceae	*Halobacterium* (rods), *Halococcus* (cocci)	
8	Gram-negative facultative anaerobic rods	Enterobacteriaceae	*Escherichia, Serratia, Proteus, Erwinia*	Small rods; peritrichous flagellation or nonmotile

NUTRITION	PATHOGENICITY OR OTHER OBVIOUS EFFECTS	OTHER IMPORTANT FEATURES
Purple nonsulfur bacteria; photoorganotrophic; anaerobic photosynthesis		Also aerobic oxidation of organic compounds
H_2S serves as H donor for reduction of CO_2; light required		Called purple-sulfur bacteria
As above, using some different pigments		Called green-sulfur bacteria
Predatory		Vegetative cell → myxospores
Many species oxidize and precipitate metals (iron and manganese oxides and hydroxides)	May clog water systems	
Metabolize one-carbon compounds (e.g., methanol)	May clog water systems due to production of insoluble iron compounds	"Complex" life cycle
Chemoorganotrophic		"Complex" life cycle
Chemoorganotrophic; some species fastidious	*Treponema* and *Borrelia* have pathogenic species	See text: Part V
Chemoorganotrophs; free-living, saprophytic, or parasitic		
Aerobic; chemoorganotrophic	Some species plant pathogens	Some species pigmented
Aerobic; chemoorganotrophic; fix N_2	See Chap. 34 (Soil Microbiology)	
Aerobic; symbiotically fix nitrogen	See Chap. 34 (Soil Microbiology)	
Methane or methanol as only source of carbon and energy		
Requires 12% salt or more for growth		
Heterotrophic; ferment many carbohydrates; catalase positive, oxidase negative	*Shigella* and *Salmonella* (800 serotypes)	Best-studied group of bacteria: to be discussed in later chapters

Bergey's Manual of Determinative Bacteriology **Kingdom Procaryotae (continued)**

PART	GROUP OF BACTERIA	SUBDIVISION(S)	EXAMPLE(S) OF GENERA	MORPHOLOGY (distinguishing characteristics)
8	Gram-negative facultatively anaerobic rods (continued)	Vibrionaceae	*Vibrio*	Short straight or curved rods; polar flag.
9	Gram-negative anaerobic bacteria	Bacteroidaceae	*Bacteroides, Fusobacterium, Leptotrichia*	Pleomorphic rods; if motile, peritrichous flagellation
10	Gram-negative cocci and coccobacilli	Neisseriaceae	*Neisseria, Branhamella, Moraxella, Acinetobacter*	Flattened cocci to short rods; singly, pairs, or short chains
11	Gram-negative anaerobic cocci	Veillonellaceae	*Veillonella; Acidaminococcus; Megasphaera*	Pairs, single, clusters, chains; nonmotile
12	Gram-negative chemolithotrophic bacteria	Nitrobacteraceae (nitrifying bacteria)	*Nitrobacter Nitrosomonas*	Diverse rods, cocci, spirals; polar flagellation
		Sulfur metabolizers	*Thiobacillus*	Gram-negative, short rods; single polar flagellation
		Siderocapsaceae	*Siderocapsa*	
13	Methane-producing bacteria	Methanobacteriaceae	*Methanobacterium, Methanospirillum*	Diverse: cocci, rods, spirals
14	Gram-positive cocci	Micrococcaceae	*Staphylococcus*	Single, pairs, fours, clusters
		Streptococcaceae	*Streptococcus*	Chains
		Peptococcaceae	*Peptococcus*	Irregular clusters, single, short chains
15	Endospore-forming rods and cocci	Bacillaceae	*Sporosarcina* are cocci in tetrads or packets; *Bacillus* (aerobic or facultative); *Sporolactobacillus* (microaerophilic); *Clostridium* (anaerobic) and *Desulfomaculum* (anaerobic) are rods that occur singly, in pairs, and in chains	
16	Gram-positive asporogenous rods	Lactobacillaceae	*Lactobacillus*	Medium length; often in chains; some curved
17	Actinomycetes and related organisms	Coryneform bacteria	*Corynebacterium,*	Gram-positive straight or curved rods; some have V Y look
			Arthrobacter	Gram-positive rods with pleomorphic life cycle

Note (spanning Micrococcaceae, Streptococcaceae, Peptococcaceae rows): 1 to 2 μm diameter

NUTRITION	PATHOGENICITY OR OTHER OBVIOUS EFFECTS	OTHER IMPORTANT FEATURES
Chemoorganotrophic	*V. cholerae* → cholera *V. parahaemolyticus* → acute enteritis	
Chemoorganotrophic; obligately anaerobic		Bacteroides numerous in intestine
Chemoorganotrophic	*N. gonorrhoeae* and *N. meningitidis*	Nonmotile
Chemoorganotrophic		
Almost all are obligate chemolithotrophs, $NO_2 \rightarrow NO_3$; Chemolithotrophs, $NH_3 \rightarrow NO_2$ Oxidation of reduced sulfur compounds $(H_2S, S^0, \text{etc.})$ Chemolithotrophs? Deposit oxides of Mn and Fe	Nitrogen cycle (see Chap. 34)	
Energy from oxidation of H_2 and $HCO \xrightarrow{CO_2} CH_3$	Ubiquitous: in animals, soil, etc.	Obligate anaerobes
Aerobic or facultatively anaerobic Aerobic or facultatively anaerobic } Chemoorganotrophs Anaerobic	Some species are very pathogenic, while others are saprophytic	Some important interactions with humans (see later chapters)
Chemoorganotrophic	*Clostridium botulinum* *Clostridium tetani*	All species produce highly resistant spores
Fastidious; anaerobic or facultative; chemoorganotrophic	In intestines of animals (nonpathogenic)	Useful in food processing
Fastidious	*Corynebacterium diphtheriae*	Human, plant, and nonpathogens
Chemoorganotrophs		Numerous in soils

Bergey's Manual of Determinative Bacteriology **Kingdom Procaryotae (continued)**

PART	GROUP OF BACTERIA	SUBDIVISION(S)	EXAMPLE(S) OF GENERA	MORPHOLOGY (distinguishing characteristics)
17	Actinomycetes and related organisms (continued)	Order: Actinomycetales: Families:		Filamenous and branched; moldlike spores
		Actinomycetaceae	*Bifidobacterium*	Diptheroid shape; form branched filaments
		Mycobacteriaceae	*Mycobacterium*	Slender rods, some filaments, rarely branched
		Actinoplanaceae	*Actinoplanes*	Sporangia at tips of hyphae → motile rods
		Streptomycetaceae (and four other families)	463 species	Hyphae; conidia; gram-positive
18	Rickettsias	See next chapter (14)		Pleomorphic (cocci-rods); gram-negative
19	Mycoplasmas (pleuropneumonia group or PPLO)	Mycoplasmataceae Acholephasmataceae		Minute; triple-layered membrane; no cell wall; "fried egg" colonies; elementary bodies (~170nm) → larger spheroids → filaments → elementary bodies
		(L forms)	Many genera	Induced in lab with penicillin in soft agar

The hyphomicrobia (Part 4) are ubiquitous in soil and water. They form sticky "holdfasts" that anchor them to solid surfaces and to one another. One-carbon compounds that are toxic to humans, such as methanol and methylamine, are preferred nutrients of most hyphomicrobia. Such a procaryote has a relatively complex life cycle. As a small, highly motile, spherical cell (less than 1 μm in diameter) it moves around until it encounters a suitable econiche. It then loses its motility, and the cell begins to grow until it it ovoid. After a time a prosthecae (stalk) appears from one pole of the cell and elongates until it is 1 to 5 μm long by about 0.3 μm in diameter. A bud forms at the **apex** of the stalk, matures, becomes motile, detaches, and "swims" away. Under optimal conditions this life cycle is completed in 2 to 24 h, depending on the species.

The myxococci, living in the competitive soil econiche (Part 2), also have a complex life cycle and display cell-cell interaction as well. The vegetative cells are slender, medium-length rods that divide by binary fission. The organisms are obligate aerobic heterotrophs and secrete powerful exoenzymes that digest pro- and eucaryotic cells. The organisms glide on solid surfaces (mechanism unknown) and secrete slime, leaving a trail behind them. Often cells follow a leader, "ingesting" matter as they progress. When conditions become less than optimal, a "message" is sent and the cells "cooperate," piling on one another to form a heap known as a *fruiting body*. The cells at the top of the heap differentiate into resistant myxospores, while the lower-level cells perish. In this way the now resistant spores are atop the fruiting body, out of "harms way." In many cases the shape of the fruiting body (governed by the way in which the cells pile together)

NUTRITION	PATHOGENICITY OR OTHER OBVIOUS EFFECTS	OTHER IMPORTANT FEATURES
Chemoorganotrophs; anaerobic	Used by dairy industry for end products	In and on animals and dairy products "mold-like" bacteria
Chemoorganotrophs; aerobes or anaerobes		Filament fragment → "diptheroid cells"
Pathogenic species are fastidious	Tuberculosis or leprosy	Acid-fast due to mycolic acid
		Aquatic
Aerobic	Antibiotic producers	Numerous in soil
Fastidious (obligate intracellular parasites)	Many human diseases	
Require sterol Do not require sterol ⎱ ⎰ fastidious In rich medium containing serum ⎰	Pneumonia and other diseases	Like mycoplasmas (little or no cell wall)

is species specific and nonrandom. The fruiting bodies are often beautifully pigmented reds, yellows, or greens. When conditions are again suitable, the myxococci germinate to vegetative cells and resume their gliding quest for food.

Programmed Self-Test

Do not begin this self test before reading the corresponding chapter in the text.

BACTERIA (Text pages 243 to 264)

_____ substances are used by the purple nonsulfur
bacteria both as carbon sources and as _____
donors for the reduction of carbon dioxide.

Chromatiaceae use reduced _____compounds as the hydrogen donor for the reduction of carbon dioxide.

Organic;
hydrogen

Myxobacters move by _____.	sulfur
Leptothrix is placed in Part 3 of *Bergey's Manual of Determinative Bacteriology* because it is surrounded by a _____.	"gliding"
"A semirigid appendage, extending from a procaryotic cell" is the definition of a _____.	sheath
Hyphomicrobia are rather distinctive in that they divide by a process of _____.	prostheca
The spirochetes range in length from 3 to _____ μm.	budding
Pseudomonadaceae are motile by means of _____.	500
Azotobacteraceae are heterotrophic, aerobic, and have the very distinctive metabolic capability of _____.	polar flagella
_____ have a symbiotic relationship with leguminous plants.	"fixing" molecular nitrogen
_____ may be the most numerous organism in the intestines of mammals.	*Rhizobium*
Nitrobacter oxidizes _____ to _____, while *Nitrosomonas* oxidizes _____to _____.	*Bacteroides*
The methane bacteria are extremely sensitive to the atmospheric gas _____, which usually kills them.	nitrite; nitrate; ammonia; nitrite
The endospore-forming bacteria are rods, except for the genus _____, which is characterized by spherical cells arranged in tetrades or packets.	oxygen
Gram-positive, asporogenous, rod-shaped bacteria (Part 16) are allocated to the genus _____.	*Sporosarcina*
The Mycobacteriaceae uniquely have the staining property of being _____.	*Lactobacillus*
The aquatic family in the order Actinomycetales is _____.	acid-fast
Streptomyces are prolific producers of _____.	Actinoplanaceae

The mycoplasmas are minute procaryotic organisms bounded by a single triple-layered membrane and lacking a typical bacterial _____[which structure?] .	antibiotics
The characteristics of _____forms of bacteria closely resemble mycoplasmas.	cell wall
	L

Multiple-Choice Test

Underline the correct answer.

1. Mycoplasma (PPLO) can be distinguished from all the other orders of bacteria because in nature they: (a) have axial filaments; (b) cannot manufacture their own ATP; (c) move by gliding; (d) have little or no cell-wall material.

2. If the largest bacteria are found among the Spirochetaceae, the smallest are found among the: (a) eubacteria; (b) Rickettsiae; (c) Mycoplasmatales; (d) Pseudomonadales.

3. Swarmer cell, stalked cell, and bud are all stages in the life cycle of: (a) *Caulobacter;* (b) Myxobacterales; (c) *Hyphomicrobium;* (d) yeasts.

4. The sheathed bacteria, exemplified by *Leptothrix*, are members of: (a) Actinomycetales; (b) Caryophanales; (c) Myxobacterales; (d) Chlamydobacteriales.

5. The family of aquatic Actinomycetales is: (a) Mycobacteriaceae; (b) Actinomycetaceae; (c) Streptomycetaceae; (d) Actinoplanaceae.

6. *Escherichia coli* is a: (a) gram-positive rod; (b) gram-negative rod; (c) gram-positive coccus; (d) gram-negative coccus; (e) gram-negative spiral.

7. Underline the letter(s) corresponding to the group(s) of bacteria that do *not* generally divide by binary fission. Choose as many answers as are required to completely answer the "question." (a) Pseudomonads; (b) *Hyphomicrobium;* (c) eubacteria; (d) Actinoplanaceae; (e) Mycoplasma.

Questions 8 to 12. Match the order of bacteria with its distinguishing characteristics. A given choice may be used more than once or not at all.

8. Pseudomonadales

9. Hyphomicrobiales

10. Actinomycetales

(a)   Members cause typhus and Rocky Mountain spotted fevers
(b)   One family is the acid-fast Mycobacteriaceae
(c)   Gram-negative; polar flagellation
(d)   Diseases caused by this group include psittacosis, lymphogranuloma, and trachoma
(e)   Utilization of one-carbon compounds; stalked

11. Myxobacterales   (f)   No cell wall; multiplication is by fragmentation into elementary
                                    bodies
12. Mycoplasmatales   (g)   Motion is by gliding on a layer of slime; forms fruiting bodies

Answers: 1. (d);   2. (c);   3. (c);   4. (d);   5. (d);   6. (b);   7. (b), (d), (e);   8. (c);   9. (e);   10. (b);
             11. (g);   12. (f).

Chapter 14

The World of Bacteria II:
Kingdom Procaryotae (continued)
Rickettsias and Chlamydias

INTRODUCTION: Rickettsia and Chlamydia, though procaryotes, are discussed separately, partly because historically they were thought to resemble viruses, being obligate intracellular parasites. All the organisms in Part 18 of *Bergey's Manual* (see Chap. 13) share these characteristics; gram-negative, divide by binary fission, nonmotile, obligate intracellular parasites, many cause disease in humans and/or animals, some are symbionts in insects and other tissues. Classification is based on mode of transmission, where the organisms multiply, and pathogenicity. In many ways chlamydia are like rickettsia except that chlamydia cannot synthesize their own high-energy compounds (e.g., ATP), which they must obtain from their hosts.

This chapter also provides a discussion of medical and diagnostic implications of the Rickettsias and Chlamydias, whereas the pathogenicity of the other groups of bacteria is elaborated in later chapters.

Expanded Outline

Classification, pathogenicity, morphology, cultivation, characteristics, and other pertinent information is condensed in the following table, which replaces the expanded outline and summary. The table also provides a nearly complete outline of the classification scheme of Part 18 of *Bergey's Manual* and thereby also serves as a cogent example of bacterial systematics in operation.

Table 14-1. Classification of the Organisms in Part 18 of *Bergey's Manual of Determinative Bacteriology*

GENERA	ORDER I: RICKETTSIALES *FAMILY I: RICKETTSIACEAE	SPECIES—DISEASE IN HUMANS (if any)

Tribe: Rickettsieae
Small, pleomorphic, mostly intracellular organisms that exist in arthropods. Some are pathogenic for certain vertebrate hosts

Rickettsia. Small coccoid to rod-shaped or pleomorphic organisms. Found intracytoplasmically in lice, ticks, fleas, and mites or extracellularly in lumen of arthropod gut. Have not been grown on cell-free media. Are not filterable. Pathogenic for human beings, in whom they produce Weil-Felix agglutinins for *Proteus* spp.	*R. prowazekii*—Typhus fever (epidemic) *R. typhi*—Murine Typhus *R. canada*—Typhus fever *R. rickettsii*—Rocky Mountain spotted fever *R. sibirica*—Siberian tick typhus *R. conorii*—Boutonneuse fever *R. australis*—Queensland tick typhus *R. akari*—Rickettsial pox *R. parkeri*—Spotted fever–like disease *R. Tsutsugamushi*—Scrub typhus
Rochalimeae. Depend on arthropod and vertebrate hosts for Natural survival. Usually reside in an extracellular environment in the arthropod host. Can be cultivated in host cell-free media.	*R. quintana*—Trench fever
Coxiella. Small pleomorphic, coccoid, or rod-shaped organisms that grow preferentially in vacuoles of the host cell (rather than in cytoplasm or nucleus). Also occur extracellularly in infected ticks. They are filterable. Parasitic for humans and other animals but do not produce Weil-Felix agglutinins in humans.	*C. burnetii*—Q fever

Tribe: Ehrlichieae
Minute spherical or pleomorphic cells. Pathogenic for some mammals but not for humans. They occur in arthropods and other invertebrates.

Ehrlichia. Small coccoid or pleomorphic cells found in cytoplasm of monocytes of certain mammalian hosts. Causative agents of tick-borne diseases of dogs, cattle, sheep, goats, and probably horses.	*E. canis* *E. phagocytophila*
Cowdria. Small spherical, rod-shaped, or pleomorphic organisms found intracellularly in ticks. Are characteristically localized in clusters in cytoplasmic vacuoles of endothelial cells of mammalian host. Cause of heartwater of cattle, sheep, and goats.	*C. ruminantium*
Neorickettsia. Small coccoid or pleomorphic rods, crescents, or rings found in the cytoplasm of reticuloendothelial cells of certain mammals or fluke vectors. They cause a helminth-borne disease of canines.	*N. helminthoeca*

*There are two other families in this order, not described here.

Table 14-1. Classification of the Organisms in Part 18 of *Bergey's Manual of Determinative Bacteriology* **(continued)**

GENERA	ORDER I: RICKETTSIALES *FAMILY I: RICKETTSIACEAE	SPECIES—DISEASE IN HUMANS (if any)

Tribe: Wolbachieae
  Coccoid, rod-shaped, or filamentous cells adapted to growth in arthropods as symbionts.

Wolbachia. Pleomorphic organisms ranging from short coccoid to filamentous forms. Mostly intracellular, but extracellular forms are found.

W. pipientis
W. melophagi
W. persica

Symbiotes. Rickettsialike pleomorphic organisms, that exist as symbionts or in a true commensalistic state with arthropod hosts. Special organs or mycetomes may be developed in host to harbor these organisms.

S. lectularius

Blattabacterium. Straight or slightly curved rods. Nonmotile. Characteristically occur as intracellular symbionts in mycetocytes in abdominal fat body tissue and in ovaries and eggs of all species of cockroaches. Not known to be pathogenic or infective to any other insect, animal, or human being.

B. cuenoti

Rickettsiella. Found in association with intracellular, crystalline inclusions. Sometimes in the nuclei of host cells. They are filterable. Causative agent of blue disease of beetle larvae.

R. popilliae

	ORDER II: CHLAMYDIALES FAMILY I: CHLAMYDIACEAE	

Chlamydia. Nonmotile, gram-negative, spheroidal (0.2 to 1.5 μm diameter). Obligate intracellular parasites in cytoplasmic vesicle. Cannot synthesize own high-energy compounds. Intracellular propagation only. Three major ecological niches: Humans (venereal and respiratory disease); birds (respiratory and general infection); nonprimate animals.

C. trachomatis—trachomas and lymphogranuloma venerium
C. psittaci—psittacosis

*There are two other families in this order, not described here.

Programmed Self-Test

Do not begin this self-test before reading the corresponding chapter in the text.

RICKETTSIAS; CHLAMYDIAS (Text pages 266 to 281)

With the exception of _____, which causes the disease _____, rickettsiae are transmitted to humans and other animals by the bites of arthropod vectors or in their excreta.

Epidemic typhus fever, caused by *R. prowazekii,* is transmitted to people by _____.	*Coxiella burnetii;* Q fever
R. rickettsii causes the disease _____.	body lice
The most effective antibiotics against rickettsial infections are _____and_____.	Rocky Mountain spotted fever
Rickettsia can be cultivated only in actively metabolizing host cells, with the exception of the genus _____, which may be cultivated on a blood agar base.	tetracycline; chloramphenicol
Certain strains of the eubacterium _____ are agglutinated by the blood serum of patients with typhus fever and some of the other rickettsial diseases.	*Rochalimeae*
The outstanding characteristic that distinguishes Chlamydias from Rickettsias is the dependence of Chlamydias on the host cells for their _____.	*Proteus vulgaris*
_____-synthesis inhibitors are effective agents against Chlamydias.	energy
Chlamydias cause ornithosis, lymphogranuloma venereum, and _____.	Protein
	trachoma (inclusion conjunctivitis)

Multiple-Choice Test

Underline the correct answer.

1. The morphology of the group of rickettsias is best characterized as: (a) rods; (b) cocci; (c) coccobacillary; (d) varied.

2. Chlamydias are relatively rich in: (a) proteins; (b) DNA; (c) phospholipids; (d) salt.

3. Which of the following is not an obligate intracellular parasite? (a) Virus; (b) chlamydia; (c) rickettsia; (d) eubacteria.

4. Ehrlichia: (a) cause disease in humans; (b) cause disease in dogs, cattle, sheep, and other animals; (c) cause plant disease; (d) are nonpathogenic.

5. Q fever is caused by the genus: (a) *Rickettsia;* (b) *Rochalimeae;* (c) *Coxiella;* (d) *Wolbachia.*

6. Which can be cultivated in host cell-free media? The causative agent of: (a) typhus fever; (b) trench fever; (c) Q fever; (d) trachoma.

7. The Chlamydiales are more host-dependent than the Rickettsiales because they (Chlamydiales) require host: (a) ATP; (b) vitamins; (c) ribosomes; (d) DNA.

Answers: 1. (a);   2. (c);   3. (d);   4. (b);   5. (b);   6. (b);   7. (a).

Chapter 15

Fungi: The Molds

INTRODUCTION: Though perhaps the main emphasis of the text involves bacteriology, fungi (molds and yeasts) are both ubiquitous and important microorganisms. This chapter describes the biology of molds and touches on their importance. Relevant functions and properties of the fungi will be reintroduced as appropriate in later chapters.

Expanded Outline and Summary

I. Importance of Fungi.
   A. As saprophytic organisms.
      1. Beneficial activities—break down complex plant and animal remains into simpler compounds that greatly enhance soil fertility.
      2. Harmful activities—rot timber, textiles, food, and other commercial products. Some species produce mycotoxins.
   B. Industrial applications—production of beer, wine, antibiotics, vitamins, cheeses, etc.
   C. As parasites, they cause diseases in plants, humans, and animals

II. Distinguishing Characteristics of Fungi.
   A. Metabolism: Chemoorganotrophic (no chlorophyll).
   B. Cell structure: Eucaryotic, filamentous, often branched. Whole fungus including spores is called a *thallus*.
   C. Reproduction: Sexual and asexual spores.

III. Morphology of the Mold Thallus.
   A. Nonreproductive structure. Microscopic tubular filaments are called *hyphae*. Aggregates of hyphae are called *mycelia*. Depending on the species, the hyphae may be *nonseptate* (coenocytic), *septate* with *uninucleate* compartments, or *septate* with *multinucleate* compartments. (See Fig. 15-5.)
      1. Vegetative mycelia—form thallus body and may penetrate the substrate to obtain nourishment.

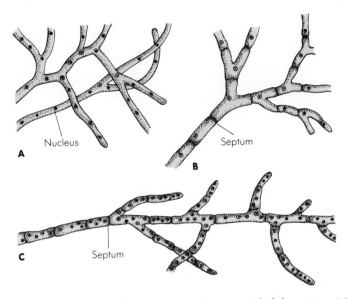

Figure 15-5. Three types of hyphae: (1) nonseptate (coencoytic); (2) septate with uninucleate cells; (3) septate with multinucleate cells.

2. Reproductive mycelia—responsible for spore production and usually extend in the air away from the medium.

B. Reproductive structures.
1. Asexual spores (terminology).
   a. *Sporophore*—spore-producing structure.
   b. *Sporangium*—sac on terminal portions of sporophore.
   c. *Sporangiophore*—sporophore with a sporangium.
   d. *Sporangiospores*—spores produced within a sporangium. (See Fig. 15-4b.)
   e. *Zoospores*—motile sporangiospores.
   f. *Zoosporagium*—contains zoospores.
   g. *Aplanospores*—nonmotile sporangiospores.
   h. *Conidiophore*—sporophore with spores born free.
   i. *Conidia*—spores born free (shape of conidia is species-specific and used in identification). (See Fig. 15-4a.)
   j. *Microconidia*—small, usually single-celled conidia. (See Fig. 15-7.)
   k. *Macroconidia*—large, usually multicelled conidia. (See Fig. 15-7.)
   l. *Sessile* conidia — those formed on the side of a hypha without any detectable conidiophores.
2. Sexual spores (terminology)—produced less frequently and less abundantly than asexual spores.

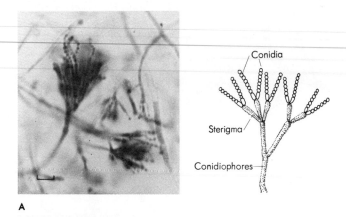

Figure 15-4a. Conidiospores of *Penicillium*.

Figure 15-4b. Sporangiospores of *Rhizopus*.

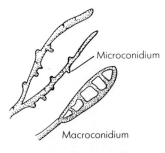

Figure 15-7. Microconidia and macroconidium of *Microsporum* sp.

a. Stages of sexual reproduction.
  i. *Plasmogamy*—the mechanism which brings two compatible nuclei together in a single protoplast.
  ii. *Karyogamy*—actual fusion of two nuclei, yielding a diploid zygote nucleus.
  iii. *Meiosis*—restores the haploid state to the nucleus. (In most fungi, the thallus is haploid, since meiosis occurs soon after karyogamy.)
b. Examples of types of sexual reproduction.
  i. Sexual spore is formed by the fertilization of the contents of a special female structure (*oosphere*) by a male sperm. The oosphere (egg) is contained within an *oogonium* produced on the mycelium, and the sperms are formed in an *antheridium* close to the organism. The spore resulting from this process is called an *oospore*.

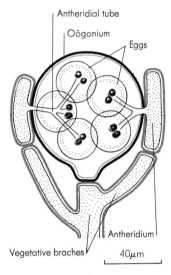

Figure 15-8. Sexual reproduction in *Saprolegnia*.

  ii. The tips of two hyphae come together and their contents fuse to produce a large, thick-walled body called a *zygospore*.

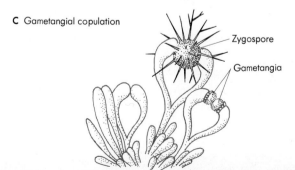

Figure 15-10c. Gametangial copulation: the direct fusion of gametangia without differentiation of gametes.

iii. Sexual spores are formed in a sac known as an *ascus;* the spores are called *ascospores.* There are usually eight such spores (see Fig. 15-4c) per ascus. In most ascus-producing fungi, these asci are enclosed in a definite fruiting body called an *ascocarp.* Ascocarps vary greatly in size and shape, and each type has its own name, like *cleistothecium, perithecium,* and *apothecium.* When the sexual spores, usually four in number, are developed from the end of a club-shaped structure called a *basidium,* the spores are *basidiospores.* (See Fig. 15-4d.)

C

Figure 15-4c. Ascospores of an ascomycete.

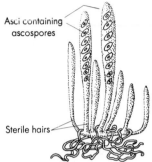

Asci containing ascospores

Sterile hairs

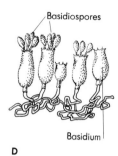

Basidiospores

Basidium

D

Figure 15-4d. Basidio-spores of a typical mush-room, a basidiomycete.

IV. Physiology and Nutrition of Molds.
    A. Tolerance. Molds often can withstand more severe stress than most other microorganisms (e.g., high concentrations of salt and sugar; wide pH range; dehydrated environment).
    B. Optimum conditions: pH, 5.6; temperature, 22 to 30°C; aerobic environment.
    C. Nutrition of saprophytes.
        1. Carbon sources: sugars, starches, cellulose, other organic compounds.
        2. Nitrogen sources: organic and/or inorganic.
        3. Vitamins: required by some species.
    D. Nutrition of parasites: special hyphal branches (haustoria) penetrate host cells to obtain food from the cytoplasm.

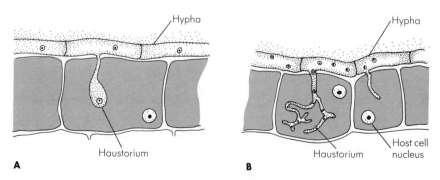

Hypha

Haustorium

A

Hypha

Haustorium

Host cell nucleus

B

V. Cultivation of Molds.
    A. Natural media: infusion of fruits, vegetables, animal cells, etc.
    B. Nonsynthetic media.

    C.   Synthetic media.

    D.   Selective media (e.g., Sabouraud media is selective for fungi because of high sugar concentration and low pH).

VI. Morphological Examination of Molds. Morphological examination is essential in the identification of fungi which can be cultivated on a slide (with media) and observed (undisturbed) under a microscope.

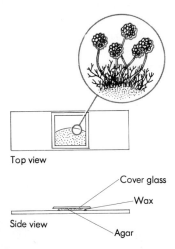

Top view

Cover glass

Wax

Side view

Agar

VII. Classification of Fungi. Classification of fungi is based primarily on the characteristics of their sexual spores and fruiting bodies. Those that do not (or are not observed to) produce sexual structures are placed with the Fungi Imperfecti and evaluated on the basis of the characteristics of their asexual spores and thalli. Some major classes of fungi are described.

    A.   Chytridiomycetes—aquatic or soil organisms, motile by means of a single posterior flagellum. Saprophytes or parasites on algae.

    B.   Hyphochytridiomycetes—aquatic organisms, motile by anterior flagellum.

    C.   Oomycetes—sexual reproduction is heterogametangic with oospore formation in oogonia. Parasitic members cause disease in fish and plants (potato blight and downy mildew of grapes).

    D.   Plasmodiophoromycetes—slime molds that parasitize plants (clubroot of cabbage and powdery scab of potatoes) and aquatic algae and fungi. Plasmodia, which develop in host cells, produce spores that release swarm cells (see IX.B, below).

    E.   Zygomycetes—sexual reproduction by gametangial copulation to form a zygospore. Terrestrial saprophytes or parasites. Some species used commercially to produce organic acids and alcohols. Other species destroy foods.

    F.   Trichomycetes—no sexual reproduction observed. Parasitic or commensalistic to arthropods.

    G.   Ascomycetes—sexual reproduction by ascospores. Also characterized (except for yeasts) by well-developed mycelia with perforated septa between cells. Some species are commercially useful or maintain soil fertility. Other species cause plant diseases (Dutch elm disease, apple scab, rusts, etc.).

    H.   Basidiomycetes—sexual reproduction by basidiospores. Binucleate hypha. Harmful activities include plant disease (rusts and smuts) and the deterioration of wooden structures. Macroscopic fungi of this class include mushrooms.

I.   Deuteromycetes (Fungi Imperfecti), 10,000 species—harmful activities include plant
     and animal disease; beneficial activities include the synthesis of industrial and phar-
     maceutical products.

VIII. Some Molds of Microbiological Interest.
   A. *Mucor*—sexual reproduction by zygospores. Asexual sporangiophores. Under high CO_2
       tension cells are yeastlike; otherwise filamentous (dimorphic). Found in soil and foods.
       Some species cause food spoilage, others are used in the manufacture of foods.
   B. *Rhizopus*—sexual reproduction by zygospores (see text fig. 15-15). Asexual sporangio-
       phores. Rhizoids ("runners") may also establish new organisms. Responsible for food
       spoilage.
   C. *Aspergillus*—Fungi Imperfecti. Septate, branching mycelia with vegetative portions sub-
       merged in nutrient. Conidia of various colors (species-specific) are produced within
       tubular sterigmata and are extruded to form spore chains. Beneficial in industrial fer-
       mentations and harmful as food spoilers.

Figure 15-16. *Aspergillus nidulans.*

   D. *Penicillium*—sexual ascospores or Fungi Imperfecti. Septate branching mycelia which
       penetrate substrate and then produce aerial hyphae on which conidiophores develop.
       Beneficial in the ripening of cheese (Roquefort, blue, and Camembert), industrial fer-
       mentations, and antibiotic production; harmful as food spoilers.
   E. *Neurospora*—sexual ascospores (some species heterothallic). Produces long strands of
       septate aerial mycelia. Branched chains of pink or red conidia. Used in the studies of
       genetics and metabolism and for industrial fermentations.
   F. *Sporotrichum*—Fungi Imperfecti. Septate mycelia with pear-shaped conidia that may
       grow in small clusters, but not chains. Cream-colored colonies. Most species are
       saprophytes, but one causes a plant disease, another spoils refrigerated meat, and a
       third causes human disease.

G. *Trichoderma*–Fungi Imperfecti. *T. viride* grows in the soil, where it ammonifies, decomposes cellulose, and produces an antibiotic against other species of fungi. Laboratory colonies are bright green.

H. *Cladosporium*–Fungi Imperfecti. Conidia produced by budding (see text Fig. 15-18). Contaminate culture media, forming discrete, olive green colonies.

I. *Alternaria*–Fungi Imperfecti. Large multicelled conidia in chains. Form brown to olive-green colonies on petri plates. Some species cause food spoilage, others are plant pathogens, and others are allergens, causing hay fever.

J. *Fusarium*–Fungi Imperfecti. Multicellular, sickle-shaped conidia borne on conidiophores arranged like spokes in a wheel. Implicated in food spoilage and plant disease. *F. moniliforme* synthesizes gibberellin.

IX. The Slime Molds. The slime molds resemble amoebas in many respects, but they do produce spores. Their taxonomic affiliation is uncertain.

A. Class Myxomycetes (the true slime molds)–vegetative phase is multinucleate mass of protoplasm called a *plasmodium*, which moves in amoeboid fashion and feeds on microorganisms or decaying organic matter. When conditions become unfavorable, the plasmodium changes into a dormant resistant form (*sclerotium*) until the return of favorable conditions. Some sporangia are borne on stalks arising from the plasmodium. Spores undergo metamorphosis and become first flagellated cells, then gametic amoeboid cells. The fusion of the gametes leads again to the development of plasmodia.

B. Class Plasmodiophoromycetes (endoparasitic slime molds)–zoospore penetrates rootlet of host plant and becomes a myxamoeba, which in turn developes into a plasmodium which lives in the tissues of the plant. Zoospores are liberated when the plant dies, and these infect new seedlings, thus causing the plant disease clubroot.

C. Order Acrasiales (cellular slime molds)–among organisms such as *Dictyostelium discoideum*, discrete amoeboid cells constitute the plasmodium.

D. Order Labyrinthulales (net slime molds)–deposit fine network of slime on their growing surface. Commonest in marine environments, as saprophytes or parasites of algae.

X. Molds and Their Associations with Other Organisms.

A. Lichens–symbiotic relationship in which an alga supplies organic carbon (via photosynthesis) to the fungus and the fungus provides protection, minerals, and water to the alga.

B. Fungi and nematodes–some fungi can capture roundworms (some of which are plant parasites) by constricting a hyphal loop around the prey. Haustoria penetrate the worm and digest it. Other trapping mechanisms include sticky hypha and hyphal webs.

C. Fungi as parasites of insects–numerous fungi cause self-limiting epidemics among flies, aphids, and other insects.

D. Mycorrhizas–fungi may infect plant rootlets, enhancing mineral absorption by the green plants but not causing disease. Truffles are subterranean fruiting bodies of certain *Ascomycetes* that grow in association with oak, beech, and other trees. The fungus and the tree exchange some essential nutrients. Other examples of Mycorrhizas include orchid-fungal and Indian pipe–fungal relationships.

Programmed Self-Test

Do not begin this self-test before reading the corresponding chapter in the text.

IMPORTANCE AND DISTINGUISHING CHARACTERISTICS OF FUNGI (Text pages 285 to 287)

Saprophytic organisms feed on _____.

Mold-produced poisons are called _____.   nonliving organic matter

The cell walls of fungi contain _____ and/or   mycotoxins
_____.

The whole fungus is called a _____.   chitin; cellulose

MORPHOLOGY OF THE FUNGAL THALLUS (Text pages 287 to 292)

Microscopic filaments of a thallus are called _____.   thallus

A sporangium is a sac on the terminal portion of the   hyphae
_____.

Nonmotile sporangiospores are called _____.   sporophore

_____ are the simplest and most primitive type of thal-   aplanospores
lospore.

Plasmogamy is the mechanism which brings two compatible   Buds
_____ together in a single protoplast.

Sexual spores, formed in a sac known as an _____, are   nuclei
called _____.

Aplanospores are defined as _____   ascus;
sporangiospores.   ascospores

PHYSIOLOGY, NUTRITION, AND CULTIVATION (Text pages 292 to 295)

Molds generally tolerate a pH range of _____ to _____.   nonmotile

Parasitic fungi often produce special hyphal branches called _____, which penetrate the host cells.	2.0; 9.0
Media with a low _____ and high concentration of _____ are tolerated by molds but are inhibitory to many bacteria.	haustoria
An example of a medium selective for fungi is _____.	pH; sugars

CLASSIFICATION OF FUNGI (Text pages 296 to 301)

Most species in the class Chytridiomycetes live in _____ environments.	Sabouraud
Endoparasitic slime molds cause two crop diseases known as _____ and _____ _____.	aquatic
Fungi of the order Entomophthorales are commonly parasites on _____.	clubroot of cabbage; powdery scab of potatoes
"Sac fungi" compose the class _____.	insects
Yeasts are placed in the class _____.	Ascomycetes
Fungi that cause Dutch elm disease belong to the class _____.	Ascomycetes
Deuteromycetes are also called _____.	Ascomycetes

SOME MOLDS OF MICROBIOLOGICAL INTEREST (Text pages 301 to 305)

In the presence of high concentrations of CO_2, mucor may grow in a _____ instead of in a filamentous form.	Fungi Imperfecti
Common bread molds belong to the species _____.	yeastlike
Aspergillus niger is used commercially to produce _____ and _____.	*rhizopus*
Roquefort, blue, and Camembert cheeses are ripened by members of the genus _____.	citric acid; gluconic acid

The conidia of *Neurospora* are colored _____.	*Penicillium*
Trichoderma viride is active in the soil in the _____ process and in the decomposition of _____.	pink or red
The mold _____ is an important allergen and one of the major causes of hay fever.	ammonification; cellulose
Fusarium moniliforme produces_____, which are plant growth stimulators.	*Alternaria*

THE SLIME MOLDS; MOLDS AND THEIR ASSOCIATIONS WITH OTHER ORGANISMS
(Text pages 305 to 308)

In their vegetative phases, Myxomycetes are multinucleate masses of cytoplasm called _____.	gibberellins
During reproduction Myxomycetes produce _____, which germinate into _____, which change into _____ that function as gametes. The zygotes, formed by the fusion of gametes, develop into _____.	plasmodia
Endoparasitic slime molds cause _____ disease.	spores; flagellated cells; amoeboid cells; plasmodia
Lichens comprise two organisms, an _____ and a _____.	clubroot
A _____ is an infected root system arising from the rootlets of a seed plant.	alga; fungus
Truffles are subterranean fruiting bodies of certain _____ which grow in association with some trees.	Mycorrhiza
	Ascomycetes

Multiple-Choice Test

Underline the correct answer.

1. Which pair of microorganisms (or group of microorganisms) is most closely related to each other? (a) Virus and rickettsia; (b) amoeba and blue-green algae; (c) algae and fungi; (d) *Escherichia coli* and *Salmonella typhosa*.

2. Fungi are: (a) eucaryotes; (b) procaryotes; (c) zooplankton; (d) afilamentous.

3. The whole fungus, including spores, is called a: (a) hypha; (b) mycelium; (c) conidia; (d) thallus.

4. An antheridium is the site of fungal _____ formation. (a) Spore; (b) sperm; (c) oosphere; (d) ascocarp.

5. Special hyphal branches of fungi that penetrate host cells to obtain food from host cytoplasm are: (a) characteristic of the Hyphochytridiomycetes; (b) conidia; (c) haustoria; (d) formed during karyogamy.

6. Dimorphic (yeast-mold) fungi are found in the genus: (a) *Mucor;* (b) *Rhizopus;* (c) *Neurospora;* (d) *Aspergillus.*

7. *Fusarium moniliforme* is used industrially to synthesize: (a) auxin; (b) gibberellin; (c) ethyl alcohol; (d) butter.

8. A vegetative mass of Myxomycete multinucleate protoplasm is called a(n): (a) plasmodium; (b) sclerotium; (c) acrasiale; (d) mycorrhiza.

Answers: 1. (d); 2. (a); 3. (d); 4. (b); 5. (c); 6. (a); 7. (b); 8. (a).

Chapter 16

Fungi: The Yeasts

INTRODUCTION: The mold-yeast transition of *Mucor*, cited in the previous chapter, underscores the classification of yeasts as fungi. It is appropriate to treat the yeasts apart from the molds, however, because yeasts are morphologically different, being afilamentous. Yeasts are very important tools of industry, and some species cause human disease. This chapter introduces you to the biology of this group of microorganisms.

Expanded Outline

I. Yeasts and Molds.
    A.   Historical importance.
        1. Fruit fermentations, leavening of bread, food production.
        2. Growth of microbiology. Hub of work by Pasteur, Hansen, et al.
    B.   Essential tool of industry (e.g., brewing and baking industries).
    C.   Contribution to scientific progress as a model of the biology of eucaryotic cell processes.

II. Classification of Yeasts (still in state of flux).
    A.   Criteria used in classifying yeasts (see Table 16-A).
    B.   General scheme of yeast classification.

Table 16-A. A Partial Classification of Yeasts: Criteria (cf. Table 16-1 of text)

			MAJOR DISTINGUISHING CHARACTERISTICS	
HIGHER TAXA	FAMILIES	SUBFAMILIES	FAMILY	SUBFAMILY
Class Ascomycetes				
Subclass Hemiascomycetidae			Ascospores	
Order Endomycetales	Spermophthoraceae		Needle-shaped spores	

Table 16-A. A Partial Classification of Yeasts: Criteria (cf. Table 16-1 of text)(continued)

HIGHER TAXA	FAMILIES	SUBFAMILIES	MAJOR DISTINGUISHING CHARACTERISTICS	
			FAMILY	SUBFAMILY
Class Ascomycetes (continued)	Saccharo-mycetaceae	Schizosaccharo-mycoideae	Various-shaped spores	Asexual fission
		Saccharomycoideae		Asexual budding
		Lipomycetoidae		Oval, amber, ascospores
		Nadsonioideae		Bipolar budding
Class Basidiomycetes Subclass Heterobasi-diomycetidae Order Ustilaginales	Ustilaginaceae (?)		Basidiospores	Asexual budding
Form-class Deutero-mycetes Form-order Moniliales	Sporbolomy-cetaceae		Asexual ballisto-spores	
	Cryptococcaceae		Arthrospores may be formed	

III. Ecology of Yeasts. They are ubiquitous in the soil and in numerous aquatic environments.

IV. Morphology of Yeasts.
   A. Cellular characteristics.
      1. Size: larger than most bacteria (1 to 5 μm wide and 5 to 30 μm long).
      2. Shape: usually egg-shaped. Some elongated and some spherical. (See p. 126.)
   B. Microscopic examination (staining).
      1. Nucleus: iron hematoxylin or Feulgen technique.
      2. Fat globules: Sudan III.
      3. Vacuoles: neutral red.
      4. Cellulose: zinc chloride–iodine.
      5. Nucleoprotein: polychrome methylene blue.
      6. Starch granules (blue) and glycogen (red-brown): potassium iodide.

V. Cytology of Yeasts (Eucaryotic Cells).
   A. Capsules—on some yeasts; usually composed of polysaccharides.
   B. Cell wall—primarily composed of glycan and usually mannan, and smaller amounts of protein and lipid. Some yeast walls have small amounts of chitin and glucosamine.
   C. Cytoplasmic membrane—about the same structure and composition as those of pro-caryotes.
   D. Protoplasmic constituents—cytoplasm rich in RNA, enzymes; endoplasmic reticulum.
   E. Nucleus—surrounded by membrane; lacks condensed chromosomes.
   F. Mitochondria—membrane-bound organelles containing respiratory enzymes.
   G. Vacuoles—one or more present in each cell; high activity of hydrolytic enzymes; con-tain phosphates or lipid when cell is in stationary phase of growth.
   H. Miscellaneous inclusions—fat, carbohydrates, protein, pigment, etc.

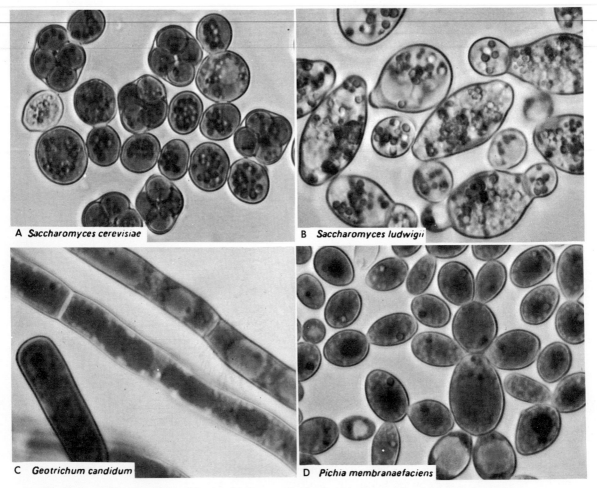

A *Saccharomyces cerevisiae*

B *Saccharomyces ludwigii*

C *Geotrichum candidum*

D *Pichia membranaefaciens*

VI. Cultural Characteristics. Yeast colonies vary in form as do bacterial colonies. Colony characteristics may be used to aid in yeast characterization.

VII. Reproduction of Yeasts.
   A. Budding (most common method)—tube is sent out from nuclear vacuole toward cell wall, which is weakened; protuberance is filled with nuclear and cytoplasmic parental material (through tube). Successive buds (about 24 per cell) are formed on different places on the cell surface.

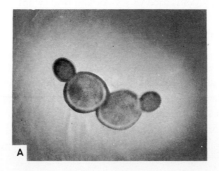

A

    B.   Combined budding and fission (bud-fission). Buds form at the cell's poles, and the inner part of the cell wall (septum) separates the buds from the parent.

    C.   Sporulation (exemplified by three different sexual cycles in basidiomycetes).

        1. Haploid mating cells fuse to form a dikaryotic mycelium; diploid chlamydospores form on the mycelium; meiosis occurs at about the time the chlamydospores germinate.

        2. Self-sporulating yeasts (no conjugation?).

        3. Numerous variations of conjugation without the formation of a dikaryotic mycelium. One variation is exemplified by the life cycle of *Saccharomyces cerevisiae* (see text Fig. 16-10).

    D.   Hybridization. Crossing of different yeasts to produce a progeny having some of the traits (hopefully the best) of each parent.

        1. By micromanipulation of ascospores from different, but compatible, parents. Resulting zygote gives rise to a hybrid colony.

        2. Gypsum-block method—involves the induction of sporulation, the killing of vegetative cells, and the subsequent rise of haploid colonies that originate from a single spore. Resulting "pure" cultures can be characterized and appropriately crossed.

VIII. Physiology of Yeasts (physiologies vary among the species but these generalizations can be made).

    A.   Nutrition.

        1. Utilization of sugars.

           a. Aerobically (respiration via the Krebs cycle; other pathways).

           b) Anaerobically (glycolysis $\rightarrow CO_2$ + ethanol).

        2. Nitrogen source—NH_3, nitrate, nitrite, and/or by amino acid deamination.

        3. Sulfur—SO_4, but some yeasts prefer organic sulfur.

        4. Trace metals—required, as with all other organisms.

    B.   Temperature—optimum for most yeast is 20 to 30°C; pathogen optimum is 30 to 37°C; psychrophilic varieties exist.

    C.   pH—depending on the strain, optimum is between 2.2 and 8.0. Most yeasts prefer an acid condition and can grow from 3.5 to 3.8.

    D.   Growth media.

        1. Nutrient agar and other synthetic media.

        2. 5% malt extract agar.

        3. Wickerham's medium.

Programmed Self-Test

Do not begin this self-test until you have read the appropriate chapter in the text.

YEASTS AND HUMANS, CLASSIFICATION OF YEASTS (Text pages 313 to 316)

Yeasts and molds compose the biological group called _____.

A _____ is one who studies yeasts.   fungi

The Schizosaccharomyces vegetatively reproduce only by _____.	zymologist
Basidiospores are sometimes called _____.	fission
The three main classes of yeast are defined according to the mode of _____.	sporidia

ECOLOGY AND MORPHOLOGY OF YEASTS (Text pages 317 to 318)

Most yeasts are saprophytes, but some have a _____ mode of nutrition.	sexual reproduction
Are yeasts motile?	parasitic
The stain Sudan III demonstrates _____.	No
The nucleus can be stained by _____ or _____.	fat globules

CYTOLOGY AND CULTURAL CHARACTERISTICS OF YEASTS (Text pages 319 to 323)

Most yeast capsules are composed of _____.	iron hematoxylin; the Feulgen technique
The major constituents in the cell wall of *S. cerevisiae* are _____ and _____.	polysaccharide
The nucleus is surrounded by a _____.	glycan; mannan
Mitochondria consist largely of lipoprotein and a small amount of _____ and _____, and function in_____.	semipermeable nuclear membrane
In the stationary phase of growth, phosphates or lipid are concentrated in the yeast _____.	RNA; DNA; aerobic energy conversion
Upon aging, yeast colonies become thicker and drier, and _____ may be produced.	vacuole

REPRODUCTION OF YEASTS (Text pages 323 to 328)

Yeasts may reproduce by sporulation, budding, or _____ .	pigments
A yeast may bud an average of only _____ during its lifetime.	fission
Saccharomycoides and *Nadsonia* asexually reproduce by a process known as _____ .	24 times
When the nuclei of two cells of similar size and shape fuse, this conjugation is termed _____ .	bud-fission
The crossing of different yeasts (or any organism) to produce an organism having the desirable characteristics of the two genetically different strains is called _____ .	isogamic

PHYSIOLOGY OF YEASTS (Text pages 328 to 329)

In yeasts, anaerobic dissimilation of sugars yields the end products _____ and _____ .	hybridization
Before a yeast culture can ferment polysaccharides, they must first be _____ .	ethyl alcohol; carbon dioxide
Most yeasts have an optimum growth temperature of _____ .	hydrolyzed
Yeasts grow well on media adjusted to pH _____, which inhibits most bacteria.	20 to 30°C
Media commonly used for the isolation of yeasts are _____ and _____ .	3.5 to 3.8
	5% malt extract agar; Wickerham's medium

Multiple-Choice Test

Underline the correct answer.

1. Yeasts are not classified as protozoa partly because: (a) they do not carry out photosynthesis; (b) they are procaryotes; (c) they are motile; (d) they have a rigid cell wall.

2. Arthrospores may be formed by yeasts belonging to the family: (a) Sporobolomycetaceae; (b) Cryptococcaceae; (c) Saccharomycetaceae; (d) Spermophthoraceae.

3. The most common morphological form among yeasts is: (a) egg-shaped; (b) rod-shaped; (c) spiral-shaped; (d) filamentous.

4. Which is never a component of the yeast cell wall? (a) Glycan; (b) mannan; (c) teichoic acid; (d) chitin.

5. Which organelle is the "powerhouse" of eucaryotic cells? (a) Vacuole; (b) mitochondrion; (c) nucleus; (d) cytoplasmic membrane.

6. Buds are progeny that are: (a) larger than the parent; (b) the same size as the parent; (c) smaller than the parent; (d) the result of a conjugal process.

7. During yeast budding, a tube is sent out from the nuclear vacuole toward a point of the cell wall nearest the: (a) cell membrane; (b) mitochondria; (c) chloroplast; (d) vacuole.

8. Which class of fungus produces a sexual zygospore? (a) Phycomycetes; (b) Ascomycetes; (c) Basidiomycetes; (d) Sarcodina.

9. Under which of the following conditions would a culture of yeast utilize chemical bond most efficiently? (a) When it is stored in a sealed flask in the refrigerator; (b) when it is fermenting grape juice to yield ethanol; (c) when it is growing aerobically; (d) when it is fermenting wort in the manufacture of beer.

Answers: 1. (d); 2. (b); 3. (a); 4. (c); 5. (b); 6. (c); 7. (d); 8. (a); 9. (c).

Chapter 17

Algae

INTRODUCTION: Algae constitute another major group of microorganisms, and these photo-synthesizers are also encountered everywhere in nature. Like the preceding chapters on molds and the subsequent ones covering protozoa and viruses, Chap. 17 highlights a wealth of known information. It is hoped that these introductions will make you more aware of the "scheme of biology" and enable you to better understand more comprehensive material as the need arises.

Expanded Outline

I. Occurrence of Algae.
   A. All aquatic systems.
       1. Phytoplankton—microscopic plant food for animals.
       2. Harmful effects—in great quantities has offensive odors and tastes; toxins; limit amount of O_2 that can penetrate deeper water.
       3. Beneficial effects—in moderate concentrations, increases O_2; removes excessive salts.
   B. Many terrestrial niches.

II. Characteristics of Algae.
   A. Morphology—wide range of sizes and shapes.
       1. Single cells—spherical; rods; spindle-shaped.
       2. Aggregates of single cells.
       3. Aggregates of cells, some differentiated.
   B. Fine structure: eucaryotic.
       1. Outer coverings.
           a. Cell walls thin and rigid in most species; surrounded, perhaps, by flexible, gelatinous *outer matrix*.
           b. Diatoms—cell walls impregnated with silica, making them thick and rigid.
           c. Motile algae (e.g., *Euglena*)—flexible cell membranes (periplasts).
       2. Chloroplasts—one, two, or many per cell; ribbonlike, barlike, netlike, or discrete discs. Contain flattened membranous vesicles (thylakoids).

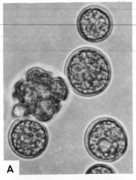
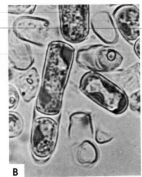

A   *Chlorococcum scabellum*

B   *Pseudobumilleriopsis* sp.

C   *Volvox spermatosphaera*

D   *Gloecapsa* sp.

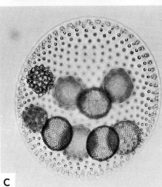
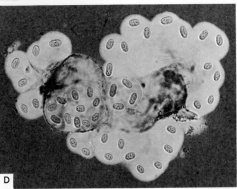

      a. Parietal—massive structures situated near the wall.

      b. Asteroidal—embedded in the midst of the cytoplasm.

C.   Algal pigments—one basis for algal classification.

    1. Chlorophylls—a, b, c, d, e.

    2. Carotenoids—lipid-soluble carotenes and xanthophylls.

    3. Biloproteins (Phycobilins)—water-soluble phycocyanin and phycoerythrin.

D.   Motility.

    1. Some algae are nonmotile.

    2. Flagella occur singly, in pairs, or in clusters at one or both ends of the cell (eyespot present near anterior end of motile algae).

      a. Whiplash—cylindrical and smooth.

      b. Tinsel—cylindrical with hairlike appendages.

      c. Ribbon or straplike.

E.   Reproduction (sexual, asexual, or both).

    1. Asexual.

      a. Fragmentation.

      b. Involving the production of zoospores (aquatic) or apanospores (aquatic).

    2. Sexual (many forms found among the algae).

      a. Gamete fusion (conjugation) → zygote.

      b. Oogamy—Ovum (large, nonmotile, female egg cell) fuses with smaller, motile male gamete (sperm cell). Sometimes there is also differentiation of the thalli that produce the egg or sperm cells.

        i. Dioecious (unisexual)—algae that produce either sperm or egg cells.

        ii. Monoecious (bisexual)—algae that produce both sperm and egg cells.

Classification of algae (see Table 17-1).

III. Economic Importance of Algae.
    A. Soil fertility.
        1. Nitrogen fixation—by blue-green algae (bacteria).
        2. Protection of nitrogen-fixing organisms from desiccation.
        3. Fertilizer—large red and brown seaweeds.
    B. Vitamin synthesis.
        1. Carotene—precursor of vitamin A.
        2. Vitamin D—To fish to humans.
        3. Vitamins B_1, C, and K.
    C. Algae as food.
        1. *Porphyra* (red alga)—cultivated in Japan.
        2. Agar.
        3. "Irish Moss"—yields carrageenan (holds substances in suspension).
        4. *Chlorella,* etc., as single-cell food.
    D. Algae and disease (few algae are pathogenic).
        1. *Prototheca*—mammalian pathogen in tropics.
        2. *Cephaleuros*—attach to leaves of tea, coffee, and pepper and cause considerable damage.
        3. *Gymnodinium* and *Gonyaulax*—produce a neurotoxin that kills fish during algal blooms (the "red tide").
        4. *Prymnesium parvum* and some blue-green algae also produce toxins.

IV. Lichens (composite organisms consisting of algae and fungi).
    A. Ecology—rocks and tree bark and other substances that do not usually support the growth of plants; survive cold Arctic climates and rarefied atmospheres; resistent to heat and desiccation; grow slowly and are long-lived.
    B. Morphology—algae (one of many greens or blue-greens) sandwiched between layers of fungi (one of many ascomycetes or one of a few basidiomycetes). Bottom fungal layer may attach to the substrate directly or by means of short, twisted hyphae (rhizines). 18,000 lichen species are described.
        1. Crustaceous—grow as mat on substrate.
        2. Fruiticose—erect and shrublike.
    C. Reproduction.
        1. Lichen reproduction—vegetative processes.
            a. Fragmentation.
            b. Soredia—knots of hyphae containing a few algal cells.
        2. Lichen components—reproduce independent of one another.
            a. Fungus—usually ascospores.
            b. Alga—cell division; occasionally spores.
    D. Symbiotic nature (contribution by each partner).
        1. Alga—food.
        2. Fungus—water, minerals, and "protection."
    E. Chemical interaction (resulting in unique organic products).
        1. Unusual fats and phenols (2 to 20 percent of lichen dry weight).
        2. Litmus.
        3. Oils—used in perfumes.

Table 17-1. Classification of Algae

	TAXONOMIC GROUP (DIVISION)	CHLORO-PHYLL	CAROTENOIDS*	PRESENCE OF BILO-PROTEINS	STORAGE PRODUCTS	FLAGELLATION AND DETAILS OF CELL STRUCTURE
A	Cyanophycophyta (blue-green algae or blue-green bacteria)	a	β-carotene, zeaxanthine, echinenone, myxoxanthophyll	✓	Glycogenlike cyanophycean starch; proteins	Flagella absent; procaryotic cells; a bacterium
J	Rhodophycophyta (red algae)	a, rarely d	β-carotene, zeaxanthine ± α-carotene	✓	Floridean starch; oils	Flagella absent
F	Xanthophycophyta† (yellow-green algae)	a, c rarely e	β-carotene, diadinoxanthin, heteroxanthin, vaucheriaxanthin ester		Chrysolaminarin; oils	Flagella: 2 unequal, apical; silica incorporated in cell wall
D	Chrysophycophyta (golden algae)	a, c_1, c_2	β-carotene, fucoxanthin		Chrysolaminarin; oils	Flagella: 1 or 2 equal or unequal, apical; in some, cell surface covered by characteristic scales
I	Phaeophycophyta (brown algae)	a, c_1, c_2	β-carotene ± α-carotene rarely ε-carotene, fucoxanthin		Laminarin; soluble carbohydrates; oils	Flagella: 2 lateral holdfasts; air bladders
E	Bacillariophycophyta (diatoms)	a, c, c_2	β-carotene ± α-carotene rarely ε-carotene, fucoxanthin		Chrysolaminarin; oils	Flagella: 1 in male gametes, apical; cell in two halves, the walls silicified with elaborate shapes
B	Euglenophycophyta (euglenoids)	a, b	β-carotene ± α-carotene, diadinoxanthin		Paramylon; oils	Flagella: 1, 2, or 3 equal, slightly apical; gullet present
C	Chlorophycophyta (green algae)	a, b	β-carotene ± α-carotene, rarely α-carotene and lycopene, lutein		Starch; oils	Flagella: 1, 2, 4 to many, equal, apical or subapical; pyrenoids
H	Cryptophycophyta (cryptomonads)	a, c_2	α-carotene ± β-carotene, rarely ε-carotene, alloxanthin	✓	Starch; oils	Flagella: 2 lateral; gullet present in some species
G	Pyrrophycophyta (motile, dinoflagellates; nonmotile, phytodinads)	a, c_2	β-carotene, peridinin		Starch; oils	Flagella: 2 lateral, 1 trailing, 1 girdling; in most, there is a longitudinal and transverse furrow and angular plates

*Only predominant xanthophylls are included.
†Some workers have recently separated a new division, Eustimatophycophyta, from this.

ECOLOGY	REPRODUCTION	MORPHOLOGY	EXAMPLES (GENERA) SEE TEXT FOR SPECIFIC DETAILS
Fresh and marine water; terrestrial	Asexual: fission; fragmentation; spores (akinetes)	Single cells; filamentous	
Most in warm marine water; subtidal zone; form algal reefs	Highly specialized; asexual: aplanospores; sexual: union of capogonia and spermatia	Usually less than 3 ft long	*Gelidium* (agar source) Chondrus crispus
Fresh and marine water; terrestrial	Oogamous; etc.	Unicellular; colonial; filamentous; tubular	*Vaucheria* ("water felt")
Fresh and marine water; moist soil	Usually asexual; occasionally isogamous	Some amoeboid forms; also some nonmotile coccoid and filamentous forms; unicellular or colonial. Silica incorporated	Ochromonas; Chrysamoeba
Cool marine waters	Asexual: zoospores; sexual: isogamous and heterogamous	Multicellular	*Kelps* (several hundred feet long); *Sargassum natans*
Fresh and marine water; moist soil; major group of plankton		Unicellular; colonial; filamentous; prominent nucleus; ribbonlike or lenslike plasmids; silica shells (frustules)	Thousands of species
Soil; water	Fission; dormant cysts formed	No cell wall; periplast; single cells	*Euglena*
Mostly fresh water; some seawater or terrestrial	Asexual: zoospores fission, etc.; sexual: diverse	Have cellulose cell walls; single cells or colonial	*Chlamydomonas; Chlorella; Volvox; Acetabularia; Desmids; Ulothrix*
	Longitudinal fission; sexual reproduction not observed	Flattened slipper-shaped, singly occurring cells; some have a cell wall	
Fresh and marine water; important plankton member	Mostly by fission	Some have prominent cell wall made of plates	*Gymnodinium* (no cell wall); *Gonyaulax* ("red killer tide")

Programmed Self-Test

Do not begin this self-test before reading the corresponding chapter in the text.

OCCURRENCE AND CHARACTERISTICS OF ALGAE (Text pages 332 to 339)

Endophytic algae live in _____.

Cell walls of diatoms are impregnated with _____ making them thick and very rigid.

other organisms

Euglena have flexible cell membranes called _____.

silica

Parietal chloroplasts are situated near _____.

periplasts

The three kinds of photosynthetic pigments in algae are _____, _____ and biloproteins.

the cell wall

Carotenes and xanthophylls are two kinds of _____.

chlorophylls; carotenoids

The pigments of the blue-green algae are borne on _____.

carotenoids

Nonmotile algal spores are called _____ and are more likely to be produced by _____ algae.

thylakoids

Union of a large, nonmotile ovum and a small, motile sperm cell is termed algal _____.

aplanospores; terrestrial

CLASSIFICATION (Text pages 339 to 349)

Filamentous blue-green algae reproduce by _____.

oogamy

_____ is an organism that is a cross between an "animal" and a plant.

fragmentation

Chlorophycophyta are commonly called _____.

Euglena

The _____ is a dense region of the chloroplasts on the surface of which starch granules are formed.

green algae

The reproduction of spirogyra by sexual means is (called) _____.	pyrenoid
Flagellated, amoeboid algae such as Chrysamoeba belong to the algal division _____.	isogamous
Shells of diatoms are called _____.	Chrysophycophyta
Vaucheria is commonly known as _____.	frustules
Brown algae (seaweeds) are most commonly found in _____.	"water felt"
A byproduct of *Gelidium* is _____.	cool ocean waters

ECONOMIC IMPORTANCE OF ALGAE (Text pages 349 to 351)

Large red and brown seaweeds are used by farmers as _____.	agar
Carotene is a precursor of vitamin _____.	fertilizer
The Japanese cultivate and harvest _____, a red alga, as a food crop.	A
One alga pathogenic for humans is _____.	*Porphyra*
Gymnodinium produces a _____ that kills aquatic animals.	*Prototheca*

LICHENS (Text pages 351 to 353)

Lichens are composite organisms consisting of a(n) _____ and a(n) _____.	neurotoxin
Blue-green and _____ algae can enter into a lichenlike relationship with many of the _____ (fungal division).	alga; fungus
_____ lichens grow closely appressed to the substrate, while _____ lichens have a shrublike morphology.	green; Basidiomycetes

Lichens produce the well-known pH indicator _____ .	Crustaceous (foliose); fruiticose
Lichen "reproductive bodies" called _____ are knots of hyphae containing a few algal cells.	litmus
	soredia

Multiple-Choice Test

Underline the correct answer.

1. Algal species number in the: (a) tens; (b) hundreds; (c) thousands; (d) millions.

2. Organisms in which class of algae are much like bacteria? (a) Cyanophycophyta; (b) Euglenophycophyta; (c) Chlorophycophyta; (d) Chrysophycophyta.

3. What form of sexual reproduction has been observed among cryptomonads? (a) Heterogamy; (b) isogamy; (c) oogamy; (d) none.

4. *Volvox* grows: (a) as single cells; (b) filamentously; (c) in masses that are several feet long; (d) in colonies of from 500 to several thousands cells.

5. A tropical plant pathogen is: (a) *Porphyra;* (b) *Euglena;* (c) *Cephaleuros;* (d) *Prototheca.*

6. "Reindeer mosses" are really: (a) algae; (b) mosses; (c) ferns; (d) lichens.

7. Chlamydomonas cells that have formed *en masse* within a gelatinized matrix are called: (a) palmelloid stages; (b) pyrenoids; (c) frustules; (d) spermatia.

8. Which of the following groups of Protista have membrane-enclosed chloroplasts? (a) Algae; (b) blue-green algae; (c) bacteria; (d) both algae and blue-green algae.

9. Algae are one of the links between the unicellular and multicellular organisms. Which of the following members normally exist in multicellular form? (a) *Protococcus;* (b) *Euglena;* (c) *Volvox;* (d) diatoms.

Answers: 1. (c); 2. (a); 3. (d); 4. (d); 5. (c); 6. (d); 7. (a); 8. (a); 9. (c).

Chapter 18
Protozoa

INTRODUCTION: This chapter on Protozoa introduces an entirely new division of micro-organisms. The morphological, physiological, and developmental diversity of this group of eucaryotes is great. Therefore, a general discussion, with some examples, constitutes the contents of the text. Again, therefore, your task is twofold:

(1) To assimilate the basic biology of the protozoa in order to broaden your understanding of microbiology.

(2) To learn the basic terminology and facts so that you will be able to comprehend additional information.

Expanded Outline and Summary

I. Introduction and Overview.
  A. Morphology—single-celled or aggregates of cells; eucaryotes.
  B. Diversity—45,000 catalogued species and many more uncatalogued species. Classified mostly by criteria of locomotion.
    1. 20,000 fossil species.
    2. 18,000 free-living forms.
    3. 7,000 parasitic.
  C. Ecological importance—food chain.

II. Ecology of Protozoa.
  A. Free-living protozoa (environmental optima resemble those of bacteria).
    1. Vegetative (trophic) stage—ubiquitously encountered in many terrestrial and aquatic environments.
    2. Encysted state (thick-walled inactive stage)—withstands greater environmental extremes than vegetative stage.
  B. Symbiotic (literally any form of coexistence between two different organisms) protozoa.
    1. Commensalistic (host neither injured nor benefited).
      a. Ectocommensalism (attachment to host's exterior).

      b. Endocommensalism (inside the host's body), e.g., protozoa that live in the alimentary tract.
2. Mutualistic (both organisms benefit), e.g., protozoa that digest cellulose in termite gut.
3. Parasitic (parasite gains; host loses), e.g., Sporozoa which cause disease.
4. Hyperparasitic (parasite of a parasite).

III. Morphology.
   A. Size—considerable variation among species.
     1. *Leishmania donovani*—1 to 4 μm.
     2. *Amoeba proteus*—600 μm.
     3. Ciliates—some reach 2,000 μm (2 mm).
   B. Cellular structures (eucaryotic).
     1. Cytoplasm.
       a. Ectoplasm—gellike.
       b. Endoplasm—more voluminous and fluid.
     2. Structures in cytoplasm.
       a. Protein fibrils (fibrillar bundles, myonemes microtubules)—parallel fibrils involved in contraction.
       b. Pigments—some species green, brown, blue, purple, or red.
       c. Membrane systems—endoplasmic reticulum.
       d. Golgi complexes (dictyosomes)—membranous sacs.
       e. Kinetosomes (blepharoplasts)—basal bodies of cilia or flagella.
       f. Other structures—mitochondria, food vacuoles, contractile vacuoles.
     3. Nucleus—eucaryotic.
       a. Types.
         i. Multiple nuclei (e.g., many ciliates).
         ii. Dissimilar nuclei: macronucleus (metabolism and regeneration) and micronucleus (reproduction), e.g., ciliates.
         iii. Two similar nuclei.
         iv. One nucleus.
       b. Structure.
         i. Chromosomes—number is species-specific.
         ii. Nuclear membrane.
         iii. Karyoplasm (nucleoplasm).
     4. Cell envelope (functions: protection, active transport, perception).
       a. Plasmalemma (cell membrane)—sole covering of some protozoa, e.g., amoeba.
       b. Pellicle—various shapes and chemical compositions, e.g., ciliates have thick, ridged pellicle.
       c. Shell, test, lorica, cyst (loose covering external to the pellicle)—these have organic matrix and are encrusted with inorganic material (e.g., calcium carbonate or silica).
       d. Cysts (temporary sheaths).
         i. Induced by unfavorable environment in some species.
         ii. Part of life cycle of parasitic species (transmissible stage).
     5. Locomotor organelles.
       a. Pseudopodium (temporary projection of cytoplasm)—characteristic of Sarcodina.

      b. Flagellum—1 to 2 per cell; sometimes as many as 8 per cell, depending on species. Characteristic of Mastigophora. Fine, filamentous extension of cell.
        i. Axoneme—elastic filament.
        ii. Contractile cytoplasmic sheath—surrounds axoneme.
        iii. Undulating membrane—found in parasitic Mastigophora.
      c. Cilia—functions: locomotion; food ingestion; tactile organelle; fine, threadlike extensions of cells in the group Ciliophora.
      d. Body flexion—responsible for gliding movement.

IV. Reproduction Processes.
    A. Asexual reproduction—binary fission (2 daughter cells), equal or unequal (budding?); multiple fission (many daughter cells formed).
      1. Binary fission.
        a. Elementary binary fission—e.g., amoebas.

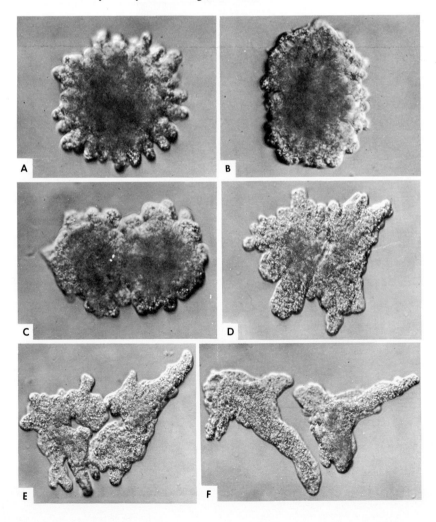

      b. Longitudinal fission—e.g., flagellates.

      c. Transverse fission—e.g., some ciliates.

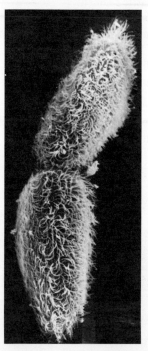

  2. Multiple fission—most common to *Foraminfera, Radiolaria,* and Sporozoa.

  3. Budding—in protozoology, sessile mother cell releases one or more smaller, swarming daughter cells.

      a. Exogenous—external formation and separation of bud.

      b. Endogenous—swarmer formed inside mother cell.

B. Sexual reproduction.

  1. Conjugation—only in Ciliophora. Temporary union of two cells, exchange of genetic material, then reproduction by fission or budding.

  2. Total conjugation—complete fusion of two organisms.

  3. Syngamy or gametogamy—sexual fusion of two gametes.

      a. Isogametes—morphologically alike.

      b. Anisogametes—not alike morphologically or physiologically.

        i. Microgametes (spermatozoa)—small and motile.

        ii. Macrogametes (ova)—large and nonmotile.

C. Regeneration—damaged nucleated cells reconstitute themselves.

V. Characteristics of Major Groups of Protozoa (cf. Table 18-1 of text)

MAJOR GROUPS	CHARACTERISTICS	EXAMPLES OF SOME GENERA	SOME DISEASE-CAUSING GENERA
A Superclass Sarcodina (amoebas) and other amoeboid Protozoa	Pseudopodia typically present; flagella, when present, restricted to developmental stages; cortical zone of cytoplasm relatively undifferentiated in comparison with other major taxa; body naked or with external or internal tests or skeletons of various types and chemical composition; asexual reproduction by fission; sexual reproduction if present, with flagellate or, more rarely, amoeboid gametes; most species free-living	*Foraminiferans* (chalky shell) and *Radiolaria* (silica shell) are two marine groups; *Amoeba proteus* (pseudopods capture food which is acid and enzyme digested in vacuoles); *Entamoeba gingivalis* (lives in human mouth)	*E. histolytica* (amoebic dysentery in humans)
B Subphylum Ciliophora (ciliates) and other ciliated Protozoa	Simple cilia or compound ciliary organelles in at least one stage of life cycle; subpellicular infraciliature universally present even when cilia absent; two types of nucleus, except in a few homocaryotic forms; binary fission in asexual reproduction; sexual reproduction by conjugation; heterotrophic nutrition; most species free-living	*Didinium* (feeds on *Paramecia*); *Paramecia* (fixed mouth pore at base of oral groove takes on food which is digested in the gullet and excreted at the anal pore)	*Balantidium coli* (dysentery)
C Superclass Mastigophora (flagellates)	One or more flagella typically present in trophozoites; solitary or colonial; asexual reproduction basically by symmetrogenic binary fission; sexual reproduction unknown in many groups; nutrition is phototrophic, heterotrophic or both	*Mastigamoeba* (feeds like amoeba); *Trichonympha collaris* (digests cellulose in gut of termite)	*Giordia lamblia* (diarrhea, mostly in children); *Trichomonas buccalis* (gingivitis); *T. hominis* (diarrhea); *T. vaginalis* (vaginal and urinary infection); *Trypanosoma gambiense* and *T. rhodesiense* (sleeping sickness); *Leishmania* (Kala azar), etc.
D Subphylum Sporozoa	Spores typically present; spores simple, without polar filaments and with one to many sporozoites; single type of nucleus; cilia and flagella absent except for flagellated microgametes in some groups; sexuality, when present, syngamy; all species parasitic; complex life cycles		*Plasmodium* (4 species) cause various forms of malaria; other species of *Plasmodium* infect chicks, ducks, canaries, or mice

Programmed Self-Test

Do not begin this self-test before reading the corresponding chapter in the text.

ECOLOGY OF PROTOZOA (Text pages 355 to 359)

Protozoan is derived from the Greek words *protos* and *zoon*, meaning _____ and _____.	
In colonial forms, individual protozoa are joined to one another by _____.	first; animal
The vegetative stage of protozoa is also termed the _____ stage.	cytoplasmic threads
Holozoic protozoa are those that eat _____.	trophic
Any type of coexistence between two organisms is termed _____.	other organisms
A relationship where the host is neither benefited nor harmed is called _____.	symbiotic
A parasite of a parasite is called a _____.	commensalistic

MORPHOLOGY OF PROTOZOA (Text pages 359 to 364)

Protozoa may survive the most severe environmental extremes when they are in the stage of development known as the _____ _____.	hyperparasite
Holozoic protozoa _____ other organisms.	encysted state
The ectoplasm is more _____ and contains more _____ than the endoplasm.	eat
Intracytoplasmic basal bodies of cilia or flagella are called _____.	gellike; organelles (structures)
The macronucleus controls _____ and _____.	kinetosomes *or* blephanoplasts

In its simplest form, the pellicle is the cell membrane or the _____, e.g., the pellicle of amoebas.	metabolic activities; regeneration processes
A temporary projection of part of the cytoplasm of amoebas is called a _____.	plasmalemma
Cilia, in addition to their locomotor function, also aid in _____ and serve often as a _____ organelle.	pseudopodium

REPRODUCTIVE PROCESSES OF PROTOZOA (Text pages 364 to 367)

Multiple division occurs commonly in the Foraminiferida, the Radiolarida, and the _____.	food ingestion; tactile
In schizogony, the multinucleate organism produces many _____ buds.	Sporozoa
Conjugation is found exclusively among the protozoa in the group _____.	uninucleate
Microgametes and macrogametes are both _____ gametes.	Ciliophora
When a protozoan is cut in two, the _____ portion regenerates.	aniso

CHARACTERISTICS OF THE MAJOR GROUPS OF PROTOZOA (Text pages 367 to 375)

Amoebas belong to the group _____.	nucleated
Entamoeba histolytica causes _____ in humans.	Sarcodina
Paramecium belongs to the group _____.	amoebic dysentery
Trypanosoma gambiense is transmitted by the _____ and causes _____.	Ciliophora
The species of *Plasmodium* that causes the most lethal form of malaria is _____.	tsetse fly; African sleeping sickness

The obligately parasitic group (subphylum) of protozoa is the _____ .

falciparum

Sporozoa

Multiple-Choice Test

Underline the correct answer.

1. Which of the following diseases is not caused by a protozoan? (a) Amoebic dysentery; (b) sleeping sickness; (c) typhoid fever; (d) malaria.

2. Protozoa are ecologically important because of their role in: (a) photosynthesis; (b) denitrification; (c) the food chain; (d) plant pathogenesis.

3. Which protozoan structure is internal to the cell envelope? (a) Dictyosome; (b) test; (c) pellicle; (d) plasmalemma.

4. A form of reproduction *not* common to the protozoa is: (a) binary fission; (b) fragmentation; (c) multiple fission; (d) schizoogamy.

5. Which species of *Plasmodium* causes benign tertian malaria? (a) *vivos;* (b) *malariae;* (c) *falciparum;* (d) *ovale.*

6. The econiche of *Trichonympha collaris* is: (a) marine water; (b) freshwater; (c) termite gut; (d) human intestine.

7. Sporozoa are all: (a) ciliates; (b) flagellated; (c) conjugating organisms; (d) parasitic.

8. Of all the catalogued, *living* protozoa, about what percent of the species are parasitic? (a) 50 percent; (b) 30 percent; (c) 10 percent; (d) 1 percent.

Answers: 1. (c); 2. (c); 3. (a); 4. (b); 5. (a); 6. (c); 7. (d); 8. (b).

Chapter 19

Viruses: General Characteristics

INTRODUCTION: Viruses are obligate intracellular parasites. More like a chemical outside the cell, they "spring to life" once they gain entry into a suitable host. Viral morphology and physiology are quite distinct from all other earthly life. Some properties of the viruses have been alluded to in earlier chapters on the history of microbiology and on genetics. In later chapters, particularly on disease, the "applied" aspects of virology will be discussed. This chapter provides some theoretical background to enable you to more fully comprehend the impact of viruses on biology and pathology. As is the case so often in a general course, familiarity with new terminology, understanding of cogent examples, and integration of a broad array of detail will put you well on your way.

Expanded Outline and Summary

I. History.
   A. Smallpox and vaccination.
      1. Jenner—cowpox virus protects against smallpox.
      2. Pasteur—attenuated (less virulent) rabies virus, when inoculated, produces active immunity against the disease.
   B. Tobacco mosaic virus and filterability.
      1. Ivanowski, Beijernick, Loeffler, and Frosch (turn of the twentieth century) found that filters that trapped bacteria did not trap viruses.
      2. Stanley crystallized (purified) the tobacco mosaic virus (TMV).
   C. Yellow fever virus.
      1. Theiler attenuated yellow fever virus by serial passage in living chick embryo tissue.
      2. Mumps, measles, and German measles vaccines are prepared today essentially by Theiler's techniques.

II. Characteristics of Viruses.
   A. Inclusion bodies—generally, aggregates of unassembled virus subunits and intact virions in infected cells.

Table 19-3. Classification of Animal Viruses

Properties used to classify animal viruses (explanations of these properties follow later in the text).

PRIMARY CHARACTERISTICS	SECONDARY CHARACTERISTICS
Nucleic acid:	Host range:
RNA: Single- or double-stranded	Species of host
DNA: Single- or double-stranded	Specific host tissues or cell types
Structure of virus particle:	
Helical capsid: Naked or enveloped	Mode of transmission (e.g., feces)
Icosahedral capsid: Naked or enveloped	
Complex structure (e.g., tail)	Immunological characteristics
Number of capsomeres	
Size of virion	
Susceptibility to inactivating agents	
Site of replication:	
Nucleus	
Cytoplasm	

Table 19-4. Outline Classification of Animal Viruses

NUCLEIC ACID	SYMMETRY	ENVELOPE	VIRION SIZE, nm	FAMILY	EXAMPLES OF GENERA
RNA	Icosahedral	No	18–30	Picornaviridae	Enterovirus
		No	54–75	Reoviridae	Reovirus
		Yes	35–80	Togaviridae	Alphavirus
	Helical	Yes	80–120	Orthomyxoviridae	Influenzavirus
		Yes	100–300	Paramyxoviridae	Paramyxovirus
		Yes	60–250	Rhabdoviridae	Lyssavirus
DNA	Icosahedral	No	18–24	Parvoviridae	Parvovirus
		No	70–80	Adenoviridae	Mastadenovirus
		Yes	110	Herpetoviridae	Herpesvirus
	Not defined	Complex coat	200 × 300	Poxviridae	Orthopoxvirus

SOURCE: G. P. Youmans, P. Y. Paterson, and H. M. Sommers, *The Biologic and Clinical Basis of Infectious Diseases,* Saunders, Philadelphia, 1975.

1. Elementary bodies (Paschen bodies) are colonies of smallpox virus growing in the cytoplasm (not real inclusion bodies). First seen by Buist (1887) and Paschen (1906).
2. Guarnieri bodies of smallpox virus.
3. Negri bodies of rabies virus.
4. Also characteristic and diagnostic of other pox viruses, herpes virus, and insect viruses.

III. Virion (intact virus particle) Structure and Composition. This knowledge is based primarily on electron microscopy (viruses are too small to be seen with light microscopes) and chemical analysis.
   A. The capsid and envelope.
      1. Protein coat (capsid) composed of protein subunits (capsomeres).
         a. Functions: Protection of nucleic acid and infection (the penetration of nucleic acid into the host cell).
         b. Specificity: Given virus infects only a particular host or class of hosts and often only particular cell types within the host. Such specificity is bestowed, at least in part, by the capsid.
      2. Envelope—present on some types of viruses; composed of lipids or lipoproteins taken from the host.
         a. Enveloped viruses sensitive to bile salts, ether, chloroform, and detergents.
         b. Nonenveloped (*naked*) viruses not sensitive to these lipid solvents, emulsifying agents, and detergents.
   B. Nucleic acids—*either* single-stranded (SS) RNA *or* double-stranded (DS) RNA *or* single-stranded DNA *or* double-stranded DNA.
      1. Plant viruses: SS or DS RNA.
      2. Bacterial viruses: SS or DS DNA or SS RNA.
      3. Animal viruses: DS DNA or SS or DS RNA.
   C. Other components which may be contained in the more complex types of virions.
      1. Carbohydrates.
      2. Trace metals.
      3. Enzymes.
      4. Vitaminlike substances.
   D. Composite virion. Capsid surrounds nucleic acid to form a nucleocapsid which may be naked or enveloped.
   E. Shapes of viruses.
      1. Icosahedral (20 triangular facets, 12 corners) or, roughly, spherical. Example: poliovirus.

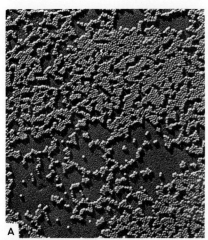

A

Figure 19-8a. Poliovirus (x 20,500). (*Courtesy of Edgar Ribi and the Rocky Mountain Laboratory, U.S. Public Health Service.*)

2. Helical—resemble long rods: capsid hollow cylinder with helical structure. Example: tobacco mosaic.

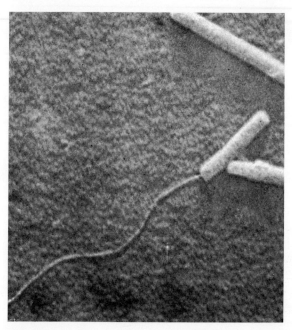

3. Enveloped—nucleocapsid icosahedral or helical, but virions appear pleomorphic since the envelope is not rigid. In enveloped helical virus, the nucleocapsid is coiled within the envelope. Examples: herpes simplex (icosahedral) and influenza (helical).
4. Complex—a few viruses have many different proteins, appendages, and/or structures. Such viruses may range from tadpole-shaped (T-2 bacteriophage) to indented spheres (pox virus).
5. Sizes of viruses—see Text Fig. 19-1.

IV. Replication. Extracellular virions are dormant "chemical entities." Processes associated with life occur only inside a suitable host cell. Life cycles of the various viruses differ in detail. For example, most DNA animal viruses usually replicate in the nucleus, while those that contain RNA usually replicate in the cytoplasm. Also, methods of host penetration and virion exodus differ. An example of the life cycle of a herpes virus is presented here, and that of a bacteriophage is presented in the next chapter. For now, the following generalizations (stages of the viral life cycle) that apply to all animal viruses can be made.

A. Attachment—between specific receptors on the host cell surface and macromolecules on the virion.
1. Preliminary attachment (adsorption) involves ionic bonds and is reversible.
2. Firm attachment.
B. Penetration (and uncoating, which takes place intracellularly).
1. By phagocytosis (pinocytosis)—naked viruses.
2. By fusion of host cell membrane and the viral lipoprotein envelope.

C. Biochemical replication—virus-coded enzymes are synthesized which in turn direct replication of the virus genome and capsid components. Host cells supply necessary structures (e.g., ribosomes), energy (e.g., ATP), and (some) biochemicals necessary for viral replication.

D. Assembly or maturation. In "industrial assembly-line" fashion, completed viral components coalesce (sometimes spontaneously without enzyme direction) in proper form around viral genome.

E. Release.
  1. Cell lyses and numerous virions are released suddenly, or
  2. Slow release (extrusion through membrane) of virions, one at a time over a specific time interval. For an example of replication of herpes simplex virus, see text Fig. 19-13.

V. Isolation and Identification of Viruses. The methods vary. Essentially they involve partial purification of the virus, viral propagation in suitable cell cultures, and viral characterization, usually by immunological methods.

VI. Cultivation of Viruses.
  A. Chick embryos (fertile hen's eggs, incubated 5 to 12 days) aseptically inoculated on chorioallantoic membrane (e.g., vaccinia virus) or the yolk sac of the embryo (e.g., influenza virus).
  B. Plasma clots—viruses inoculated into plasma congealed around tissue.
  C. Tissue culture—widely used to grow viruses and observe induced cytopathic changes. Useful for propagating viruses for vaccines. Tissue (e.g., monkey kidney or human HeLa cells) are propagated in complex synthetic media. Viruses are inoculated, and tissue deterioration (cytopathic effect or CPE) can be observed as evidence of viral multiplication.

VII. Are viruses living organisms? Viruses behave as living organisms only when they are inside their appropriate host cell.

Programmed Self-Test

Do not begin this self-test before reading the corresponding chapter in the text.

HISTORY (Text pages 377 to 383)

Like Rickettsia, viruses are obligate _____.

Jenner introduced a vaccine which protects against_____.   intracellular
                                                                         parasites

---

A word meaning "render less virulent" is _____.   smallpox

The initials TMV stand for _____.	attenuate
Rubeola is the scientific name for the _____ virus.	tobacco mosaic virus
The mumps virus, when cultivated for vaccine production, is propagated in _____.	measles

CLASSIFICATION AND CHARACTERISTICS OF VIRUSES (Text pages 383 to 390)

Animal viruses are classified primarily by the kind of _____ _____ within the capsid.	eggs (chicken embryos)
An example of an enveloped, icosahedral, RNA animal virus is _____.	nucleic acid
The largest DNA animal viruses belong to the _____ group.	arbovirus
Aggregates of unassembled and intact smallpox virions, within the host cell, are called _____.	pox
A capsid is composed of protein subunits called _____.	Guarnieri bodies
Animal viruses have all types of nucleic acids except _____.	capsomeres
Viral envelopes are composed of _____ or _____.	single-stranded DNA
Viruses that are unenveloped are termed _____.	lipid; lipoprotein
The shape of polio virus is _____, whereas that of the tobacco mosaic virus is _____.	naked
The intact virus particle is called a _____.	icosahedral; helical

REPLICATION (Text pages 390 to 393)

Several steps of viral infection that are common to all animal viruses are attachment, penetration, uncoating, replication, _____, and _____.	virion

Preliminary virus attachment to the host is by _____.	assembly *or* maturation; release
Naked animal viruses penetrate the host cell by a process known as _____.	ionic bonds
The assembly of the herpes virion is initiated in the _____ of the host cell.	phagocytosis (pinocytosis)

ISOLATION, IDENTIFICATION, AND CULTIVATION OF (ANIMAL) VIRUSES (Text pages 393 to 395)

Some viruses grow in the embryo yolk sac, and others can be cultivated on the _____ of fertile hen's eggs.	nucleus
Tissue-culture vaccines have an advantage over embryo-culture vaccines in minimizing the possibility of a patient developing hypersensitivity to _____.	chorioallantoic membrane
Poliovirus, for the Salk vaccine, was cultivated on _____.	egg albumin
The deterioration of virus-infected cells is termed _____ _____ and is indicative of viral activity.	(monkey) kidney cells
Influenza virus, which does not cause pronounced CPE, can be detected instead by the _____.	cytopathic effect (CPE)
If cells are infected with influenza virus, _____ can be adsorbed on their surface.	hemadsorption technique
	erythrocytes

Multiple-Choice Test

Underline the correct answer.

1. Which of these statements is most accurate? (a) Viruses multiply inside any plant, animal, or bacterium, but extracellularly; (b) viruses multiply inside any living or dead cell; (c) viruses multiply in nutrient broth supplemented with yeast extract; (d) viruses multiply inside living cells.

2. A virion: (a) is the intact virus particle; (b) is the protein coat of any virus; (c) functions in virus multiplication; (d) is the complex structure of a pox virus; (e) is a capsid.

3. Plant viruses usually contain: (a) DNA; (b) RNA; (c) both RNA and DNA; (d) DNA, RNA, and cytoplasm.

4. A viral capsid is composed of: (a) mucopeptide; (b) lipid; (c) capsomeres; (d) DNA.

5. Viruses multiply by the process of: (a) mitosis; (b) binary fission; (c) budding; (d) none of these.

6. Which of the following microorganisms has no cytoplasm? (a) Bacteria; (b) algae; (c) viruses; (d) fungi.

7. Which of the following is not an obligate intracellular parasite? (a) Virus; (b) chlamydia; (c) rickettsia; (d) eubacteria.

8. A virus that is naked is: (a) polio; (b) measles; (c) herpes; (d) mumps.

9. Viral envelopes are composed of: (a) nucleic acid; (b) protein; (c) lipid or phospholipid; (d) polysaccharide.

Answers: 1. (d); 2. (a); 3. (b); 4. (c); 5. (d); 6. (c); 7. (d); 8. (a); 9. (c).

Chapter 20

Viruses: Bacteriophages
and Phages of
Other Protists

Morphologically and physiologically all viruses are basically alike. Nucleic acid and capsid are common to all viruses. A few viruses possess a slightly more complex structure. All viruses are obligate intracellular parasites, depending on their hosts for many things. This chapter describes viruses that infect procaryotes. Some of these viruses have been characterized more completely than *any* other biological entity. Therefore, in this chapter, fresh virological concepts and information can be introduced. Pertinent examples are included. It is hoped that you can broaden your knowledge of viruses and, through examples, attain a better understanding of viral characteristics in general. One of the purposes of this study guide is to condense and summarize textual material so that you can more clearly envision trends and the most essential information. However, this section expands on some textual material (reproduction of bacterial viruses). Hopefully, this will increase your understanding of it.

Expanded Outline and Summary

  I. General Characteristics. Bacterial viruses (bacteriophages) exist for most, and possibly all, bacteria.
    A. Morphology — like other viruses, but some have a "tail" through which they inject their genome into the host.
    B. Importance — as a research tool.
    C. Bacteriophage (phage) life cycles.
      1. Lytic cycle (virulant cycle) — phage genome injected into host and directs production of numerous progeny. Bacterial cell lysis releases phage progeny.
      2. Lysogenic cycle (avirulent cycle) — some phages are *temperate,* meaning they can undergo the lytic and lysogenic cycles. In lysogeny, viral infection is inapparent. A viral-produced repressor turns off the viral genes coding for lytic-cycle functions. Temperate-phage DNA is incorporated (integrated) into host DNA and becomes part of it (a prophage). The prophage is now "controlled" by the host and is replicated when host DNA is replicated, to be passed (in this inapparent state — still integrated into bacterial DNA) to bacterial progeny. Either spontaneously or

through the use of mutagenic agents (induction), the repressor is destroyed, the prophage is excised from the bacterial chromosome, and the lytic cycle occurs.

II. The Discovery of Bacteriophages by Twort (1915) and d'Herelle (1917). They found that something in sewage lysed intestinal bacteria.

III. Morphology and Structure — illustrated below. Forms I, II, and III are unique to phage.

Type	A	B	C	D	E	F
Morphology	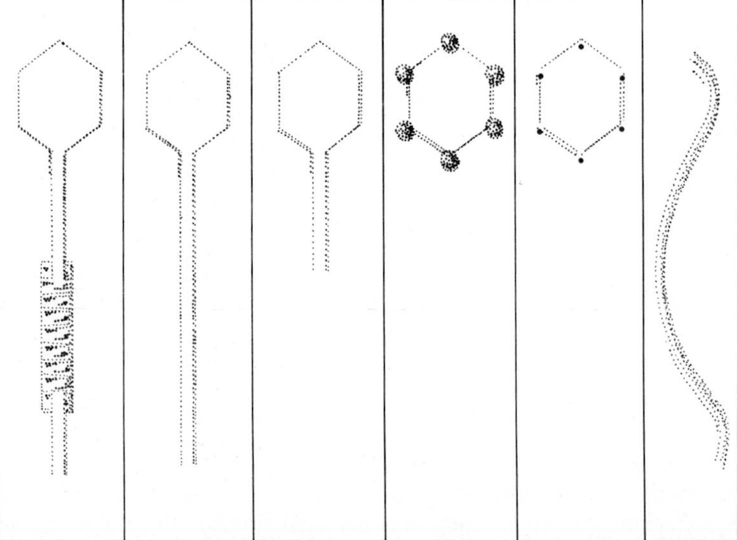					
Description	Contractile tail	Long noncontractile tail	Short noncontractile tail	No tail, large capsomeres	No tail, small capsomeres	No head flexible filament
Nucleic acid type	2-DNA	2-DNA	2-DNA	1-DNA	1-RNA	1-DNA

Fig. 20-2. Morphological types of bacteriophages. *(As described by David E. Bradley in "Ultrastructures of Bacteriophages and Bacteriocins," Bacteriol Rev, 31:230–314, 1967.)*

IV. Some Bacteriophages of *Escherichia coli.*
  A. T (for tadpole) phages of *E. coli* B (genome: double-stranded DNA).
    1. T2, T4, T6 — hexagonal heads; long tails; volume 1/1000 that of *E. coli* host; 5-hydroxymethylcytosine replaces cytosine in DNA. (See figure on facing page.)
    2. T1 and T5 — longer and more slender tails than T-even phages.
    3. T3 and T7 — rudimentary tails.
  B. Phages with genomes other than double-stranded DNA.
    1. Linear, single-stranded RNA — F2, which is much smaller than the T phages and does not have a tail.
    2. Circular, single-stranded DNA.
      a. Icosahedral (cubic) — ØX174.
      b. Filamentous (helical) — M_{13}, fd, f1.

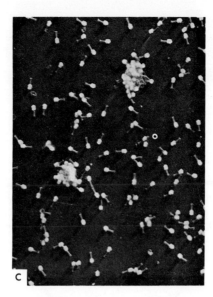

V. Isolation and Cultivation of Bacterial Viruses. Like all viruses, phage are cultivated in their living host cell, in this case a bacterium.
   A. Broth bacterial cultures — for obtaining large yields of viruses. Culture clears as cells lyse.
   B. On agar, "lawns of bacteria" — useful for titering phage, as one virus yields one plaque ("hole" in the lawn of bacteria).
VI. Reproduction of Bacterial Viruses (exemplified by T-even coliphages).

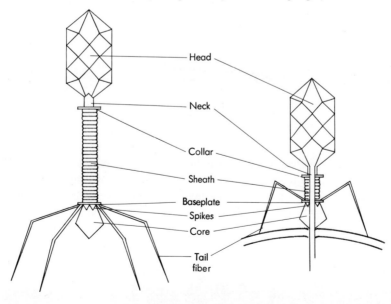

Head
Neck
Collar
Sheath
Baseplate
Spikes
Core
Tail fiber

A. Adsorption and penetration.
   1. Adsorption — the baseplate spikes on the tail and the now extended tail fibers at-
       tach to specific receptor sites of the bacterial cell wall.

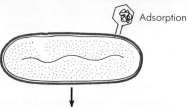

Adsorption

   2. Penetration — the viral sheath contracts, thrusting the core into, and past, a lyso-
       zyme-weakened bacterial cell wall. DNA in the head of the phage is injected
       through the core and into the bacterium. The now empty phage capsid remains
       outside the bacterium.

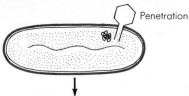

Penetration

B. Replication, assembly, and lysis.
   1. Replication — nonessential host machinery is shut down, and the host genome is
       degraded. Thus, the bacterium is under phage control and is "working for the
       phage."
       a. Phage DNA is transcribed into mRNA, which codes for enzymes that replicate
           phage DNA and synthesize phage capsid (e.g., heads, baseplates, sheaths, tail
           fibers, etc.).
       b. Translation involves host ribosomes, energy, and some precursor materials like
           nucleotides and amino acids.

Replication

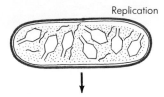

   2. Assembly — after viral components are manufactured within the bacterium, the
       parts are "put together" in a manner analogous to the manner in which a car is put
       together — in "assembly-line fashion." Many of the component-joining steps are
       under enzymatic direction, while some occur spontaneously. Head capsomeres
       surround the phage genome, and additional components are added as illustrated on
       page 404 of your text.

Assembly

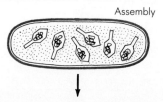

3. Lysis. The infected bacterium bursts for at least three reasons.
   a. The reduced metabolism of the infected bacterium limits cell-wall repair.
   b. Phage-produced lysozyme weakens the cell wall.
   c. The bacterium is "swollen" with phage and phage components.
   Figures below show a bacterium just before lysis and a diagrammatic sketch of the process.

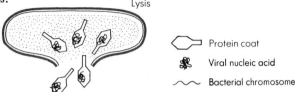

C. The timing of the infection cycle of the T-even bacteriophage — the *one-step growth curve.* Phage replication is demonstrated when one adds the viruses to an actively growing broth culture of bacteria and counts the viruses in the culture (on bacterial lawns as plaque-forming units, or PFUs) at several-minute intervals. When this is done, this pattern of "growth" is noted.

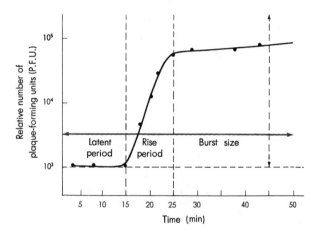

1. 0 to 30 min — phage are adsorbing to and penetrating bacteria. Titer declines, as at this point intracellular phage DNA and attached ghost capsids are incapable of producing a plaque.
2. 3 to 15 min — latent period. The initial part of the latent period is called the *eclipse phase.* During the eclipse phase, viral components are manufactured, but no virions have yet assembled. Thus, during the eclipse phase, no infectious particles exist within the bacteria. During the later part of the latent period virions begin to assemble but are trapped within the bacteria.
3. 15 to 25 min — rise period. Bacteria lyse, releasing infectious particles (PFUs). The T-even growth curves are termed "one-step" because, theoretically, one second there are no extracellular virions and the next the bacteria have burst, releasing hundreds of virions per cell. Of course, in actuality, not all bacteria in the culture are lysed simultaneously, so the rise period is not completely vertical.
4. Burst size — the first round of infection is complete. The burst size is defined as the number of virions that are released per infected cell.

VII. Lysogeny – see Part I.C.2 of this chapter.

VIII. The Bacteriocins.
   A. Production – plasmid-coded polypeptides (see Chap. 12).
   B. Specificity – act on closely related organisms not possessing the plasmid coding for the production of bacteriocins.
   C. Structure – some resemble phage capsid.
   D. Dissimilarity to phage – bacteriocins do not multiply in victim, do not normally lyse the victim, and are degraded by the enzyme trypsin.
   E. Mode of action – adsorb to specific receptors on the cell wall and inhibit DNA synthesis, transcription, and/or translation.
   F. Spectrum – found in many bacteria (e.g., *E. coli*, colicin; *Aerobacter aerogenes*, aerocin; etc.).

IX. Cyanophages. These are viruses much like bacteriophages, except that their hosts are blue-green algae, which are really photoautotrophic bacteria.
   A. Cyanophage groups (four main viral groups).
   B. Cyanophage composition – like bacteriophage except that all discovered, to date, contain linear double-stranded DNA.

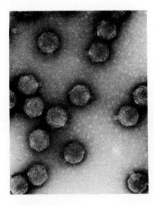

Fig. 20-10. Particles of purified LPP-1 cyanophage.

   C. Growth cycle of cyanophages – data as yet incomplete and complicated by the filamentous nature of the hosts.
      1. Cyanophage LPP-1 lytic cycle.
         a. Timing – like that of T viruses except slower. The infectious process takes 6 h, and the burst size is 350 PFU.
         b. Adsorption and penetration – like T-even bacteriophages.
         c. Replication – in the vicinity of the nucleoplasm; long helices formed between the photosynthetic lamellae.
         d. Assembly – at the *virogenic stroma* (spaces formed by the invagination of the photosynthetic lamellae).
         e. Release – like T-even bacteriophages.
      2. Lysogenic cycle – temperate cyanophages (LPP-1D and LPP-2SPI) were recently discovered.

X. Algal Viruses. Some have reportedly been seen, but actual proof of their existence has not yet been presented.

XI. Mycoviruses. Viruses attacking various fungi are common.
   A. Structure — those described, to date, are small polyhedrons, about 40 nm in diameter, which contain double-stranded RNA (mycorna viruses).
   B. Habitation — many viral aggregates seen in older hyphal regions (many in vesicles) and in spores.

Programmed Self-Test

Do not begin this self-test before reading the corresponding chapter in the text.

CHARACTERISTICS, DISCOVERY, STRUCTURE, AND CULTIVATION OF BACTERIO-PHAGES (Text pages 397 to 401)

_____ bacteriophages are capable of entering the lysogenic cycle.	
Viruses that infect bacteria were observed first by Twort and soon afterward by _____ .	Temperate
The contractile component of a T2 bacteriophage is called a _____ .	d'Herelle
T-even phages have _____ in their DNAs in place of the usual cytosine.	sheath
The type of nucleic acid in phage f2 is _____ .	5-hydroxy-methylcytosine
The replicative form of ∅X174 DNA is _____-stranded.	linear, single-stranded RNA
On agar plates clear zones caused by phage multiplication on bacterial "lawns" are called _____ .	double

REPRODUCTION OF BACTERIAL VIRUSES (Text pages 401 to 405)

The first step in the reproduction of bacteriophage is _____ .	plaques

In T-even phage infection, predominantly _____ enters the host cell.	adsorption
Complete viral capsids that are devoid of nucleic acids are called _____ .	DNA
About _____ min after initial T-even phage infection, about _(number)_ new bacteriophages will have been assembled.	ghosts
The _____ of the T-even bacteriophage "punctures" the bacterial cell wall.	25; 200
T-even phages carry and produce the enzyme _____, which aids in host penetration and escape.	core
A _____ growth curve characterizes the T-even replication cycle.	lysozyme
T4 bacteriophage DNA has been mapped. The locations of at least _(number)_ of the genes are known.	one-step

BACTERIOCINS, CYANOPHAGES, AND MYCOVIRUSES (Text pages 405 to 409)

Bacteriocin production is directed (coded for) by a _____ .	75
Chemically, bacteriocins are _____ .	plasmid
Pyocin is produced by _____ .	proteins (polypeptides)
Bacteriocins kill by degrading DNA, inhibiting DNA or RNA synthesis, or interfering with _____ synthesis.	*Pseudomonas aeruginosa*
The hosts of cyanophages are _____ .	protein
The latent period of cyanophage LPP-1 lasts for about _____ h, and the average burst size is _____ PFUs.	blue-green algae
LPP-1 is assembled in the _____ of its host.	6; 350
Are there any temperate cyanophages?	virogenic stroma

The name _____ has been proposed for the small icosahedral mycovirus containing double-stranded RNA.	Yes
May fungal spores contain mycoviruses?	mycorna
Young apical regions of fungal hyphae are generally _____ of virus particles; older regions contain _____ particles.	Yes
	free; many

Multiple-Choice Test

Underline the correct answer.

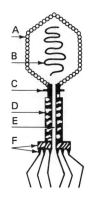

Questions 1 to 3 refer to the diagram.

1. Pictured here is a: (a) plant virus; (b) bacteriophage; (c) animal virus; (d) rickettsia.

2. Of all the labeled components, which one enters the host cell? (a) A; (b) B; (c) D; (d) F.

3. Which one (protein) confers specificity on the virus for a given host? (a) A; (b) C; (c) D; (d) F.

4. The tail fibers on coliphage T2 function in: (a) firmly attaching the virus to the *E. coli* cell wall; (b) "injecting" viral DNA; (c) locating the host; (d) giving the tail structural rigidity.

Questions 5 to 8. Define the stages of the one-step growth curve by choosing the correct answer from the right-hand column. Use each answer once.

5. Eclipse period   (a) Viruses emerging from lysed bacteria
6. Late latent period   (b) No intra- or extracellular virions
7. Burst size   (c) Number of virions released per infected cell
8. Rise period   (d) Intra- but no newly formed extracellular virions

9. Which word does not fit with the others in terms of alternative viral life cycles? (a) Vegetative; (b) virulent; (c) lytic; (d) prophage.

10. Bacteriocins generally act by: (a) denaturing enzymes; (b) adversely affecting various components of genetic "machinery"; (c) rupturing the cell membrane; (d) inducing prophages to resume the lytic cycle.

Answers: 1. (b); 2. (b); 3. (d); 4. (a); 5. (b); 6. (d); 7. (c); 8. (a); 9. (d); 10. (b).

Chapter 21

Fundamentals
of Control

INTRODUCTION: Up to now the text has dealt with the biology of microorganisms. The cultivation, physiology, genetics, classification, and other attributes of microorganisms — particularly bacteria — have been presented. Major groups of protista have been introduced and briefly described. Thus, much of the preceding material was theoretical, presenting the ideas, facts, and terminology that will enable you to deal intelligently with microorganisms.

From this point, the text becomes a little more applied, and the building blocks of knowledge that you have accumulated can now be used to fashion microbiology into a discipline that serves humanity. Along the way, new ideas, facts, and terminology will continue to be added to your repertoire.

Chapter 21 has just this intent. It introduces three subsequent chapters that deal with ways to control microorganisms. Good control of microorganisms minimizes the risk of infectious disease, cures once some diseases have struck, and retards overwhelming economic loss caused by spoilage. This chapter provides general principles by which this can be accomplished.

Expanded Outline and Summary

   I. Importance of Microbial Control. Good control helps prevent disease, microbial contamination, and spoilage.

  II. Definition of Terms. You must know these, as each word conveys a precise meaning that "binds" industry, affects medicine, and guides the researcher.
     A. Sterilization — kills all microorganisms.
     B. Disinfectant and germicide — agent that kills vegetative cells but not necessarily spores of microorganisms.
     C. Antiseptic — agent that must at least inhibit the growth and activity of microorganisms.
     D. Sanitizer — agent that reduces microorganisms to "safe" levels by killing 99.9 percent of growing bacteria.
     E. Bactericide, fungicide, viricide, and sporicide — agents that kill bacteria, fungi, viruses, or spores, respectively.

F. Bacteriostasis — inhibition, but not death, of bacteria.

G. Antimicrobial agent — one that interferes with growth and activity of microbes.

H. Therapeutic agent — antimicrobial agent used to treat infections.

III. The Pattern (and Rate) of Bacterial Death.

A. Definition of death — in microbiology, the irreversible loss of the ability to reproduce.

B. "Instantaneous death" — some processes (e.g., incineration) kill bacteria quickly and simultaneously.

C. Target theory — many agents kill cells at a constant exponential rate (e.g., if there are 1 million cells when the agent is added, there may be 100,000 after 1 min 10,000 after 2 min, etc.)

1. Rationale — like randomly aimed bullets hitting a target; it is just as hard to kill the last nine bacteria as it was to kill the first 900,000.

2. Concentration effect — generally, up to a point, the higher the concentration of the agent, the faster cells will be killed.

IV. Conditions Influencing Antimicrobial Action.

A. Temperature — agents kill more rapidly at higher temperatures.

B. Kind of microorganisms — sporeformers are most resistant; species vary in their susceptibility to various agents.

C. Physiological state of cells — young, actively metabolizing cells are more susceptible than old, dormant cells.

D. Environment — a considerable number of factors have a considerable effect on antimicrobial action; two are cited.

1. pH — for example, heat kills more quickly in acid material.

2. Extraneous organic matter — reduces the action of an antimicrobial agent.

a. May combine with disinfectant to neutralize it.

b. May precipitate out disinfectant.

c. May accumulate on cell surface in a protective layer.

V. Measurement of Microbial Death. One must be sure that growth conditions permit treated survivors to multiply, so that measurements of bacteriostatic or bacteriocidal conditions are valid.

A. Choose the correct growth medium.

B. Remove (or neutralize) the antimicrobial substance from the growth medium (e.g., cells treated with mercury are subcultured in thioglycolate broth to neutralize mercurial compounds).

VI. Mode of Action of Antimicrobial Agents. Any structure or metabolic process common to microorganisms is subject to attack. The cell membrane, enzymes, and the genetic code apparatus render bacteria most vulnerable.

A. Damage to cell wall — a damaged cell wall may lead to lysis.

1. Enzymes (e.g., lysozyme, which is most effective on gram-positive bacteria).

2. Penicillins — see Chap. 24.

B. Alteration of cell permeability — healthy membranes are essential to cell survival. Detergents, soaps, and quarternary ammonium compounds damage membranes, causing first ion leakage and later the loss of other vital functions.

C. Alteration of protein and nucleic acid molecules — high temperatures and numerous chemical agents can denature enzymes and nucleic acids or otherwise interfere with their activity.

D. Inhibition of enzyme action (discussed, also, in Chap. 9).
   1. The cell is most quickly affected by interference with enzymes that mediate energy-supplying reactions:
      a. Cyanide – inhibits cytochrome oxidase.
      b. Fluoride – inhibits glycolysis.
      c. Trivalent arsenic compounds – block the TCA cycle.
      d. Dinitrophenol – uncouples oxidative phosphorylations.
   2. Oxidizing agents that break sulfhydryl bonds quickly denature enzymes.
E. Antimetabolites – block certain metabolic pathways (e.g., sulfanilamide blocks folic acid biosynthesis; see Chaps. 9 and 24).
F. Inhibition of nucleic acid synthesis.
   1. Compounds that interfere with the synthesis of nucleotides.
   2. Compounds that inhibit the polymerization of nucleotides into nucleic acids.

Programmed Self-Test

Do not begin this self-test before reading the corresponding chapter in the text.

DEFINITION OF TERMS (Text pages 414 to 415)

Sterilization is the process of destroying _____ forms of microbial life.	
A disinfectant kills growing forms but not necessarily the resistant _____ forms of disease-producing microorganisms.	all
A sanitizer kills _____ percent of growing bacteria.	spore
A bacteriostatic agent is one that _____ bacteria.	99.9
Antimicrobial agents used to treat infections are called _____.	inhibits the growth of

THE PATTERN OF BACTERIAL DEATH AND CONDITIONS INFLUENCING ANTIMICROBIAL ACTION (Text pages 415 to 420)

The probability of randomly hitting a target is proportional to _____.	therapeutic agents

As the temperature decreases, the effectiveness of disinfectants _____ .	the number of targets (and the concentration of the agent)
_____ cells are apt to be more easily destroyed by many agents than older, dormant cells.	decreases
Heat is a more effective bacteriocidal agent in _____ material.	Actively metabolizing (younger)
The presence of extraneous organic matter can significantly reduce the efficacy of an antimicrobial chemical agent by _____ or _____ .	acid
_____ broth can neutralize mercurial compounds.	inactivating the agent; protecting the microorganism from the agent

MODE OF ACTION OF ANTIMICROBIAL AGENTS (Text pages 420 to 423)

The cell walls of some gram-positive bacteria are attacked by the enzyme _____ .	Thioglycolate
Synthetic detergents, soaps, and quarternary ammonium compounds each alter _____ .	lysozyme
High temperatures denature _____ and/or _____ .	cell-membrane permeability
Sulfanilamide blocks the synthesis of _____ .	protein; nucleic acids
Oxidative phosphorylations may be uncoupled by_____ .	folic acid
Of all metabolic pathways, inhibition of _____ may be particularly detrimental to cell survival.	dinitrophenol
Halogens and hydrogen peroxide are both strong _____ agents.	energy-supplying reactions
	oxidizing

Multiple-Choice Test

Underline the correct answer.

1. Our culture (in the sociological sense) has been bombarded with terms referring to the killing of odor-causing, hazardous, and other villainous types of microorganisms. Sometimes these terms are incorrectly used. Which of the following types of agents that control microflora is most lethal? (a) Disinfectant; (b) sanitizer; (c) sterilizer; (d) antiseptic.

2. A disinfectant is an agent, usually a chemical, that _____ of disease-producing micro-organisms. (a) Kills growing forms and spore forms; (b) inhibits vegetative cells; (c) inhibits vegetative cells and kills spores; (d) kills growing cells but perhaps not spores.

3. Which of the following kinds of agents does not necessarily kill all *growing* bacteria? (a) Sterilizer; (b) disinfectant; (c) sanitizer; (d) bacteriocide.

4. "To render free from all living organisms" would be a definition of the process of: (a) pasteurization; (b) sterilization; (c) antisepsis; (d) sanitization; (e) bacteriostasis.

5. In general, when is a culture of bacteria most susceptible to a lethal agent? (a) In the logarithmic phase of growth; (b) in the late stationary phase of growth; (c) when the temperature is $10°C$ below the optimum growth temperature; (d) after it has formed dormant spores.

6. A chemical agent which halts bacterial growth but does not kill the cells would be termed: (a) bactericidal; (b) a disinfectant; (c) bacteriostatic; (d) a chemisterilant.

7. Sulfanilamide inhibits or kills many bacterial cells by: (a) denaturing their enzymes; (b) inhibiting the synthesis of DNA; (c) competing with folic acid for an active site on an enzyme; (d) inhibiting the synthesis of folic acid by competing with PABA for an active site on an enzyme; (e) a process called noncompetitive inhibition.

8. Heavy metals kill bacteria predominantly by: (a) denaturing DNA of cells; (b) destroying the integrity of cell membranes; (c) inhibiting motility; (d) combining with cellular proteins and denaturing them.

9. Fluorides exert the most pronounced effect upon which one of these energy-supplying pathways? (a) Cytochrome system; (b) glycolysis; (c) TCA cycle; (d) oxidative phosphorylation.

Answers: 1. (c); 2. (d); 3. (c); 4. (b); 5. (a); 6. (c); 7. (d); 8. (d); 9. (b).

Chapter 22

Control by
Physical Agents

INTRODUCTION: Microorganisms tolerate a wide range of physical conditions. When that range is exceeded, microorganisms are inhibited or killed. Thus, by manipulating their environment, microorganisms can be controlled. As a layperson, you work to control microorganisms each day. As a scientist, you should know what methods of control work well and when and why they work well. The purpose of this chapter is to give you that knowledge.

Expanded Outline and Summary

I. Temperature, Water, and Life. Chemical reactions occur in water, and their rates are directly related to temperature. These two conditions must be considered together.
   A. Excessive temperatures kill.
   B. Subminimum temperatures often produce stasis.

II. Susceptibility of Microorganisms to High Temperatures.
   A. Principles of susceptibility.
      1. Moist heat (coagulates proteins) kills more effectively than dry heat (oxidizes chemical constituents).
         a. Moist heat — spores of *Clostridium botulinum* are killed in 4 to 20 min at $120°C$.
         b. Dry heat — spores of *Clostridium botulinum* are killed in 2 h at $120°C$.
      2. Vegetative cells are more sensitive to heat than spores.
         a. Vegetative cells — moist heat for 5 to 10 min kills:
            i. Bacteria at 60 to $70°C$.
            ii. Fungi at 50 to $60°C$.
            iii. Viruses at 60 to $70°C$.
         b. Spores — moist heat for 5 to 10 min kills spores of:
            i. Bacteria above $100°C$.
            ii. Fungi at 70 to $80°C$.
   B. Measurements of susceptibility — these have many important applications (e.g., the canning industry).
      1. Thermal death point — lowest temperature at which a suspension of bacteria is killed in 10 min.

      2. Thermal death time — shortest period of time required to kill a suspension of bacteria (or spores) at a prescribed temperature and under specific conditions.

      3. Decimal reduction time — number of minutes required to reduce the population by 90 percent.

III. Application of High Temperatures for Destruction of Microorganisms.
   A. Moist heat.
      1. Steam under pressure (the autoclave) — the hot steam rather than the pressure kills. Widely used for the sterilization of aqueous solutions ($121°C$ for 15 or more minutes).
      2. Fractional sterilization (tyndallization) — used to sterilize those substances that are not adversely affected by steam at $100°C$ but are adversely affected at higher temperatures. Method involves heating the material to $100°C$ on three successive days with intermittent incubation periods. This allows for spore germination; on subsequent exposure to heat, vegetative cells can be destroyed.
      3. Boiling water — kills vegetative cells. Disinfects rather than sterilizes.
      4. Pasteurization — see Chap. 39. Involves use of moderate temperatures to kill many pathogens, but not all organisms. Some of the flavor and nutrition of the food may still be retained.
   B. Dry heat.
      1. Hot air sterilization — used for substances that may be inaccessible to steam (e.g., glassware, oils, etc.). Usually 2 h at $160°C$ sterilizes.
      2. Incineration — used to destroy carcasses, etc.

IV. Low Temperatures. Usually microbiostatic. As the temperature decreases, metabolic activity decreases until it ceases at subzero C.

V. Desiccation. Drying causes a cessation of metabolic activity, followed by some cell die-off. Microorganisms vary widely in their susceptibility to desiccation, some dying in hours (gonococci) and some not at all (microbial spores).

VI. Osmotic Pressure. Most microorganisms are inhibited by 10 to 15% concentrations of salt and 50 to 70% concentrations of sugar because plasmolysis occurs and the cells become dehydrated.
   A. Plasmoptysis — "salt" concentration outside cell is less than salt concentration within cell. Water flows into cell to equalize osmotic pressure.
   B. Plasmolysis — "salt" concentration outside cell is greater than salt concentration within cell. Water flows out of cell to equalize osmotic pressure.

VII. Radiations. Ionizing radiations (gamma and x-rays) create free hydrogen and hydroxyl radical plus peroxides which damage the cell. Nonionizing radiations (ultraviolet light) may be absorbed by specific compounds, which become "excited" and engage in a variety of chemical reactions, often detrimental to the cell.
   A. Ultraviolet light — radiations from 150 to 3900 Å. Wavelengths about 2650 Å are most bactericidal. These rays do not penetrate matter and may thus be used to sterilize only surfaces.
      1. Mode of action — ultraviolet light is absorbed mainly by nucleic acids, where it dimerizes adjacent bases, which leads to inhibition of DNA replication and causes mutation.

2. Photoreactivation — process by which a (visible) light-dependent enzyme system cleaves dimers and repairs DNA.
3. Excision repair (dark reactivation) — a second system, but light-dependent, for repairing ultraviolet-induced DNA damage. Two different enzymes cleave damaged sections of DNA. Two other enzymes replace the cleaved section with the proper undamaged bases.

B. X-rays (Roentgen rays) — these are not useful for controlling microorganisms, as they are expensive to produce and difficult to control.
C. Gamma rays — these have shorter wavelengths than x-rays and consequently great penetrating power and lethal effects. May have potential use in sterilizing large packages.
D. Cathode rays (electron-beam radiation) — these are accelerated electron beams that are used to sterilize medical and other materials.

VIII. Other Physical Means to Control Microorganisms.
A. Electricity — this can kill organisms by generating high temperatures and causing chemical change. Its use has been limited (e.g., pasteurization of milk has been tried).
B. Surface tension — depressants of surface tension (e.g., soaps, bile salts, phenols) impede cellular processes.
C. Filtration — used to sterilize fluids that are thermolabile (destroyed by heat). There is a wide variety of filters, with various size pores, that can trap microorganisms. Because of the minute pore sizes, negative pressure must be applied to pull the liquid through the filter. In another application of filtration, air is passed through high-efficiency particulate air (HEPA) filters to sterilize it before it is admitted to a room or an enclosure.

Programmed Self-Test

Do not begin this self-test before reading the corresponding chapter in the text.

CONTROL OF MICROORGANISMS BY HIGH TEMPERATURE (Text pages 426 to 431)

Low temperatures generally produce stasis, while excessively high temperatures generally _____ cells.	
Moist heat kills microorganisms by _____ and is much more rapid and effective than dry heat, which destroys microorganisms by _____ their chemical constituents.	kill
Cells of most bacteria are killed in 5 to 10 min at _____ to _____ °C (moist heat).	coagulating protein; oxidizing
Most bacterial spores are killed only by temperatures above _____ °C.	60; 70

The _____ refers to the lowest
temperature at which a suspension of bacteria is killed in 10 min.

100

The _____ is the time (in minutes)
for the thermal-death-time curve to pass through one log cycle.

thermal death
  point

The laboratory apparatus designed to use steam under regulated
pressure is called an _____.

decimal reduction
  time

Generally, although not always, the autoclave is operated at a
pressure of about 15 lb/in^2, which produces a temperature of
_____°C.

autoclave

During tyndallization, intermittant incubation allows for

_____.

121

Boiling water brings about _____ rather than
sterilization.

spore germination

When one uses dry heat, a 2-h exposure to a temperature of
_____°C is sufficient for sterilization of laboratory
glassware.

disinfection

ADDITIONAL METHODS OF CONTROLLING MICROORGANISMS (Text pages 431 to 442)

When the salt concentration in the medium is so low that water
enters the cell, the process is called _____.

160

When microbial growth is inhibited by plasmolysis, the cells are
unable to metabolize because they are in a _____
state.

plasmoptysis

Ionizing radiations have energies of more than _____
eV.

dehydrated

Pyrimidine dimers in DNA are the result of _____
radiation.

10

Intracellularly, pyrimidine dimer lesions may be removed by
_____ and/or _____.

ultraviolet

Because of their great penetrating power and their microbial effect, _____ rays are attractive for use in sterilizing materials of considerable thickness.	photoreactivation; excision repair
Accelerated electron beams are also called _____ rays.	gamma
A surface force that exists between two immiscible liquids and at the interface between a solid and a liquid is called _____ .	cathode
_____ , _____ , and _____ have surface-tension-depressing effects.	interfacial tension
HEPA filters together with a system of _____ airflow are now used extensively to provide dust- and bacteria-free air.	Soaps; bile salts; phenols
	laminar

Multiple-Choice Test

Underline the correct answer.

1. Which of the following microorganisms would not survive dry heat of 120°C (248°F) for 40 min? (a) *Bacillus anthracis;* (b) *Clostridium botulinum;* (c) *Clostridium welchii;* (d) *Escherichia coli.*

2. To be sure of sterilizing laboratory media, one must employ: (a) dry heat at 121°C for 1 h; (b) moist heat (steam at 121°C for 15 min); (c) boiling water at 10 lb/in^2 pressure; (d) methods of pasteurization; (e) cold temperatures of 1°C.

3. Consideration of thermal death point is of prime importance in which of the following? (a) Frozen food industry; (b) water treatment plant; (c) food canning industry; (d) chlorination of water.

4. When nonhalophilic and nonhalotolerant microorganisms are placed in a 25% salt solution, they are inhibited primarily by: (a) mutation; (b) asphyxiation; (c) lysis; (d) salt precipitation in the cytoplasm; (e) dehydration.

5. Ultraviolet light damages many parts of the cell. However, its *primary* lethal action is: (a) formation of pyrimidine dimers, thus mutating the genetic code; (b) destroying enzyme activity; (c) damaging cell walls; (d) inhibiting water-soluble vitamins.

6. Ultraviolet light is most bactericidal at a wavelength of 3900 Å. (a) True; (b) false.

7. Photoreactivation refers to: (a) the emission of light by living organisms; (b) the action of a light-dependent enzyme that recognizes dimers in DNA and cleaves them so that the normal DNA structure is restored; (c) the reversal of a prototrophic mutation so that the organism is restored to auxotrophy; (d) the process in which energy of light and chlorophyll are used by plants to synthesize carbohydrates from carbon dioxide and water.

8. Ionizing radiation with energies of more than 10 eV and with wavelengths shorter than 10^2 Å is: (a) infrared; (b) ultraviolet; (c) visible; (d) gamma rays.

9. The organism most quickly killed by desiccation is: (a) gonococcus; (b) *Streptococcus;* (c) *Mycobacterium;* (d) sporulated *Clostridium.*

10. Which of these processes sterilizes? (a) Boiling; (b) pasteurization; (c) freezing; (d) incineration.

Answers: 1. (d); 2. (b); 3. (c); 4. (e); 5. (a); 6. (b); 7. (b); 8. (d); 9. (a); 10. (d).

Chapter 23

Control by
Chemical Agents

INTRODUCTION: This chapter describes how chemical agents adversely affect microorganisms. From the treatment of a minor wound to the sterilization of an operating room, this information is useful, if not essential. You should learn how the major classes of chemicals act (on cells) and learn how to select the agent that is most effective in a particular situation. This information is personally useful and professionally necessary.

Expanded Outline and Summary

I. Characteristics of an Ideal Disinfectant (i.e., the closer a disinfectant comes to these properties, the better it is).
   A. Antimicrobial activity — kill a broad spectrum of organisms.
   B. Solubility — in sufficient concentrations in water and other solvents.
   C. Stability — not lose germicidal activity.
   D. Nontoxicity — to all but the target organisms.
   E. Homogeneity — uniform composition to ensure reproducible application.
   F. Noncombination with extraneous organic material — so it is not "inactivated."
   G. Toxicity to microorganisms at room or body temperature.
   H. Capacity to penetrate — allows for subsurface action.
   I. Noncorroding and nonstraining.
   J. Deodorizing ability — or no odor.
   K. Detergent capacities — also improves effectiveness of disinfectant.
   L. Availability — in large quantities at a reasonable price.

II. Selection of Antimicrobial Chemical Agent. Based on:
   A. Nature of the material to be treated.
   B. Type of microorganisms.
   C. Environmental conditions (recall Chap. 21).

III.   Major Groups of Chemical Antimicrobial Agents

MAJOR GROUP	MODE OF ACTION	ADDITIONAL CHARACTERISTICS
A. Phenol and phenolic compounds	Denature protein; damage cell membrane	Derivatives (hexylresorcinol) greatly reduce surface tension
B. Alcohols	Denature protein; damage cell membrane; dehydrating agents; detergent action	More carbons in the alcohol make it more germicidal
C. Halogens 1. Iodine	Halogenation of tyrosine; inactivating enzymes and other proteins?	Effective against all bacteria; may kill some spores
2. Chlorine (and chlorine compounds)	Combines with proteins of cell membranes and enzymes	Chlorine used to disinfect water. Chlorine compounds are easier to apply and have many applications
D. Heavy metals	Oligodynamic action; sulfhydryl group attacks ($HgCl_2$)	
E. Dyes 1. Triphenylmethane	Interferes with cellular oxidation?	More effective against gram-positive bacteria
2. Acridines		More effective on gram-positive bacteria. Not antifungal
F. Synthetic detergents	Depress surface tension	Soaps mechanically remove microorganisms
G. Quarternary ammonium compounds (cationic detergents)	Denature proteins? Damage to cell membrane?	More germicidal than other detergents; most bactericidal against gram-positive bacteria; fungicidal
H. Strong acids and alkalies	Ionization	Strong alkalies most effective vs. gram-negative bacteria and viruses
I. Aldehydes	Break hydrogen bonds; denature protein	Effective against all microorganisms, but not bacterial spores
J. Gaseous chemosterilizers	Ethylene oxide: alkylates organic compounds; inactivates enzymes	Kill *all* forms of life

(SPECIFIC) COMPOUNDS	RECOMMENDED USE	LIMITATIONS
Cresols (more germicidal than phenol); hexylresorcinol	General disinfectant	Microbial effectiveness limited; irritating and corrosive
Methyl (least bactericidal, most toxic); ethyl (least toxic, used in 50-70% concentration); propyl, butyl, amyl, etc.	Skin antiseptic; 60% concentration kills viruses if there is no extraneous carbon	Antiseptic
Tincture of iodine (dissolved in alcohol); iodophors (+ surface active agents)	Disinfect skin	Irritating to mucous membranes
Hypochlorites (sanitize utensils and equipment); Chloramines (oxidizing agents, also)	Water disinfection	Inactivated by organic material; pH-dependent for effectiveness; objectionable taste and odor unless strictly controlled
Silver nitrate	Treating burns	Possible irritation
Mercurials	Skin disinfection	Slow acting; toxic
Malachite green Brilliant green Crystal violet	Selective media	
Acriflavine Proflavine	Burns, wounds; ophthalmic application	Being replaced by chemotherapeutic agents
Anionic (detergent property resident in anion); nonionic	Cleaning applications	Nonanionic detergents have no germicidal action
Cetylpyridinium Cl. Zephiran Phemerol	Skin disinfection; sanitizing agents	Some viral resistance; not sporicidal
Lye (disinfectant) Lime (CaO) does not disinfect		Protozoa and acid-fast bacteria resistant to alkalies. Corrosive
Glutaraldehyde	Sterilizing instruments; fumigation	Stability limited
Formaldehyde; aqueous formalin	Sterilizing instruments; fumigation; tissue preservation	Permeation poor; corrosive
Ethylene oxide	Sterilizing heat-sensitive materials, instruments, and large equipment	Flammable; potentially explosive in pure form; comparatively slow action
β-propiolactone	Sterilizing instruments and heat-sensitive materials	Lacks penetrating power; carcinogenic?

IV. Evaluation of Disinfectants and Antiseptics. Agent is tested against a selected organism (test organism).

    A. Tube dilution and agar-plate techniques.

        1. Organism and test agent are mixed together. Periodic transfers are made to growth-supporting media. Procedure tests for killing power with time and the bactericidal properties of the agent.

        2. Agent, organism, and broth are mixed, incubated, and organism scored for diminished growth vs. control.

        3. Application of antimicrobial substance to inoculated plate; zone of inhibition develops if compound is active.

        4. Paper strips impregnated with known quantity of spores are exposed to gaseous chemosterilizer and then cultured for survivors.

    B. Phenol-coefficient method. This makes use of the procedure outlined in IV. A. 1. To a series of dilutions of disinfectant being tested (5 ml/tube), 0.5 ml of 24-h broth culture of test organism (*Salmonella typhi* or *Staphylococcus aureus*) is added. Parallel dilutions of phenol are likewise tested. At intervals of 5, 10, and 15 min incubation (at 20°C), subcultures are made to sterile media. *The greatest dilution of the disinfectant killing the test organism in 10 min but not in 5 min is divided by the greatest dilution of phenol giving the same result.*

Programmed Self-Test

Do not begin this self-test before reading the corresponding chapter in the text.

CHARACTERISTICS OF AN IDEAL DISINFECTANT; SELECTION OF ANTIMICROBIAL CHEMICAL AGENT (Text pages 444 to 446)

The most important requirement of a disinfectant is

_____.

Good disinfectants are active at _____ temperature.	ability to kill microorganisms
The choice of an antimicrobial agent depends on _____ _____, _____, and _____.	room or body
Escherichia coli is much more resistant to cationic disinfectants than _____.	nature of material to be treated; type of microorganism; environmental conditions

MAJOR GROUPS OF CHEMICAL ANTIMICROBIAL AGENTS (Text pages 446 to 460)

Phenols act primarily by _____ and _____.	*Staphylococcus aureus* (gram-positive bacteria)
The antimicrobial activity of phenolics is reduced at an _____ pH and by _____ compounds.	denaturing proteins; damaging membranes
A derivative of phenol, hexylresorcinol, is a strong *(mechanism of action)* reductant.	alkaline; organic
There is a progressive increase in germicidal power of alcohols as their _____ increases.	surface-tension
Ethyl alcohol, in concentrations between _____ and _____ percent, is effective against vegetative cells.	molecular weight
Are 70% concentrations of alcohol effective against viruses?	50; 70
_____ is one of the oldest and most effective germicidal agents.	Yes
Iodophors are mixtures of iodine with _____ agents.	Iodine
It is suggested that iodine exerts antimicrobial activity by halogenating _____ units of enzymes.	surface-active
Compressed liquid chlorine gas is widely used to purify _____.	tyrosine
The chemical formula for calcium hypochlorite is _____.	municipal water supplies
Products containing 5 to 70 percent calcium hypochlorite are used for sanitizing _____ and _____.	$Ca(OCl)_2$
The ability of extremely small amounts of certain metals, particularly silver, to exert a lethal effect upon bacteria is called _____.	dairy equipment; eating utensils in restaurants

Heavy metals act antimicrobially by combining with _____ and _____ them.	oligodynamic action
Three triphenylmethane dyes are _____, _____, and _____.	proteins; denaturing
_____ bacteria are most susceptible to both triphenylmethane and acridine dyes.	malachite green; brilliant green; crystal violet
Surface-tension depressants employed primarily for cleansing surfaces are called _____ .	Gram-positive
Quarternary ammonium compounds are _____ionic detergents.	detergents
The bactericidal power of the quarternaries is highest against _____ bacteria.	cat-
Are the quarternaries relatively good detergents?	gram-positive
Lime is calcium oxide, *(chemical formula)*; when added to water it becomes calcium hydroxide, *(chemical formula)*.	Yes
A 2% solution of glutaraldehyde is a _____ .	CaO; $Ca(OH)_2$
In pure form ethylene oxide is dangerous because it is _____ and _____ .	sterilant
Ethylene oxide is effective against all life (even bacterial spores); another outstanding feature of this gas is its ability to _____ .	flammable; explosive
The mode of ethylene oxide is believed to involve _____ reactions on organic compounds such as protein.	penetrate
β-propiolactone, while more active than ethylene oxide, has two drawbacks; its lack of _____ and its alleged _____ properties.	alkylation
	penetration; carcinogenic

Multiple-Choice Test

Underline the correct answer.

1. The highly germicidal agent hexachlorophene has been banned from soaps, creams, and deodorants because of its high toxicity to humans. Part of the phenol class of compounds, it kills bacteria by: (a) denaturing proteins and damaging cell membranes; (b) preventing transcription and translation; (c) inhibiting cell-wall and cell-membrane formation; (d) mutating the genetic code.

2. The phenol coefficient test shows: (a) that phenol is the most suitable antiseptic for general use; (b) that no bacteria can resist 5% aqueous phenol for a half hour; (c) the relationship between other compounds and phenol as regards comparable bactericidal activity; (d) the pronounced bacteriostatic activity of weak solutions of phenol; (e) the pronounced fungistatic activity of phenol.

3. The phenol coefficient is defined as the greatest dilution of the disinfectant killing the test organism in 10 min but not in 5 min, divided by the greatest dilution of phenol showing the same result. (a) True; (b) false.

4. Ethylene oxide, β-propiolactone, and formaldehyde can all be used: (a) as antiseptics in large wounds; (b) to routinely disinfect laboratory workbenches; (c) as antibiotics in strep throat infections or as an ingredient in mouthwashes; (d) as gaseous chemosterilizers.

5. To which class of antimicrobial agents does proflavin belong? (a) Phenols; (b) halogens; (c) dyes; (d) detergents.

6. Which class of detergents possesses the least antimicrobial activity? (a) Cationic; (b) anionic; (c) nonionic; (d) quarternary ammonium.

7. Which of these is not a characteristic of an ideal disinfectant? (a) Homogeneity; (b) stability; (c) flammability; (d) detergent capacity.

8. Which of the following agents kills bacterial spores relatively quickly? (a) Alcohols; (b) nonionic detergents; (c) β-propiolactone; (d) quarternaries.

Answers: 1. (a); 2. (c); 3. (a); 4. (d); 5. (c); 6. (c); 7. (c); 8. (c).

Chapter 24

Antibiotics and Other Chemotherapeutic Agents

INTRODUCTION: This last chapter on the control of microorganisms deals with a special type of chemical agent, one that is administered internally where it must kill target cells alone. Thus, specificity is the key.

As few agents are entirely specific and nontoxic, they should be used only when resistance and immunity fail, and then very judiciously. Numerous chemotherapeutic agents exist, and each is indicated only for specific infections in specific circumstances. One must always balance the need of the sick individual with the consequences of chemotherapy.

After reading this chapter, you should certainly know these principles relating to chemotherapeutic agents:

(1) Ideal properties
(2) Modes of action
(3) Spectra of action
(4) Potential side effects
(5) Laboratory assays
(6) Antibiotic resistance and dangers of overuse

General understanding is a must, while specific, and ever-changing, detail can always be looked up.

The (sometimes innocent) overuse of antibiotics can be harmful to both individual patients and generations unborn. Therefore, whether you prescribe, test the efficacy of, or receive chemotherapy, the information in this chapter should serve you well.

Expanded Outline and Summary

I. Chemotherapeutic Agents.
  A. Meaning and scope — chemical substances used for treatment of infectious disease or malignancies.
    1. Antibiotic — special class of chemotherapeutic agents that is naturally occurring. Most are obtained from their living source (e.g., molds), and some are modified by a chemist (semisynthetic).
    2. Chemotherapeutic agents are not:

   a. Antitoxins or other substances produced by infected animals.

   b. Compounds (disinfectants, etc.) that inhibit growth in vitro.

 B. Selective toxicity for parasite (a key property that most, if not all, disinfectants lack).

  1. Agent must destroy or inhibit parasites but not host cells.

  2. Agent must last in host, reach the proper location, and penetrate organs and/or host cells so that it may act.

  3. Agent must not interfere with host's defense mechanisms (e.g., phagocytosis).

II. History of Chemotherapy.

 A. Quinine — used for centuries to treat malaria.

 B. Salvarsan — an arsenical compound, prepared by Ehrlich (1910), used to treat syphilis.

 C. Sulfonamides — Domagk (1935) prepared *Prontosil,* which contained sulfanilamide.

 D. Antibiotics.

  1. Early events — used by Chinese to treat food infections; effects observed by Tyndall (1881), Pasteur, and Jobert; Emmerich and Low (1901) reported that material from *Pseudomonas aeruginosa* protected rabbits against anthrax.

  2. Actinomycetin — found by Gratia and Dath (1924) after a systematic search for an antibiotic.

  3. Penicillin — discovered "accidentally" by Fleming (1929).

  4. Gramicidin and tyrocidine — found by Dubos (1935).

  5. Streptomycin — found by Waksman (1940).

III. Properties of a Useful Antibiotic.

 A. Many of those of a good disinfectant (see Chap. 23-I of this guide). Possess antimicrobial activity, solubility, stability, nontoxicity, homogeneity, noncombination with extraneous molecules, toxicity to microorganisms at body temperature, and availability.

 B. Selectivity, which is described in part I.B. of this chapter.

 C. Furthermore, ideally, it should:

  1. Act on many pathogenic species (broad spectrum).

  2. Prevent the evolution of antibiotic-resistant pathogens.

  3. Not produce side effects (allergic reactions, nerve damage, etc.).

  4. Not eliminate normal (and protective) host flora.

IV. The Search for New Antibiotics.

 A. Reason — though there are hundreds of useful compounds, microorganisms develop resistance to them. New agents need to be found as the old are rendered less effective.

 B. Focus of the search — soil organisms, particularly *Bacillus, Penicillium, Streptomyces,* and *Cephalosporium.*

 C. Screening method — test organism (often *Staphylococcus aureus*) is spread (lawn) on an agar plate on which plugs or impregnated disks of the test materials are placed. A clear zone (no growth) suggests antimicrobial activity.

V, VI, and VII. The table on pp. 184–187 of this guide contains a summary of the material contained in the "Types of Antibiotics," "Synthetic Chemotherapeutic Agents," and "Mode of Action of Chemotherapeutic Agents" sections of Chap. 24.

 A. Sections of the table list many often-used chemotherapeutic agents.

  1. Class — contains major groups of chemotherapeutic agents (each including many very related compounds) or some lone agents as appropriate.

Chemotherapeutic Agents

CLASS	SPECIFIC AGENTS (TRADEMARK OR PROPERTY)	MODE OF ACTION
Sulfonamides	Sulfanilamide ⎫ Sulfapyridine ⎬ etc., see text Table 24-1 Sulfathiozole ⎭	Interfere with folic acid metabolism; PABA analogs
Penicillin	Penicillin G Penicillin V (oral use) Staphicillin ⎫ (for penicillin- Methicillin ⎬ resistant strains) Ampicillin (broader spectrum)	Interferes with cell-wall synthesis; prevents incorporation of *N*-acetyl-muramic acid peptide in the cell-wall structure
Cephalosporins	Cephaloridine, cephaloglycin, cephalexin (Keflin)	Structure and mechanism of action like penicillins
Streptomycin		Produces abnormal protein synthesis
Erythromycin		Interferes with protein synthesis
Chloramphenicol	Chloromycetin is a common trademark	Interferes with protein synthesis
Tetracyclines	Chlortetracycline (Aureomycin) Oxytetracycline (Terramycin) Tetracycline	Interferes with protein synthesis; bacteriostatic
Polymyxins	Polymyxin B	Damages cell membrane
Colistin	(Colymycin)	Damages cell membrane
Neomycin		Produces abnormal protein synthesis
Bacitracin		Inhibits cell-wall synthesis
Lincomycin	(Lincocin)	Inhibits protein synthesis

SPECTRUM	MAIN USAGE	MAIN SIDE EFFECTS
Broad	Meningococci, *Shigella,* rheumatic fever; urinary and respiratory infections	Kidney toxicity
Gram-positive bacteria and cocci	Drug of choice for sensitive organisms and nonallergic patients	Possibility of severe allergic reaction
Rather broad	Penicillin-resistant strains; many infections	"Same" allergin as penicillin
Broad	Tuberculosis, salmonellosis and other infections that do not respond to safer antibiotics	Damage to VIIIth cranial nerve, resulting in deafness and dizziness
Like penicillins; rickettsiae	Substitute for penicillin when there is allergy or penicillin-resistant bacteria	Gastric distress
Very broad	Only for severe, nonresponsive bacterial infections	In a rare patient it may cause a fatal blood disease
Very broad	A wide variety of gram-positive and gram-negative infections; prescribed often	Relatively few and minor
Gram-negative bacteria	Topical; *Pseudomonas* infections (see below)	Very toxic when administered internally
Pseudomonas; Proteus	For gram-negative species that are otherwise very resistant to antibiotics	Somewhat toxic; neurological disturbances
Broad, including *M. tuberculosis*	Topical (ointment)	Many, very toxic
Gram-positive	Topical	Toxic
Gram-positive	Resistant *Staphylococcus* infections	Severe intestinal upset

Chemotherapeutic Agents (continued)

CLASS	SPECIFIC AGENTS (TRADEMARK OR PROPERTY)	MODE OF ACTION
Novobiocin	(Cathomycin)	Inhibition of DNA polymerization
Oleandomycin		Inhibits protein synthesis
Vancomycin	(Vancocin)	Inhibits cell-wall synthesis
Nalidixic acid	(Negram)	Inhibits DNA synthesis
Viomycin		Inhibits protein synthesis
Rifampin	Rifamycin	Inhibits transcription
Kanamycin		Induces abnormal protein synthesis
Cycloserine		Inhibits cell-wall synthesis
Isonicotinic acid hydrazide	(Isoniazid)	Blocks pyridoxine-catalyzed reactions (antimetabolite)
Nystatin		Damages fungal membrane; (combines with ergosterol)
Griseofulvin		Interferes with fungal cell-wall and nucleic acid synthesis
Nitrofurans	Over 1000 compounds	
Amphotericin B		Interferes with membrane function
Cycloheximide	(Acidione)	Inhibits protein synthesis
Fumagillin	(Phagopedin sigma)	Inhibits protein synthesis

SPECTRUM	MAIN USAGE	MAIN SIDE EFFECTS
Gram-positive	Resistant infections	
Rickettsiae; gram-positive	Resistant infections	
Gram-positive; Neisseria, *Cl. tetani*	Life-threatening infections that do not respond to other agents	Very toxic; renal damage; deafness, etc.
Gram-negative; not *Pseudomonas*	Urinary tract infections	Gastrointestinal disturbances; allergy
M. tuberculosis	Treatment of tuberculosis	
Fairly broad; *M. tuberculosis*	Treatment of tuberculosis	
Fairly broad; *M. tuberculosis*	Urinary and blood infections; treatment of tuberculosis	
M. tuberculosis	Treatment of tuberculosis	
M. tuberculosis	Treatment of tuberculosis (alternated with streptomycin)	
Yeasts and fungi	Treatment of mycosis, including intestinal *Candida*	
Yeasts and fungi	Superficial and some deep-seated mycoses	
Very broad, including some fungi and protozoa	Fungal and protozoan infections; not usually drug of choice	
Fungi	Treatment of deep-seated mycoses	
Eucaryotes	Plant mycoses	
Amoebas	Protozoan infections	

2. Specific agents – contains some widely used agents within each class. One great problem in drug administration, for both the practitioner and the consumer, is the use of trademarks. For example, a given penicillin that is manufactured by ten different companies may have ten different trademarks. Generic names are predominantly used here, and some of the more common trademarks are indicated parenthetically.

3. Mode of action – general primary physiological effects are listed; specific molecular targets are not.

4. Spectrum – the broadest spectrum of action is an attack on most, if not all, living organisms (e.g., Puromycin). These agents are too toxic to the host and are not clinically used to combat microorganisms. Therefore, spectrum refers to bacteria (few agents are effective against viruses). Broad would signify action against both gram-positive and gram-negative bacteria. Where the agent is effective against eucaryotic microorganisms, it is so noted.

5. Uses and side effects – these are, of course, generalizations and may vary substantially, depending on the situation.

B. Purpose of presenting the table – as a reference and to allow you to draw general conclusions (rote memorization would be counter-productive).

1. Reference – penicillin and tetracyclines are two of the oldest and most widely used agents in the physician's arsenal. Yet organisms are becoming resistant to these and other antibiotics, which may diminish their value. Also, new and possibly less toxic agents may be discovered. Thus, this chart may provide a basic "vocabulary," but keep in mind that some agents may be deleted from this list or be used for different purposes, while others will be added.

2. General conclusions (many can be drawn; two examples are given).

   a. The arsenal – each drug has a characteristic spectrum of action and set of side effects. Diseases should be treated with the least toxic drug that will do the job. Therefore:

      i. Common respiratory and ear infections: penicillin, cephalosporins, erythromycin, and tetracyclines are often prescribed.

      ii. *Proteus* or *Pseudomonas* infections: more toxic drugs, such as polymyxins, colistin, or kanamycin, may be required.

      iii. Potentially lethal, nonresponsive diseases (e.g., some rare cases of typhoid fever): chloramphenicol may be required, and one would have to risk the rare possibility of an antibiotic-induced blood disorder.

      iv. Tuberculosis: streptomycin, Isoniazid, etc., often in combination, have been effective.

   b. Mode of action.

      i. Chemotherapeutic agents that directly affect protein synthesis: streptomycin, erythromycin, chloramphenicol, tetracycline, etc. There are many agents with this focus of attack.

      ii. Agents that affect bacterial cell-wall synthesis: penicillins, cephalosporins, vancomycin.

      iii. Agents that affect cell membranes (these are generally toxic to the host also): polymyxins, colistin.

VIII. Resistance to Antibiotics. If there is one resistant organism in a population of billions, then in the presence of the antibiotic, sensitive strains will be inhibited or killed, and eventually the resistant organism will dominate.
    A. Mechanisms of drug resistance.
        1. Enzymes that inactivate or degrade drug (e.g., penicillin).
        2. Competitive inhibition of drug by an essential cell metabolite.
        3. Development of an alternative metabolic pathway that bypasses the effect of the drug.
        4. Synthesis of excess enzymes over the amount that can be inactivated by the drug.
        5. Inability of the drug to penetrate the cell.
        6. Organelle modification (e.g., ribosomes that do not bind streptomycin).
    B. Transmission of drug resistance — by conjugation and resultant transfer of R factor plasmid among gram-negative eubacterial rods.
    C. Minimizing the spread of antibiotic-resistant bacteria.
        1. Avoiding the indiscriminate use of antibiotics where they are of no real clinical value.
        2. Refraining from the use of antibiotics commonly employed for generalized infections for topical applications.
        3. Using correct dosages of the proper antibiotic to overcome an infection quickly.
        4. Using combinations of antibiotics of proven effectiveness.
        5. Using a different antibiotic when an organism gives evidence of becoming resistant to the one used initially.

IX. Laboratory Determination of Microbial Susceptibility to Chemotherapeutic Agents.
    A. Susceptibility tests.
        1. Tube-dilution technique — to determine the smallest amount (MIC, or minimal inhibitory concentration) required to inhibit the growth of the organism in vitro.
        2. Paper-disc-plate method — small paper discs, impregnated with known amounts of drug, are placed on the surface of an inoculated plate. Zones of inhibition are equated with varying degrees of susceptibility or resistance.
    B. Microbiological assays of antibiotics.
        1. Chemical assay of potency — the strength of purified antibiotics can be expressed in micrograms per milligram of specimen.
        2. Biological assay of potency — expressed in terms of micrograms (or units), determined by comparing the action of the test drug to that of a standard preparation of the test drug.

X. Nonmedical Uses of Antibiotics.
    A. Growth stimulation of livestock. The addition of tetracyclines, penicillin, or streptomycin (!) to feeds increases the animal's growth rate by 10 to 50 percent.
    B. To prevent bacterial contamination of virus propagation media.
    C. Isolation and identification of some bacteria.

Programmed Self-Test

Do not begin this self-test before reading the corresponding chapter in the text.

HISTORY, TYPES, AND MODES OF ACTION OF CHEMOTHERAPEUTIC AGENTS (Text pages 466 to 485)

Microorganisms producing the largest number of useful antibiotics belong to the genera *Bacillus, Penicillium, Cephalosporium,* and _____ .	
The term _____ usually refers to naturally occurring chemotherapeutic agents.	*Streptomyces*
Ehrlich synthesized (1910) an arsenical drug that he called _____ .	antibiotics
Quinine has been used for centuries to treat _____ .	Salvarsan
The first very effective chemotherapeutic agent, Prontosil, was antibacterial due to its _____ moiety.	malaria
Organisms that reside in the _____ are the most common producers of antibiotics.	sulfanilamide
The semisynthetic penicillin called _____ has a relatively broad action spectrum.	soil
Streptomycin is toxic to humans because it may damage the _____ .	ampicillin
Selman Waksman discovered streptomycin and _____ .	VIIIth cranial nerve
Erythromycin is often prescribed when penicillin is indicated to those patients with _____ .	erythromycin
Chloramphenicol has a _____ spectrum of action.	allergies
The cephalosporins are closely related in structure and action to the _____ .	broad
Nystatin is used to treat nonsystematic _____ infections.	penicillins

Polymyxins are administered internally to treat systematic infections caused by the bacterial genus _____ .	fungal
To treat tuberculosis the drug called _____ is often given alternately with streptomycin.	*Pseudomonas*
Nalidixic acid is most effective against _____ bacteria.	Isoniazid
Sulfanilamide is a metabolic analog (similar structure) of _____ .	gram-negative
Penicillin inhibits _____ formation.	*p*-aminobenzoic acid (PABA)
Polymyxins combine with the bacterial _____ .	cell-wall
Nystatin combines with _____ in fungal cell membranes.	cell membrane
Actinomycin selectively inhibits _____ synthesis.	sterols (ergosterol)
Generally, agents that damage the cell wall or membrane are _____ ; those which interfere with enzyme action are _____ .	RNA
The specific site of interference with protein synthesis by chloramphenicol is believed to be at the stage of _____ from their soluble RNA complex to ribosomes.	bactericidal; bacteriostatic

MICROBIAL RESISTANCE AND SUSCEPTIBILITY TO CHEMOTHERAPEUTIC AGENTS; NONMEDICAL USES OF ANTIBIOTICS (Text pages 485 to 492)

Penicillinase converts penicillin into inactive _____ .	transfer of amino acids
Antibiotic resistance in gram-negative enteric organisms may be quickly spread by transmission of _____ .	penicilloic acid
The letters MIC stand for _____ .	R factors
1,667 units of penicillin is the equivalent of what quantity of the pure drug?	minimal inhibitory concentration

It has been suggested that pigs respond dramatically to the addition of Terramycin to their diet because the antibiotic inhibits the growth of _____ in their intestintes.	1 mg
Antibiotics in the feed of swine or poultry increases the animals' _____.	*Clostridium perfringens*
	rate of growth

Multiple-Choice Test

Underline the correct answer.

1. Why, do you suppose, is it better to treat a *Streptococcus* sore throat infection with an antibiotic with a gram-positive spectrum than to use a broad-spectrum antibiotic to treat the infection? (a) The antibiotic with a gram-positive spectrum is most likely to kill the pathogen; (b) broad-spectrum antibiotics are generally the most expensive; (c) broad-spectrum antibiotics are always more toxic to eucaryotic systems than those limited to gram-positive spectrum; (d) the broad-spectrum antibiotic may also kill normal intestinal bacteria, thus rendering the patient more susceptible to enteric infections.

2. Which one of the following is a broad-spectrum antibiotic? (a) Penicillin; (b) nalidixic acid; (c) erythromycin; (d) tetracycline.

3. Penicillin is no longer effective against many staphylococci because many of these bacteria produce an enzyme that: (a) alters the antibiotic; (b) prevents the antibiotic from entering the cell wall and membrane; (c) modifies their cell wall; (d) modifies the ribosomes.

4. Which of the following antibiotics competitively inhibits a bacterial enzyme (one not possessed by mammalian cells) and yet, despite this specificity, is still toxic to mammals because it is relatively insoluble? (a) Penicillin; (b) actinomycin; (c) chloramphenicol; (d) sulfanilamide.

5. The mode of action of the antibiotic penicillin is: (a) inhibition of protein synthesis; (b) inhibition of transfer RNA; (c) inhibition of cell-wall synthesis; (d) the destruction of penicillinase.

6. Which one of the following antibiotics inhibits DNA synthesis, thereby preventing chromosome replication and cell division? (a) Actinomycin; (b) polymyxin; (c) chloramphenicol; (d) nalidixic acid.

7. Which one of the following antibiotics primarily prevents DNA-dependent RNA synthesis (transcription)? (a) Actinomycin; (b) tetracycline; (c) chloramphenicol; (d) nalidixic acid.

8. To retard the appearance of resistant bacterial populations: (a) broad-spectrum antibiotics should be employed; (b) two different antibiotics should be used simultaneously: one that is bacteriostatic and one that is effective only on multiplying bacteria; (c) antibiotics can be used in synergistic combinations; (d) antibiotics should be used frequently, often before disease symptoms become apparent.

9. Which of the following is an antibiotic that does not inhibit some function inherent in the genetic code (DNA replication, transcription, or translation)? (a) Polymyxin B; (b) Mitamycin C; (c) chloramphenicol; (d) Actinomycin D.

10. A patient has complained of a "burning sensation" in the urogenital tract. The urine is cloudy and has been sent to the laboratory for microbial analysis. The report returns: "5,000 gram-negative rods/cc." There is no time to await the results of a sensitivity test, so the patient is administered: (a) penicillin; (b) nalidixic acid; (c) bacteriophage T2; (d) chloramphenicol.

11. Which antibiotic is usually most effective against bacteremia caused by *Pseudomonas*? (a) Penicillin; (b) nalidixic acid; (c) chloramphenicol; (d) polymyxin.

12. Chloramphenicol was once a commonly prescribed antibiotic. Now it is administered only rarely, as in the treatment of typhoid fever. It has fallen out of favor because: (a) most bacteria are now resistant to it; (b) it precipitates in the kidneys, damaging them; (c) it causes a fatal blood disease in about 1 out of every 30,000 or so people; (d) it is effective only in multiplying bacteria.

Answers: 1. (d); 2. (d); 3. (a); 4. (d); 5. (c); 6. (d); 7. (a); 8. (c); 9. (a); 10. (b); 11. (d); 12. (c).

Chapter 25

Host-Microbe
Interactions

INTRODUCTION: In essence, Chapters 25 through 32, on Microorganisms and Disease, cover the ongoing battle between the protists that would parasitize and their potential hosts, which have evolved numerous defenses against the would-be invaders. The numerous factors involved in human resistance will be discussed, and then the parasites will be identified and characterized. But before that can be done, some introductory information and concepts are in order. That is the purpose of Chap. 25. After reading this chapter, you should have acquired the vocabulary and information you will need to comprehend the next seven chapters. But more than that, if you were to read only the chapters on disease, you might come away with the simplistic conclusion that a given organism causes a given disease and "that is all there is to it." Actually, an understanding of the biology of the interactions—their dynamics, their evolution, their delicate balance—is required to most effectively treat (or even to understand the nuances of proper treatment of) infectious disease. This chapter should impart some of that understanding along with vocabulary and concepts.

Expanded Outline

I. Theories of the Cause of Disease (History).
    A. Primitive superstitions.
        1. Evil "disease" spirits excised by torturing the ill.
        2. Greek legend (Pandora released disease spirits).
            a. Aesculapius—warded off diseases with caduceus.
            b. Hygeia—prevented disease (hygiene).
            c. Panacea—neutralized disease in hosts (panacea).
    B. The humoral concept—espoused by Hippocrates and believed for 2,000 years. Led to symptomatic treatment but also blood-letting.
    C. The beginnings of scientific reasoning.
        1. Galen (130–200)—modified humoral theory.
        2. Paracelsus (1493–1541)—cause of disease.
        3. Harvey (1578–1657)—anatomy.
        4. Sydenham (1624–1689)—disease symptoms response to "morbific matter."

II.   Pathogenicity and Virulence (Terminology).
   A.   Infection—interaction between two organisms, host and parasite, with competition for superiority.
   B.   Infestation—as above, but parasite is an animal (e.g., worm, flea, etc.).
   C.   Parasitism—antagonism that exists when one organism lives at the expense of another.
   D.   Pathogen—organism capable of producing disease.
   E.   Pathogenicity—ability of parasite to invade and cause disease.
   F.   Virulence—degree of pathogenicity (e.g., pathogenic organism has the potential for producing disease, but will do so only if the organism is sufficiently virulent to enter a host and overcome its defense mechanisms). Sometimes pathogenicity and virulence are used synonymously because under a given set of circumstances *any* organism may cause disease.
   G.   Opportunists—microorganisms, normally not pathogenic, that cause disease if the host's defenses are sufficiently weakened.

III.   Dynamics of Infectious Disease.
   A.   Molecular basis of disease—this section makes the point that disease is not solely correlated with toxin production. Often the host must also provide a suitable environment for parasite invasion. The example offered is *Brucella,* which grows well in pregnant mammals (leading to abortion) but not in nonpregnant mammals (mild diseases).
   B.   Initiation of infection—parasite must survive on mucous surfaces and then penetrate the host.
   C.   Production of the disease syndrome—organism (usually) must multiply in tissues and continuously combat host's defenses.

IV.   Some Virulence Factors.
   A.   Toxins.

Table 25-1. Some Characteristics of Exotoxins and Endotoxins

FEATURE	EXOTOXINS	ENDOTOXINS
Bacterial source	Excreted by gram-positive bacteria predominantly	Released from cell walls of lysed gram-negative bacteria
Chemical nature	Protein	Lipopolysaccharide
Heat tolerance	Inactivated easily at 61–80°C	Will withstand autoclaving
Immunology	Can be converted to toxoids and readily neutralized by antitoxin	Cannot form toxoids; neutralization with antitoxin not possible or only with difficulty
Pharmacology	Specific for a particular type of cell function	Various effects, but mostly symptoms of generalized shock or hypersensitivity
Lethal dose	Small	Much larger

B.   Enzymatic and other factors.

Table 25-2. Factors Influencing Virulence

FACTOR	ACTION	REMARKS
Hyaluronidase (spreading factor)	Facilitates spread of pathogens and toxic materials through host tissue; increases permeability of tissue spaces	Probably an inducible enzyme produced by several clostridia, cocci, and other bacteria
Coagulase	Causes resistance to phagocytosis	Produced by virulent staphylococci; may wall off boils
Hemolysins	Destroy red blood cells and other tissue cells	A variety of hemolytic substances produced by various bacteria
Lecithinase or "alpha toxin"	Causes lysis of red blood cells and other tissue cells	A hemolysin produced by *Clastridium perfringens*
Collagenase	Dissolves collagen	Produced by *Cl. perfringens*
Leucocidin	Kills leucocytes	Produced by virulent staphylococci and some streptococci
Streptokinase (streptococcal fibrinolysin), streptodornase	Dissolves human fibrin	Of doubtful importance in pathogenicity; useful as diagnostic test
Exotoxins	Cause degeneration of host cells; block essential metabolites, i.e., enzymes; render substrates unsusceptible to bacterial enzymatic digestion; prevent enzyme synthesis by the cell	Proteins; antigenic
Endotoxins	Not clearly established	Lipopolysaccharide
Capsules	Enable some bacteria to resist phagocytosis	Polysaccharides; antigenic

V.   Normal Flora of the Human Host. We harbor a wide variety of bacteria which coexist in delicate balance on and within our bodies. Normally these organisms do little, if any, harm, and in fact may be quite helpful (e.g., food digestion; keeping more virulent organisms from invading). However, if the delicate balance is upset, these normal flora can cause disease.
A.   Weakened resistance of patient—infections by *E. coli, K. pneumoniae, P. mirabilis* cause more disease in North America than do (for example) the plague, typhoid, and cholera bacteria.
B.   Antibiotic administration—"wipes out" normal flora, permitting invasion by other, antibiotic-resistant bacteria (called *superinfection*).

VI. Some Factors Influencing Infection.
    A. Tissue affinity—many parasites grow best in a specific tissue or cell type (e.g., typhoid bacillus grows best in lymphoid tissue of the intestional cell wall).
    B. Portal of entry—many parasites are most likely to cause disease when they invade via a specific route (e.g., diptheria bacteria via the respiratory passages, gonococci via the urogenital tract, etc.). The more organisms that invade through their most "preferred route," the more likely it is that disease will result.
    C. Communicability or transmission of disease.
        1. Transmission dependent on:
            a. Escape of pathogen from host.
            b. Survival of pathogen en route.
            c. Entrance of pathogen into a susceptible host.
        2. Common modes of transmission.
            a. Contact (little or no survival outside host)—e.g., syphilis.
            b. Airborne—e.g., respiratory infections.
            c. Food- and waterborne—e.g., enteric infections.
            d. Insect-borne—e.g., malaria.

Summary

This chapter focuses on the factors that determine whether or not an organism will cause disease. History, vocabulary, and core information have been covered in the preceding outline. Therefore, in this section, the dynamics of host-organism-disease interaction will be highlighted. The factors that determine whether or not one becomes ill are so numerous that many remain unknown. Nevertheless, the situation is summarized by this equation:

$$\text{Probability of disease} = \frac{\text{number of organisms} \times \text{virulence (toxicity + invasiveness)}}{\text{host resistance}}$$

NUMBER OF ORGANISMS (AND PORTAL OF ENTRY): All other factors being equal, the more organisms that "attack," the more difficult it will be for the body's defenses to "neutralize" all the invaders. Those organisms that gain access through the "prime" portal will survive better, while those that enter through a "secondary" portal may survive less well. For example, inhalation of a droplet teeming with millions of pneumococci is more likely to initiate pneumonia than inhalation of a few airborne organisms. Similarly, pneumococci have evolved means of penetrating through the respiratory passages, whereas they would be likely to perish in the stomach, if ingested.

VIRULENCE (DEGREE OF PATHOGENICITY): Almost any microorganism possesses some virulence and, therefore, may cause disease in sufficient numbers or if the host's resistance is weak. Virulence is dependent on two main factors:

1. *Toxicity* (see IV. A. above)—Many organisms produce substances that impair the function of eucaryotic cells and organisms. Bacteria may produce endotoxins and/or exotoxins. Exotoxins are potent substances that attack specific cell functions. Many exotoxins are now known to be

coded for by a provirus. In fact (from one point of view), some exotoxin producers, e.g., *Clostridium botulinum,* may be inadvertent pathogens, deriving little, if any, benefit from the host. Other exotoxins, like that produced by *Corynebacterium diphtheriae,* may aid the organism's invasiveness.

Endotoxins, on the other hand, affect the entire individual in a nonspecific manner, rather than a specific molecular physiological function. Some scientists regard an endotoxin as a warning signal to the body's defenses: "Danger, invader present." Then these defenses respond. Fever, coughing, and other endotoxin-related symptoms are essentially mechanisms to rid the body of the invader. Sometimes the reaction is so severe that it may be fatal.

2. *Invasiveness—*To survive, we have evolved numerous defense mechanisms against microorganisms that would invade, multiply, and finally destroy us. To survive, microorganisms that must parasitize have evolved numerous mechanisms to neutralize the defenses of their host and establish themselves within their host. Some of these invasive factors are listed in IV. B. A delicate balance has been achieved between many microorganisms and their hosts. If the organism becomes too invasive or too toxic, or the host too weak, both may die. This is exemplified by (a) superinfections and (b) diseases caused by some opportunist pathogens.

Thus, more virulent organisms, all other factors again being equal, are more likely to cause disease. Some pathogenic bacteria are extremely toxic and relatively noninvasive (e.g., *C. botulinum*), while others can be very invasive and less toxic (e.g., anthrax bacillus). Many pathogens (e.g., *S. aureus*) are both toxic and invasive.

HOST'S RESISTANCE: A very weak host with little or no resistance (e.g., due to genetic deficiency or severe trauma) may be quickly overwhelmed by any microorganisms in small numbers. Other individuals are capable of resisting exposure to many virulent organisms. The factors that contribute to resistance and immunity are the subject of the next chapter.

Programmed Self-Test

Do not begin this self-test before reading the corresponding chapter in the text.

THEORIES OF DISEASE; PATHOGENICITY AND VIRULENCE (Text pages 498 to 513)

A single cure for all diseases is referred to as a _____.

Symptomatic treatment was based on the _____.   panacea
theory of disease.

Infestation indicates the presence of _____ para-   humoral
sites in the host.

Any agent capable of producing disease is called a _____.   animal

The degree of pathogenicity, or ability of an organism to cause infection, is termed _____.	pathogen
A normally "avirulent" organism that causes disease in a weakened host is called an _____.	virulence
Brucella abortus grows better in the presence of the sugar called _____, which is found in large quantities in the placenta of pregnant cattle, goats, sheep, and sows.	opportunist pathogen
_____toxins are proteins.	erythritol
Endotoxins are relatively heat-_____.	Exo
The spreading factor is the enzyme _____.	stable (resistant)
Lecithinase is especially active in the lysis of _____ _____.	hyaluronidase
Coagulase protects staphylococci against _____.	red blood cells
Streptokinase is produced by _____-hemolytic strepto-cocci.	phagocytes
Superinfections may occur when _____ are administered.	beta
Peyer's patches in the lymphoid tissue of the intestine are filled with the organism _____.	antibiotics
Neisseria gonorrhoeae is transmitted only by _____ _____.	*Salmonella typhi*
Malaria is transmitted by _____.	direct contact
Can a person carry *Escherichia coli, Klebsiella pneumoniae,* and/or *Proteus mirabilis* in large numbers (millions or more) and still be healthy?	arthropods
	Yes

Multiple-Choice Test

Underline the correct answer.

1. The more virulent a bacterium is, the greater the chance that it will cause disease upon infection. Virulence is a function of: (a) the number of organisms involved and the host's resistance (b) toxicity; (c) sensitivity to antibiotics; (d) toxicity and invasiveness.

2. The bacterium that is the causative agent of anthrax often kills its host because: (a) it produces a powerful exotoxin; (b) it specifically damages the nervous system; (c) it infects only weakened animals; (d) it is so invasive.

3. Generally, a *species* that is obligately parasitic will increase its chances of survival when it: (a) becomes so lethal as to kill its host quickly; (b) becomes less virulent, so that the hosts barely suffer from its presence; (c) loses its capability to be easily transmitted from host to host; (d) "learns" to utilize the screen pass to move (behind good blocking) 10 nm down the intestine.

4. Which of the following bacteria produces a toxin of great potency but is practically noninvasive? (a) *Corynebacterium diphtheriae;* (b) *Clostridium botulinum;* (c) *Staphylococcus aureus;* (d) *Diplococcus pneumoniae.*

5. Which one of the following is characteristic of an *exotoxin*? (a) Produced by pathogenic strains of *E. coli*; (b) a component of gram-negative-type cell walls; (c) relatively nonspecific in its mode of action; (d) usually a heat-labile protein.

6. Virulent staphylococci synthesize coagulase, which: (a) is a powerful endotoxin; (b) inhibits the clotting factor in blood; (c) causes resistance to phagocytosis, thus contributing to the invasiveness of the organism; (d) lyses white blood cells, thus contributing to the toxicity of the organism.

7. Which of these factors does not directly destroy red blood cells? (a) Coagulase; (b) lecithinase; (c) hemolysins.

8. Which organism's main portal of entry is through abrasions in the skin? (a) *Bordetella pertussis;* (b) *Streptococcus pneumoniae;* (c) *Francisella tularensis;* (d) *Salmonella typhi.*

Answers: 1. (d); 2. (d); 3. (b); 4. (b); 5. (d); 6. (c); 7. (a); 8. (c).

Chapter 26

Resistance and Immunity

INTRODUCTION: Because microorganisms cause infectious disease, their hosts' defense mechanisms are an integral part of the science of microbiology. Humans and other animals ward off disease by chemical and physiological means (resistance) and by the production of unique proteins and the actions of certain cells (immunity). This chapter discusses the various factors that lead to resistance and introduces the basics of immunology. In the next chapter, details and applications of the immune response will be covered.

Expanded Outline

I. Natural Resistance.
    A. Species resistance (related to inherent traits of the species).
        1. Temperature of animal, e.g., anthrax infects only those animals with a body temperature of about 37°C.
        2. Herbivorous animals are often resistant to diseases of carnivorous animals.
    B. Racial resistance (certain populations of a species have evolved resistance to a particular organism).
        1. Brahman cattle resistant to vector of tick fever.
        2. American Indians more susceptible to tuberculosis than Caucasians.
    C. Individual resistance (due to anatomical, genetic, and other factors).

II. External Defense Mechanisms (first line of defense: mechanical and chemical).
    A. Unbroken skin and mucous membranes.
    B. Lactic and fatty acids in sweat and sebaceous glands.
    C. Mucous secretions in respiratory, digestive, and urogenital tracts.
    D. Peristalsis, coughing, sneezing, tearing, perspiring, and salivating.
    E. Lysozyme and other chemicals in secretions.

III. Internal Defense Mechanisms (second line of defense)—consist of those mechanisms shown on p. 202 (right-hand side of the figure). Each will be discussed in turn.

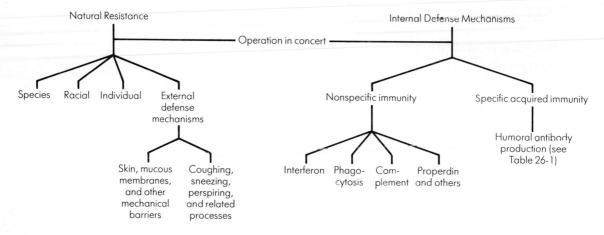

Figure 26-2. Interrelationships between defense mechanisms.

IV.   Specific Immune Responses. Animals form specifically reactive proteins and cells in response to foreign organic molecules. These complex and important responses are crucial means of defense.

A.   **Table 26-1. Types of Specifically Acquired Immunity**

TYPE	SOURCE	DEGREE AND DURATION
Active	Antibodies are produced by the body as a result of stimulation of living, killed, or attenuated organisms or their products (antigens); immunity develops slowly and becomes effective in several weeks	Usually complete and enduring
Natural	Antibody formation is stimulated by presence of living organisms or their products which cause the disease	Lifelong immunity is common
Artificial	Antigens composed of living, killed, or attenuated microorganisms, or toxic or detoxified products administered to host, stimulate antibody production	Solid protection for many years reinforced by "booster" inoculations
Passive	Antibodies produced by active immunization in one individual are transferred to another; provides immediate but temporary protection	Protection is of short duration
Natural	Transferred to young from an immune mother by placental transfer or colostrum	Complete but temporary; may last up to 1 year
Artificial	Conferred by injection of serum from an immune animal or human being to a susceptible individual; used to provide immediate protection in cases of known exposure to infection or during epidemics	Complete for 2 to 3 weeks

B.   Antigens—any substances that stimulate antibody production and react specifically with their antibodies.

1. Chemical nature: protein, nucleoprotein, lipoprotein, and polysaccharides of considerable size. Also smaller molecules (haptens) suitably linked to proteins or
   synthetic polypeptides.
2. Origin: usually substances foreign to the body in which they act.
3. Functional parts.
   a. Portion that determines antibody reaction specificity.
   b. Portion that stimulates antibody production.
4. Types (some examples).
   a. Bacterial (most pathogenic bacteria are good antibody stimulators).
      i. Exotoxins–stimulate antitoxin production.
      ii. Surface (cell wall and capsule) antigens (O).
      iii. Flagella (H) antigens.
   b. Fungal (weak human antibody stimulators).
   c. Heterophile antigens–stimulate the production of antibodies that cross-react
      with a wide variety of tissues.
   d. Isoantigen–present in some, but not all, members of a species (e.g., A and B
      antigens on human erythrocytes).
   e. Vaccines–suspensions of killed or attenuated (weakened virulence) cultures of
      microorganisms, used as antigens to produce immunity.
   f. Toxoids–made by destroying the poisonous portions of toxins without altering
      the antigenic portion.
C. Antibodies (immunoglobulins).
   1. Structure–all antibodies are basically this configuration, although the amino acid
      sequences vary (particularly at the antigen binding site) among the numerous kinds
      of antibodies.

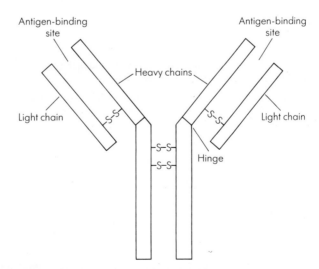

**Figure 26-3. Schematic model of an antibody (immunoglobulin) molecule with two heavy and
two light polypeptide chains held together by interchain disulfide bonds. The molecule can
flex at the hinge.**

a. Light chain—consists of about 214 amino acids each. Two basic kinds of light chains exist (kappa or lambda).

b. Heavy chains—consist of about 446 amino acids each. Five basic kinds of heavy chains exist. A given kind of chain has a characteristic amino acid sequence (relatively constant). Amino acid sequences of the light and heavy chains determine the class and biological role of the antibody.

c. Antibody binding site—very variable amino acid sequence which determines the specificity of the antigen for the antibody.

2. Classes of immunoglobulins.

IMMUNO-GLOBULIN	SITE FOUND	COMPLE-MENT FIXATION	CROSS PLA-CENTA	FUNCTIONS	CONFIGU-RATION	PERCENT OF Ig (NORMAL SERA)
IgG	Internal body fluids, particularly extravascular	+	+	Major line of defense against infection during the first few weeks of a baby's life; neutralizes bacterial toxins; binds to microorganisms to enhance their phagocytosis	Monomer	85
IgM	Largely confined to bloodstream	+	−	Efficient agglutinating and cytolytic agent; effective first line of defense in cases of bacteremia	Pentamer; also J chain	6
IgA	Serum, exocrine secretions	−	−	Protects mucosal surfaces from invasion by pathogenic microbes	Monomer, dimer (secretions), or trimer	10 (monomer)
IgD	Serum, on lymphocyte surface of newborn	?	−	May be an early receptor which later gives way to IgM and other immunoglobulins	Monomer	1
IgE	Serum, fixes to mast cells and basophils	−	−	Responsible for severe acute and occasionally fatal allergic reactions; combats parasitic infections	Monomer	0.002

3. Roles of antibodies.
   a. Antitoxins—neutralize toxins.
   b. Agglutinins—clump cells.
   c. Precipitins—precipitate soluble antigen (e.g., flagella).
   d. Lysins—lyse cells.
   e. Complement-fixing antibodies—in conjunction with complement, they lyse cells.
   f. Opsonins—aid in phagocytosis.
   g. Neutralizing antibodies—neutralize pathogen's invasiveness and/or toxicity.

D. The two systems of (specific) immunity

1. Humoral immunity system—based on antibodies, discussed above. Effective against bacterial infections and viral reinfections.
2. Cell-mediated immunity—protects against certain infectious agents (e.g., tubercle bacilli), rejects grafted cells from genetically different individuals of the same species (allografts), and may be a defense mechanism against cancer.
    a. Mechanism one:
        i. Antigen specifically combines with particular lymphocytes.
        ii. The activated lymphocytes enlarge.
        iii. They produce lymphokines.
        iv. Lymphokines incite local inflammatory reactions and eliminate foreign substances.
    b. Mechanism two: phagocytosis (relatively nonspecific).

V. Nonspecific Immunity. Mechanisms that act against invasion in general, rather than against a specific organism (e.g., in specific immunity a particular antibody may neutralize only a particular strain of bacteria, whereas nonspecific mechanisms act on many different organisms simultaneously).
    A. Inflammation—increased capillary permeability and other processes allow phagocytes and microbicidal substances to accumulate at the affected area.
    B. Phagocytosis—ingestion and removal (killing) of bacteria and other foreign matter.
        1. Cell types.
            a. Neutrophils (polymorphonuclear leukocytes).
                i. First line of internal defense.
                ii. Relatively short-lived cells, produced in bone marrow.
                iii. About $7,000/mm^2$ in blood, lymph, and tissue.
                iv. Have numerous microbicidal chemicals (in lysosomes).
            b. Macrophages (reticuloendothelial system cells).
                i. Relatively long-lived cells, also produced in bone marrow.
                ii. Found in tissue and blood.
                iii. May multiply and differentiate.
                iv. Lysozymes and other germicidal chemicals are found only after contact with antigen.
        2. Mechanism (stages) of phagocytosis. (See Fig. 26-6.)

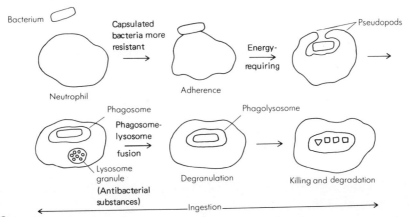

Figure 26-6.

C.   Complement system—eleven proteins plus cell-specific antibody that participate in cell lyses during infection, the inflammatory response, and allergy (immune system acting on host's own cells).
1.   Lysis pathways.
   a. Antibody—identifies invading cell and activates the complement attack.
   b. Proteins C_{1s}, C_{1a}, and C_{1R} participate in cell recognition.
   c. C_2, C_{3b}, and C_{4b} activate cell (C_3 and "properdin" activate cell directly, by-passing above steps).
   d. C_{5b} and C_{6-9} attack and puncture cell.
2.   Other functions of complement.
   a. C_{3a} and C_{5a} release histamine from leukocytes, mast cells, and platelets. Histamine increases capillary permeability so that leukocytes may penetrate tissues to combat infection or foment allergy.
   b. Certain complement fractions are chemotactic for leukocytes, attracting them to sites of immune reactions.
   c. IgE, C_{3a}, C_{5a}, and histamines are all involved in *anaphylaxis.*
D.   Interferon (antiviral protein).
1.   Properties.
   a. Intracellular action.
   b. Viral nonspecificity—once elicited, it protects against many kinds of viruses (because it acts on a cellular mechanism, not a specific virus).
   c. Host specificity—e.g., human interferon does not protect cells of other mammals or birds.
   d. Short duration of action—once elicited, interferon is produced for only about 10 days and is constantly degraded.
2.   Induction—interferon is elicited by virus infection or administered by foreign nucleic acids. Double-stranded RNAs appear to be the most potent inducers.
3.   Mechanism of action—interferon appears to stimulate the production of proteins that inhibit viral replication.
4.   Role of interferon—a main function is to combat rapidly multiplying viruses until specific immune mechanisms act.

Summary

Higher organisms frequently remain free of infectious disease because would-be invaders do not find species, races, or individuals that are suitable hosts. In other words, over millions of years certain parasites have adapted to certain hosts. For the host species to survive, it had to evolve defenses. The first line of defense—physical and chemical barriers like skin and sweat—bars many invaders. Should these barriers be insufficient, complex internal mechanisms act in concert to repel microbial parasites.

The immune response is one of the most important defense mechanisms. Specific antigens induce the production of specific antibodies which react with, and neutralize, only those specific antigens. After systematic exposure to many organisms, vertebrates continuously produce the antibodies that confer protection. Thus, they may become immune to the particular disease.

Acting synergistically with the humoral immunity system are cells that incite inflammatory responses or those that phagocytize antigens. Also proteins such as complement lyse cells, while interferon represses viral multiplication until antibodies become effective.

In short, just as much genetic capability has evolved to keep species "safe" from external predators, so perhaps even more genetic code is devoted to keeping species "safe" from internal parasites.

Programmed Self-Test

Do not begin this self-test before reading the corresponding chapter in the text.

NATURAL RESISTANCE (Text pages 516 to 519)

Natural resistance provides defense against infection by a number of mechanical and _____ barriers.	
Lack of natural resistance is called ____ _____.	chemical
Brahman cattle are resistant to _____ fever.	susceptibility
Most bacteria are inhibited by lactic acid and _____ acids in sweat.	tick
_____ of the respiratory tract, the digestive tract, the urogenital tract, and other tissues form a protective covering which collects and holds microorganisms until they can be disposed of.	fatty

INTERNAL DEFENSE MECHANISMS: SPECIFIC AND NONSPECIFIC (Text pages 519 to 531)

An antigen has two properties: _____ and reactivity.	Mucous secretions

The specificity portion of an antigen that reacts with specific antibodies but cannot incite antibody production is called a partial antigen or _____.	immunogenicity
H antigens are found on the _____ of some bacteria.	hapten
Heterophile antigen was first demonstrated in 1911 by _____.	flagella
Toxoids are made by destroying the poisonous portions of toxins without altering the _____ portion.	Forssman
"Antibodies produced by active immunization in one individual and transferred to another" is a definition of _____ acquired immunity.	antigenic
The immunoglobulin that mediates acute allergic reaction is _____.	passive
Ig____ is ordinarily a pentamer.	IgE
The variable regions on the terminal portions of both heavy and light chains (on antibodies) are _____ binding sites.	M
Opsonins render microorganisms more susceptible to _____.	antigen
Grafted cells from genetically different individuals of the same species are called _____.	phagocytosis
Activated lymphocytes enlarge, divide, and provide mediators, called _____, which incite local inflammatory reactions.	allografts
Two kinds of white blood cells that phagocytize are _____ and _____.	lymphokines
The neutrophil does not divide after leaving the _____ and survives in tissues for only _____.	neutrophils; macrophages
When the mature macrophage is "activated" by contact with a microbe, the organelle that forms is the _____.	bone marrow; a few days

Within the _____ of white blood cells, most bacteria are usually killed within a few minutes.	lysosome
Complement is normally present in serum and consists of a group of related _____.	phagolysosome
C_1 proteins act in cell _____.	proteins
C_{3a} and C_{5a} complement "fragments" cause the release of _____, from leukocytes, mast cells, and platelets.	recognition
Interferons are _____-specific and nonspecific for _____.	histamine
Interferon can be induced by nucleic acids, particularly _____.	host; viruses
	double-stranded RNA

Multiple-Choice Test

Underline the correct answer.

1. The secretions of the human eye contain an enzyme that contributes to natural resistance by alone lysing bacteria. This enzyme is: (a) catalase; (b) hyaluronidase; (c) complement; (d) pronase; (e) lysozyme.

For each of the following examples (questions 2 to 5), indicate whether the immunity is: (a) passively acquired artificial immunity; (b) passively acquired natural immunity; (c) actively acquired natural immunity; or (d) actively acquired artificial immunity.

2. There is an epidemic of influenza. The children of the Smith household, age 3, 7, and 10, catch it. The two-month-old *baby* is *immune* to it.

3. After recovering from the flu, the three Smith children are now immune to that strain of it.

4. During the epidemic, Grandmother Smith, who has a history of heart trouble, receives an injection of gamma globulin.

5. Father Smith, who told his physician that he could not afford to miss a day of work, receives the influenza vaccine.

6. In 1880, Pasteur achieved the first deliberate active artificial immunization against a bacterial disease. The vaccine used was a culture of living cells which had lost the ability to cause disease, that is, they had become: (a) axenic; (b) toxigenic; (c) attenuated; (d) antigenic.

7. Which portion of the IgG molecule specifies affinity for a special antigen?   (a) Light chain; (b) heavy chain; (c) variable regions; (d) constant regions.

8. How many antigen binding sites are there on each IgG antibody? (a) None; (b) one; (c) two (d) three; (e) four.

9. Antibody molecules are best characterized as: (a) rigid along the entire length of the molecule; (b) flexible along the entire length of the molecule; (c) flexible only on the active sites; (d) flexible at dual hinge points.

10. In an immediate hypersensitivity reaction, IgE "reacts" with mast cells, which in turn: (a) attack infected tissues; (b) release mucous; (c) differentiate into T-cell precursors; (d) release chemicals like histamine and serotonin.

11. A patient has been diagnosed, and the onset of botulism is suspected. Which type of antibody would have to be administered quickly? (a) Antitoxin; (b) opsonin; (c) precipitin; (d) agglutinin.

12. Substances that stimulate the production of antibodies capable of reacting with tissues of a wide variety of unrelated animals or plants (for example, Forssman antigen) are called: (a) isoantigens; (b) isophile antigens; (c) γ-immunoglobulin; (d) heterophile antigens.

13. An opsonin is an antibody with the function of: (a) neutralizing toxins; (b) enhancing phagocytosis; (c) lysing bacteria; (d) precipitating soluble antigens.

14. Complement is associated with: (a) antigen agglutination; (b) antigen precipitation; (c) cell lysis; (d) neutralization of toxins.

15. Which of the following chemicals is the first to respond to a viral invasion and prevent viral replication? (a) Complement; (b) lysin; (c) interferon; (d) antibodies.

Answers: 1. (e); 2. (b); 3. (c); 4. (a); 5. (d); 6. (c); 7. (c); 8. (c); 9. (d); 10. (d); 11. (a); 12. (d); 13. (b); 14. (c); 15. (c).

Chapter 27

The Immune Response in Theory and Practice

INTRODUCTION: For many years immunology-serology has been adapted to meet many needs. It has been used to monitor the resistance of individuals to disease, diagnose disease, identify microorganisms, and detect protein origins.

At present, basic mechanisms of antibody induction, formation, and action are being elucidated. This knowledge may lead to a better understanding of cellular differentiation and to better treatments for a large number of diseases.

After reading this chapter, you should understand the workings of the immune system and appreciate the specific methods of serology.

Expanded Outline and Summary

I. Development of the Immune System. The production of the cells that confer immunity is summarized below.

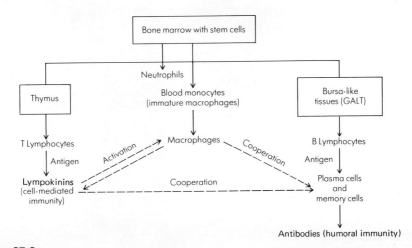

Figure 27-2.

A.   Stem cells in the bone marrow—these are the "pre-embryo" white blood cells. They may differentiate and give rise to all the other cells described below and in the preceding chapter.

B.   Neutrophiles—as described in the previous chapter, these cells phagocytize, kill, and/or remove "foreign" particles and organisms. (See Fig. 27-3c.)

C.   Macrophages—these cells mature from monocytes in the blood. As indicated in the previous chapter, they, too, phagocytize, but after they ingest and process an antigen, they may activate cell-mediated immunity and/or cooperate in triggering humoral immunity (antibodies). These interactions are further described below. (See Figs. 27-3d and 27-3a.)

D.   T lymphocytes and cell-mediated immunity—some stem-cell-produced lymphocytes may pass through the thymus (thymocytes are lymphocytes in the thymus) and interact with it. There they are induced to differentiate into T cells. T cells are activated by antigen and undergo further differentiation into mature lymphoblasts. These may then be activated by macrophages. As previously noted, activated lymphoblasts produce lymphokinins, leading to inflammation, destruction of some microorganisms

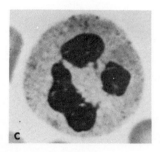

Figure 27-3c. Neutrophil.

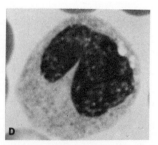

Figure 27-3d. Monocyte; immature macrophage.

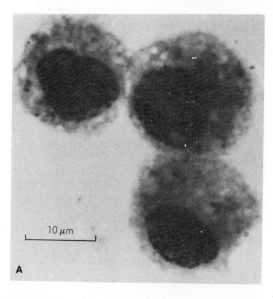

10 μm

Figure 27-3a. Macrophage.

(tuberculosis bacillus), rejection of tumor cells (?) and allografts, allergy, and other processes. Lymphoblasts also interact with, and stimulate, macrophage phagocytosis and the humoral response. (See Figs. 27-3f and 27-1, T lymphocyte.)

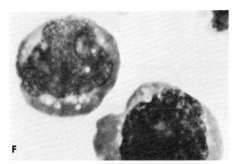

Figure 27-3f. Mature lymphoblasts.

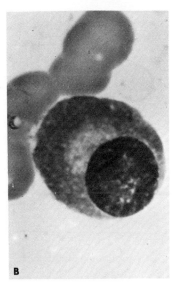

Figure 27-3b. Plasma cell.

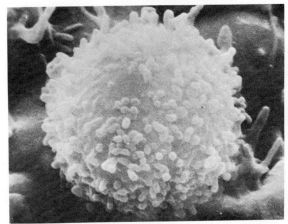

Figure 27-1. T lymphocyte.

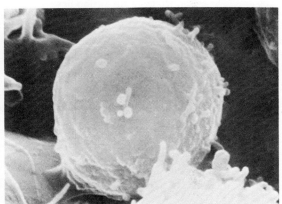

Figure 27-1. B lymphocyte.

E. Lymphocytes and the humoral response—in a manner analogous to the cell-mediated mechanism (thymus interaction), stem-cell progeny interact in humans with gut-associated lymphoid tissues (GALT), such as tonsils, appendix, Peyer's patches, and lymphoid follicles (in birds, the interaction is with the bursa of Fabricius; hence the term B cells). The "embryo" stem-cell progeny then differentiate into B lymphocytes. (See Fig. 27-1 above.) After stimulation by antigen and, somewhere along the line, macrophages, these B cells further differentiate into plasma cells and memory cells. (See Fig. 27-3b.) A plasma cell synthesizes and secretes about 2,000 identical antibody molecules (specific for a particular antigen) per second until it dies. The memory cells enable an individual who has been exposed to an antigen once to produce more antibodies, more quickly, for a longer period of time upon subsequent exposures to the antigen (anamnestic response).

II. Measurement of Humoral Antibodies. Antibodies cannot be seen, but can be quantitated by numerous procedures (e.g., neutralization and precipitation reactions) to be described later.

III. Selective and Instructive Theories of Antibody Formation.
   A. Classical theories—now believed to be at least partially untenable.
      1. Instructive theory—antigen combines with protein antibody and molds it to antigenic-specific configuration.
      2. Selective theory—cells exist that continuously make specific antibody. A particular antigen stimulates a specific group of cells (producing specific antibody to the antigen) to multiply and increase antibody production.
   B. Clonal-selection hypothesis of Burnet—a modification of selective theories. Differs from selective theory in that little or no antibody is postulated to be produced until a particular clone of cells is stimulated. Evidence for this theory:
      1. Specific antigen binds to a small ratio of lymphocytes.
      2. One plasma cell produces one kind of antibody at a time.

IV. Genetic Theories of Antigenic Variability. These theories relate to questions such as these: If one kind of antibody molecule is specific for only one kind of antigen, considering the many thousands of antigens, how may a corresponding number of unique antibodies be genetically encoded? Can the genetic code contain the information necessary to translate the 10^4 to 10^5 different amino acid sequences inherent to the antibody complement?
   A. Germ-line theory—all cells, including lymphocytes, contain the 10^4 to 10^5 genes necessary to code for antibodies.
   B. Somatic theory—mutant cells arise (thymus produced?), thus accounting for the genetic variability necessary for antibody variability.

V. Mechanisms of Antigen-Antibody Reactions—combination of reactants followed by visible reaction (precipitate). The *lattice hypothesis* supposes that antigens and antibodies are polyvalent (many combining sites), so that the pictured complex arises. The formation of large lattices requires that antigen and antibody concentrations be roughly equivalent (why?).

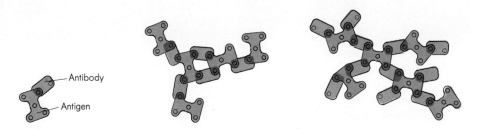

Figure 27-6. The lattice hypothesis of antigen-antibody reactions.

VI. Diagnostic Applications of Antigen-Antibody Reactions (Serology).
   A. Agglutination tests (clumping of insoluble antigens, e.g., bacteria, by specific or homologous antisera).
      1. Uses (because agglutination tests are easy to perform and interpret, they are widely used).
         a. Identification of unknown organisms (use of known specific antisera).
         b. Widal test (designed for diagnosis of typhoid fever)—heat-killed organism mixed with patient's serum.

    c. Weil Felix reaction—tests for certain rickettsial infections. Proteus antigen (similar to some rickettsial antigens but easier to prepare) mixed with patient's serum.

2. Methods.

    a. Tube agglutination (most widely used method)—serum diluted in series of test tubes and mixed with antigen (semiquantitative). Agglutination in tubes with the more diluted serum indicates a higher antibody titer.

    b. Macroscopic slide agglutination test—presumptive (screening test). Serum and antigen mixed on slide.

    c. Microscopic slide agglutination test—reaction mixture (cells are sera) examined under microscope. Possible observations are shown:

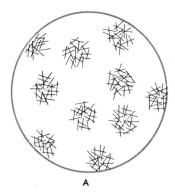 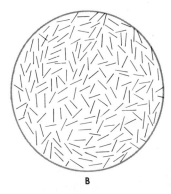

A   B

Positive Test: Cells Agglutinated   Negative Test: Cells Not Agglutinated

Figure 27-9.

    d. Whole blood agglutination tests (most commonly used to detect swine erysipelas)—blood (not serum) mixed with antigen.

    e. Agglutinin-adsorption tests—used to test serological relatedness (shared antigens) among groups (genera) of organisms.

B. Precipitin tests—reaction between soluble antigen and homologous antibody.

1. Examples of uses.

    a. Diagnostic.

    b. Typing of streptococci and other bacteria.

    c. Medicolegal.

    d. Detecting adulteration of foods.

2. Methods—antigen prepared from extracts of cells.

    a. Ring test—antigen layered over sera. Precipitate forms where proper concentration of antigen contacts proper concentration of homologous antibody. (See Fig. 27-11a.)

    b. Agar diffusion methods—provide greater accuracy and separation of components than other precipitin tests.

      i. Single-diffusion method (Oudin)—antigen overlaid on agar gel containing antiserum. Antigen diffuses through agar. (See Fig. 27-11b.)

      ii. Double-diffusion methods. (See Fig. 27-11c.)

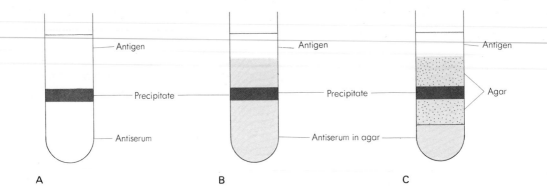

Figure 27-11.

    A. One-dimensional—antiserum in agar in bottom of tube, overlayered with agar gel; two reactants diffuse toward each other.

    B. Two-dimensional (Ouchterlony)—various antigens and antisera can be compared directly. Reactants diffuse from wells cut in agar in a petri dish.

    iii. Immunoelectrophoresis—electric current separates antigens in agar. Antibody (sera) is placed in trench in agar. Antigen and homologous antibody meet and form precipitation bands.

  c. Precipitin test for streptococcus typing—Streptococci produce various somatic carbohydrate antigens (C substance). They are serologically classified based on the kind of carbohydrate they synthesize.

  d. Precipitin (flocculation) tests for syphilis.

    i. Kahn test—presumptive due to high sensitivity. Antigen is beef heart muscle plus cholesterol.

    ii. Kline test—screening test (positives require confirmation). Microscopic-slide test using beef heart cholesterol antigen. Similar to VDRL test.

C. Complement-fixation tests.

  1. Methodology and rationale. (See Fig. 27-12.)

  2. Uses—diagnosis of many infectious disease (e.g., syphilis).

    a. Wasserman test—antigen is cardiolipin + cholesterol + lecithin (combines with but cannot induce syphilitic antibodies).

    b. *Treponema pallidum* complement-fixation (TPCF) test—similar to Wasserman test, but virulent (difficult to cultivate) treponemes are the antigen.

    c. Reiter protein complement-fixation (RPCF) test—as above, but antigen is protein extract of avirulent *T. pallidum.*

    d. *Treponema pallidum* immobilization (TPI) test—live, virulent *T. pallidum* + complement + patient's serum are incubated. If patient has syphilis, antibodies render *T. pallidum* nonmotile (observed under dark-field microscope).

    e. *Treponema pallidum* immune adherence (TPIA) test—*T. pallidum* + complement + patient's serum + red blood cells. If syphilitic antibody is present in serum, *T. pallidum* adheres to red blood cells (visible under dark-field microscope).

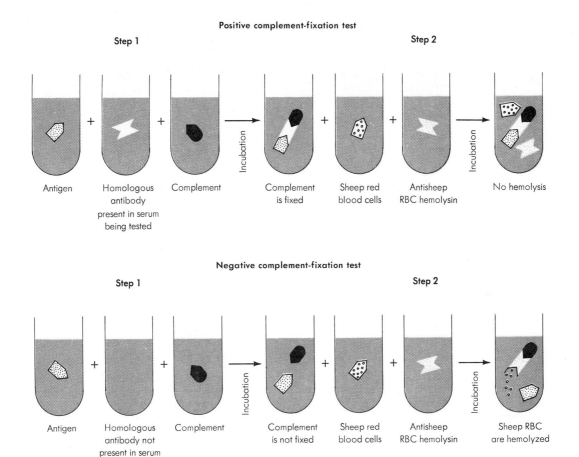

Figure 27-12. Complement-fixation test is based on the fact that if complement (found in blood) is "fixed" by reacting with antigen and its homologous antibody, lysis of sheep red blood cells does not occur even though specific hemolysin is present.

    D. Other serological tests.
        1. Fluorescent-antibody technique—known antibody, tagged with fluorochrome, attaches to specific cells, rendering them highly visible under an untraviolet microscope.
        2. Neufeld Quellung (swelling) reaction—pneumococci produce at least 80 different kinds of polysaccharide capsules that can be serologically typed. Specific antibody increases the refractive index of the specific capsule, making it appear prominent under the brightfield microscope.
        3. Opsonocytophagic index—of limited use in diagnosis of brucellosis. *Brucella* is mixed with the patient's blood, and phagocytosis by neutrophiles is monitored. Active phagocytosis (e.g., more than 20 bacteria per cell) suggests immunity.
        4. Detection of heterophile antibodies—for infectious mononucleosis; based on agglutination of sheep red blood cells by the serum of the patient.

5. Hemagglutination test—influenza, mumps, ECHO, and some other viruses agglutinate certain red blood cells. Tests can be used to titer these viruses.

6. Hemagglutination inhibition test—antibody from patient with hemagglutinating-virus infection retards hemagglutination. This is the basis for several diagnostic tests for viral infections.

7. Neutralizing antibodies—during viral infection, antibodies are produced that inactivate the virus. Patient's serum can be mixed with virus and inoculated into test animals. Degree of protection afforded the animals by the serum is both diagnostic and a measure of the patient's immunity.

E. Tests to evaluate virulence (bacterial).

1. Fibrinolysin (streptokinase) test for beta-hemolytic streptococci—coagulated human plasma + streptococcus. A liquefied clot is indicative of fibrolysin production.

2. Antifibrinolysin (antibody specific for fibrinolysin)—coagulated human plasma + fibrinolysin-producing streptococcus + test serum. Longer lysing times indicate the presence of the antibody.

3. Test for antistreptolysin O—Group A streptococci may produce a hemolytic, oxygen-labile factor (streptolysin). Presence of antibody against this factor is indicative of a streptococcal infection, which may lead to rheumatic fever and other serious complications. Increased titers of antistreptolysin O are indicative of a progressing infection. In this test, diluants, patient's serum, streptolysin O, and red blood cells are mixed. Nonlysis of red blood cells is indicative of antistreptolysin O.

4. Coagulase test—pathogenic staphylococci produce coagulase, which reproducibly clots human and rabbit plasma. The test staphylococci are mixed with plasma and, in a positive test, a clot forms in 2 h.

F. Intracutaneous diagnostic tests. Toxin or organism is injected into patient. Reaction (edema) indicates hypersensitivity or lack of immunity. Examples:

1. In the Dick test (scarlet fever) and Schick test (diphtheria), a positive reaction indicates lack of immunity.

2. In the tuberculin test, a positive reaction indicates hypersensitivity (often previous exposure to the organism).

Programmed Self-Test

Do not begin this self-test before reading the corresponding chapter in the text.

DEVELOPMENT OF THE IMMUNE SYSTEM (Text pages 533 to 535)

_____ cells in the bone marrow give rise to neutrophils, monocytes, and lymphocytes.

Monocytes mature into _____.   Stem

Antibodies are produced by _____ cells.	macrophages
Lymphoblasts synthesize _____, which trigger cell-mediated immunity.	plasma
Stem-cell progeny interact with the _____ gland before they differentiate into T lymphocytes.	lymphokinins
The acronym GALT stands for _____ _____.	thymus
A plasma cell synthesizes and secretes about ___*(number)*___ identical antibody molecules per second until it dies.	gut-associated lymphoid tissues
In birds, stem-cell progeny interact with the _____ _____ before they differentiate into B lymphocytes.	2,000

SELECTIVE AND INSTRUCTIVE THEORIES OF ANTIBODY FORMATION; GENETIC THEORIES OF ANTIGENIC VARIABILITY (Text pages 538 to 540)

Is the instructive theory of antibody formation believed to be correct?	bursa of Fabricius
A group of cells descended from the same cell is called a _____.	No
How many kinds of immunoglobulin molecules does one plasma cell make at one time?	clone
The clonal-selection model proposed by _____ is generally regarded as an acceptable working model for antibody synthesis.	One
In a single individual it has been estimated that there are about ___*(number)*___ different antibody specificities.	Burnet
The _____ genetic theory of antigenic (antibody) variability assumes that some antibody-producing cells are mutants.	10^4 to 10^5

DIAGNOSTIC APPLICATIONS OF ANTIGEN-ANTIBODY REACTIONS (Text pages 541 to 557)

In the Widal test for typhoid fever, _____-killed organisms are mixed with the patient's serum.	somatic

A precipitin test involves the reaction between a _____ antigen and homologous antibody.	heat
To enhance the sensitivity of precipitin reactions, the single agar diffusion method was devised by _____, the double-diffusion method was devised by _____, and the two-dimensional double-diffusion method was devised by _____.	soluble
The Kahn test (for _____) makes use of _____ _____as antigen.	Oudin; Oakley-Fulthorpe; Ouchterlony
In complement-fixation tests, if the sheep red blood cells lyse, the results are reported as _____.	syphilis; beef heart muscle plus cholesterol
In the RPCF test, the antigen is a protein extract of _____.	negative
The Neufeld Quellung reaction had been routinely used to type _____.	avirulent *T. pallidum*
The opsonocytophagic index is of limited use in the diagnosis of _____.	pneumococci
Influenza, mumps, and ECHO viruses each _____ certain red blood cells.	brucellosis
Fibrinolysin is also called _____.	agglutinate.
Coagulase is produced by some pathogenic _____.	streptokinase
In the Dick test for _____ and the Schick test for _____, a positive reaction indicates a lack of _____.	staphylococci
	scarlet fever; diphtheria; immunity

Multiple-Choice Test

Underline the correct answer.

1. One of the characteristic features of the anamnestic response is that after a second antigen exposure, circulating antibodies last longer. This is because: (a) less antigen is required for stimulation; (b) the antibodies are not degraded; (c) 0.003 μg of diphtheria toxin elicits a primary but not a secondary response; (d) antibodies are synthesized for a longer period of time.

2. In the anamnestic (secondary) antibody response, it is known that the threshold stimulus is lower than in the primary response. This means that in the secondary response: (a) antibodies are made for a longer period of time; (b) greater quantities of antibodies are made; (c) antibodies are made more quickly after stimulation; (d) less antigen is required to stimulate an antibody response.

3. Anaphylaxis refers to: (a) the severe reaction following reinjection intravenously of the antigen in a sensitized animal; (b) the severe reaction following primary injection of protein solutions; (c) the state of immunity developed by repeated injection of any substance; (d) the severe reaction resulting from sensitivity to common allergens.

4. The clonal-selection theory of antibody formation implies that: (a) antigen enters the antibody-producing cell and becomes a direct template from which the antibody takes its final complementary form; (b) the cell is "born" with a pattern complementary to the specific antigen, and the antigen stimulates proliferation of the cell that has the right pattern; (c) the antigen incorporates an image of itself in the genetic mechanism of the cell; (d) clones of cells proliferate in response to challenge with a given carcinogen.

5. Beef heart muscle and cholesterol cross-react with antibodies specific for: (a) *S. typhi;* (b) *T. pallidum;* (c) *O. Ouchterlony;* (d) *Brucella.*

6. Which of the following is usually an in vivo test? (a) Neutralizaion; (b) agglutinin; (c) precipitin; (d) complement fixation.

7. In a positive Widal test for typhoid fever, antibodies in the serum most often agglutinate: (a) the capsular antigen of the *Salmonella;* (b) the flagella of the *Salmonella;* (c) killed suspensions of the intact organism; (d) secondary viral invaders.

8. Which one of these is not a serological test for syphilis? (a) Wasserman; (b) *Treponema pallidum* immobilization; (c) Kahn; (d) Schick; (e) Reiter protein (avirulent *T. pallidum*) complement-fixation test (RPCF).

9. The double-diffusion Ouchterlony test makes use of: (a) complement-fixation reaction; (b) an agglutination reaction; (c) an opsonin reaction; (d) a precipitin reaction.

10. Which cell type is central to the humoral immune response? (a) T lyphocyte; (b) B lymphocyte; (c) neutrophil; (d) monocyte.

Answers: 1. (d); 2. (d); 3. (a); 4. (b); 5. (b); 6. (a); 7. (c); 8. (d); 9. (d); 10. (b).

Chapter 28

Human Airborne
Infections

INTRODUCTION: The next three chapters deal with many of the human invaders. The diseases they cause are the focal point. First airborne, then waterborne, and finally contact diseases will be discussed. Thus, organizationally, main routes of transmission are deservedly granted importance. (It is also possible to treat the subject according to the etiological agent—e.g., diseases caused by bacteria, viruses, etc.)

To help you build your knowledge of the microbiology of infectious disease, these chapters will be summarized in comprehensive tables. You may use these outline formats as concise references, as memory aids, and/or as a study guide.

Summary

Organisms whose *main* route of transmission is via the air (inhalation) usually cause respiratory disease. However, some airborne pathogens proceed from the lungs via the bloodstream to other parts of the body, where they do damage (e.g., miningococcus damages the spinal cord).

The incidence of respiratory disease is highest in the colder months. Organisms may be spread in droplets (mucous secretions) or by fomites. Most respiratory disease remains undiagnosed; about a third is caused by viruses and about 10 percent by bacteria.

Airborne infections leading to respiratory and other diseases are summarized in tabular form on pps. 224-225.

In the tables dealing with disease, the main causative organisms are identified and very briefly described. Main (not all) symptoms are listed, and common treatments are mentioned. Control of disease is usually by vaccine, and where one is available it is parenthetically noted. Under epidemiology, the general frequency of occurrence of the disease, tests for susceptibility, and "unusual" routes of transmission are often indicated.

Where exotoxins contribute to disease, they are noted. No mention, however, is made of endotoxin action, certain virulence factors (e.g., coagulase), or laboratory diagnostic procedures. This, and other information, has been presented in previous chapters or is contained in the text.

Programmed Self-Test

Do not begin this self-test before reading the corresponding chapter in the text.

HUMAN AIRBORNE INFECTIONS (Text pages 560 to 594).

Corynebacterium diphtheria organisms may impair breathing and food ingestion because they produce a _____ in the throat.	
Nonpathogenic *Corynebacterium* are called _____.	pseudomembrane
Corynebacterium is a gram-_____ rod.	diphtheroids
Nonlysogenic strains of *Corynebacterium* are _____.	positive
The case/fatality ratio of diphtheria is around _____.	nontoxigenic
The scarlet fever rash is due to an _____ toxin produced by the organism _____.	10 percent
The drugs of choice for scarlet fever are _____ and _____.	erythrogenic; *Streptococcus pyogenes*
A positive _____ test indicates susceptibility to scarlet fever.	penicillin; erythromycin
Rheumatic fever victims may suffer much _____ disability.	Dick
There are about ___*(number)*___ cases of tuberculosis in the United States, of which _____ are active.	cardiac (heart)
_____*tuberculosis* is the causative agent of tuberculosis.	1 million; two-thirds
Ninety-five percent of bacterial pneumonias are caused by _____.	*Mycobacterium*
Streptococcal pneumonia is characterized by a _____ onset while Mycoplasma pneumonia is characterized by a _____ onset.	*Streptococcus pneumoniae*

Human Airborne Infections

DISEASE	CAUSATIVE ORGANISM(S)	DESCRIPTION OF CAUSATIVE ORGANISM(S)
Diptheria	*Corynebacterium diptheriae* strains *gravis, intermedius, mitis*	Gram-positive short, curved rods; palisade arrangement
Scarlet fever ————————— Rheumatic fever	Streptococci; usually beta-hemolytic belonging to Lancefield groups A, B, or D	Gram-positive cocci; short to long chains
Tuberculosis	*Mycobacterium tuberculosis;* human and bovine species, also atypical (Runyon) groups	Slender acid-fast rods; occasional branching
Pneumococcus pneumonia	*Streptococcus pneumoniae*	Gram-positive, oval cells in pairs (short chains), 80 SSS antigenic types
Mycoplasma pneumonia	PPLO	Small, pleomorphic, gram-negative spheres
Meningococcus meningitis	*Neisseria meningitidis* (Serotypes B, C, and Y)	Gram-negative kidney-shaped or spherical cocci; pairs
Whooping cough	*Bordetella pertussis*	Short, oval, gram-negative rod; bipolar staining
Smallpox (variola)	Variola major (30% mortality); variola minor (0.1% mortality)	Viruses; brick-shape; multilayered envelope
Chicken pox (varicella)	Herpes virus	Icosahedral; DNA virus like zoster (shingles) virus
Measles (rubeola)	Measles virus	Paramyxovirus
German measles	Rubella virus	Enveloped single-stranded RNA; similar to togavirus group
Mumps	Mumps virus	Paramyxovirus (single-stranded RNA; helical; enveloped)
Epidemic influenza	Strains: A (2–3-yr cycle) pandemics B (3–6-yr cycle) C (sporadic outbreaks)	Orthomyxoviruses (helical, single-stranded DNA), hemagglutinin spikes; mushroom-shaped neuraminidase projections
Common cold	Rhinoviruses; 55 serotypes	Picornavirus group (little, nonenveloped RNA)
Poliomyelitis (infantile paralysis)	Polio virus, type 1 (epidemic); types 2 and 3	Picornavirus
Psittacosis	Chlamydia (PLT)	Small spheroidal, gram-negative bacteria

PATHOLOGY, SYMPTOMS, TOXINS	TREATMENT (CONTROL)	EPIDEMIOLOGY
Throat (pseudomembrane); exotoxin damages cells, particularly heart, nerves, kidneys	Antitoxin and antibiotics (effective vaccine)	Shick test. About 100 cases/year in U.S., 10% fatal
Sore throat; rash (erythrogenic toxin)	Penicillin G; Erythromycin, rest; Hormones for rheumatic fever	Dick test; low frequency in U.S.
Also allergic reaction involved. Fever, aches; heart valve damage		Occurs most often in children and young adults
Lung lesions; tissue destruction (hypersensitivity reactions)	Rest; chemotherapy: INH, SM, PAS (BCG vaccine)	1,000,000 new cases/year in world; 30,000 new cases in U.S./year (still a very formidable disease)
Acute swift infection of lungs; sometimes bacteremia	Antibiotics	Cause of most bacterial pneumonias
Gradual onset of headache, chills, fever, cough with bloody sputum	Tetracyclines (1% mortality)	25% of pneumonias in young adults
Flulike symptoms, followed by paralysis; if not treated early, is often fatal	Chemotherapy; symptomatic	Infrequent epidemics; endemic—about 1,000 cases/year in U.S.
Paroxysmal cough, vomiting	Tetracyclines (pertussis vaccine)	Low incidence in U.S. due to vaccine
Rash; very high fever	Gamma globulin	Vaccine may eradicate variola
Skin eruptions on back, later spreading to all areas; mild disease except for rare involvement of CNS	None	Worldwide childhood disease
Fever, cough; conjunctivitis, red rash, mucous membrane	Gamma globulin (vaccine)	Fewer cases in U.S. each year
Mild (3-day) measles, but kills or malforms fetuses	(Vaccine)	Was epidemic in U.S. (7–10 yr cycle)
Infection of glands (particularly parotid); sterility in adults; hearing complications	(Imperfect vaccine)	Attacks most children (5–15 age group)
Aches, fever, prostration (incubation period: 1–3 days); acute respiratory symptoms	(Imperfect vaccine)	1918–1919 pandemic killed 20 million (hog flu); 1957–1958, killed 8,000 in U.S. (A2)
Infection of respiratory passages (slight temperature)	Self-limiting (2–7 days)	
Early: flulike and vomiting; infection of the motor function of the spinal cord	(Vaccine)	Also food- and waterborne; many inapparent infections
Pneumonialike; duration of about 3 weeks, followed by death or recovery; frequent relapses	Tetracyclines	Bird contact

Probably no other microorganism rivals the ability of _____ to produce fulminating illness and death in a few hours.	sudden; gradual
Neisserias are gram-_____ cocci.	*Neisseria meningitidis*
Bordetella pertussis is the causative agent of _____.	negative
Are antibiotics very effective against viruses?	whooping cough
Generally chicken pox is a mild disease, although complications sometimes occur, the most serious being the involvement of the _____.	No
Morphologically, the chicken pox virus is identical to the _____ virus.	central nervous system
Rubeola is another term for _____.	herpes simplex
German measles is a relatively mild disease, but it is very virulent in _____.	measles
The rubella virus shares physical and chemical characteristics with the _____ group.	fetuses
The mumps virus is a member of the _____ group, which has genomes of _____.	togavirus
The external surface of influenza virus has spikes that are _____ and mushroom-shaped protrusions composed of _____.	paramyxovirus; single-stranded RNA
Only type _____ influenza viruses cause pandemics.	hemagglutinins; neuraminidase
Influenza viruses, types A, B, and C, have been named _____.	A
It is believed that new subtypes of influenza virus A arise from _____ of preexisting strains.	orthomyxoviruses
The common cold is caused by _____, which belong to the _____ group.	hybridization (recombination)

The poliovirus causes an inflammation of the gray matter of the spinal cord, especially the anterior horn, in which the _____ _____ are located.	rhinoviruses; picornavirus
The polio virion has _____ symmetry, with 32 capsomeres enclosing an _____ core.	motor-cell bodies
Psittacosis predominantly infects _____ but can be transmitted to humans.	icosahedral; RNA
The causative agents of psittacosis are _____.	birds
Oral infections of *Candida albicans* are called _____.	Chlamydias
	thrush

Multiple-Choice Test

Underline the correct answer.

Questions 1 and 2: Usually after recovering from a viral disease, one acquires immunity and cannot catch the same disease again. However, at least one virus evolves during the course of an epidemic, so that the newly produced strain can again cause epidemics, reinfecting the same population years later. Another virus is made up of so many strains that we can be infected with a new strain scores of times during the course of our lives. From this list: (a) smallpox; (b) polio; (c) cold; (d) influenza; (e) mumps, pick out the virus that:

1. frequently forms recombinant strains.

2. has many (scores of) strains and substrains.

3. A disease that is not caused by a virus is: (a) influenza; (b) whooping cough; (c) measles; (d) chicken pox.

4. What do these diseases have in common: strep throat, scarlet fever, rheumatic fever, bacterial arthritis? (a) All are caused by a powerful exotoxin; (b) all are resistant to chemotherapy; (c) all are caused by the same genera of bacteria; (d) all are transmitted primarily by direct contact.

5. Which of these sets of viruses is (most closely) structurally (size, shape, nucleic acid) related? (a) Cold and influenza. (b) shingles and chicken pox; (c) smallpox and chicken pox; (d) polio and measles.

6. The simplest and most expedient means of isolating beta-hemolytic streptococci from a sputum specimen is to: (a) streak a plate of blood agar; (b) inoculate enriched broth; (c) inoculate a guinea pig; (d) prepare a gram stain.

7. Another name for the virus that causes German measles is: (a) rubella; (b) rubeola; (c) vaccinia; (d) variola.

8. The first vaccine ever used is no longer routinely administered in this country. It protects against: (a) polio; (b) smallpox; (c) measles; (d) influenza.

9. Which strain of influenza virus has infected more people than any other (most epidemic)? (a) A; (b) B; (c) C; (d) D.

10. This excerpt has been copied from the Center of Disease Control weekly report (April 2, 1976), *Morbidity & Mortality.*

> Ten cases of active ____?____ have been traced to 1 source, a 30 year-old Montgomery County (Maryland) man. . . . The patient had been ill for about 7 months, with symptoms which included a productive cough, intermittent fever, night sweats, and weight loss of about 60 pounds . . . microscopy positive (numerous acid fast bacilli), and culture positive ($>$50 colonies). He was started on 3 drugs for his illness. A report of the case was submitted by the hospital nurse epidemiologist to the county health department, and an investigation of the patient's contacts was begun.
>
> All 24 persons identified as household or close contacts of the patient were examined. Seven of these individuals were 21 years of age or older. The other 17 ranged in age from 2–13 years. One adult and 9 children had negative initial skin tests and remained negative on retesting.
>
> The remaining 14 contacts (6 adults and 8 children) were found to have the infection as indicated by skin test reactions . . . .Seven of these 8 children, and 1 of the adults, were classified as having primary active ____?____ ; 3 of the children were hospitalized. Thirteen of these contacts were started on daily isoniazid (INH) and one 2 year-old child was started on INH and para-amino-salicylic acid (PAS). One child (the index patient's daughter) with a 0 nm skin test reaction was started on INH preventive therapy.

The disease the article describes is: (a) pneumonia; (b) scarlet fever; (c) diphtheria; (d) tuberculosis.

11. Which one of these diseases is not caused by a virus? (a) Smallpox; (b) Rocky Mountain spotted fever; (c) mumps; (d) polio.

12. A person is admitted to a hospital suffering from a severe sore throat, among other serious symptoms. A swab of the infected area is taken, and a gram stain is made. Under the microscope, irregularly staining gram-positive short rods, in a palisade arrangement, predominate. Chemotherapy is then initiated for: (a) strep throat; (b) botulism; (c) staph throat; (d) diphtheria.

Answers: 1. (d); 2. (c); 3. (b); 4. (c); 5. (b); 6. (a); 7. (a); 8. (b); 9. (a); 10. (d); 11. (b); 12. (d).

Chapter 29

Food- and Waterborne
Human Infections

INTRODUCTION: This chapter discusses microorganisms that enter and exit the host via the oral-intestinal route. You should become familiar with these agents and the diseases that they cause.

Summary and Outline

I.   Types of Diseases Caused by Enteric Organisms.
   A.   Those that cause gastrointestinal upsets (e.g., cramps, nausea, vomiting, diarrhea, etc.).
      1.   Organisms that gain access to the intestine, multiply there, and produce enterotoxins (those that act on the intestine). Some examples:
         a.   Enterotoxin-producing *Escherichia coli.*
         b.   *Vibrio cholerae* and *V. parahaemolyticus.*
         c.   *Shigella* and *Salmonella.*
      2.   Organisms that gain access to the intestine and multiply there, causing damage (little or no toxin production). Some examples:
         a.   Enteropathogenic *E. coli.*
         b.   *Entamoeba histolytica.*
         c.   Adeno-, Coxsackie-, polio- and other viruses.
      3.   Bacteria that produce a powerful exotoxin that causes disease (the organisms themselves are not adapted to the intestine). Example: *Staphylococcus aureus,* coagulase positive.
   B.   Those that cause diseases other than the gastrointestinal syndrome.
      1.   Organisms that gain entrance to other parts of the body from the intestine.
         a.   *Brucella abortus.*
         b.   Hepatitis A virus.
      2.   Bacteria that produce powerful toxins that enter through the oral route. Example: *Clostridium botulinum.*

Food- and Waterborne Human Infections

DISEASE	CAUSATIVE ORGANISM(S)	DESCRIPTION OF CAUSATIVE ORGANISM(S)
Gastroenteritis (*Escherichia coli*)	Opportunistic *E. coli*	Normal gut flora
	Enteropathogenic *E. coli*	Mainly serotypes O_{111} and O_{55}
	Enterotoxin-producing *E. coli*	Plasmid carrier (see cholera)
Gastroenteritis (Salmonellosis)	More than 1,800 *Salmonella* serotypes	Gram-negative, motile rods; typed by Kauffman-White scheme
Typhoid fever	*S. typhi*	As above. Live in water for week or more; multiply in milk
Shigellosis (dysentery)	*S. boydii* (rare); *S. flexneri* (6 subtypes) *S. sonnei* (most common)	Gram-negative; nonmotile rods
Bacillary dysentery	*S. dysenteriae* (10 subtypes)	As above
Cholera	*Vibrio cholerae* El Tor biotype with O_1 antigen	Gram-negative curved rods, motile
Vibrio food poisoning	*V. parahaemolyticus*	As above
Brucellosis (Malta or undulant fever in humans; Bang's disease in cattle)	*Brucella abortus* (bovine); *Br. melitensis* (caprine); *Br. suis* (porcine)	Small, gram-negative, nonmotile coccobacilli, require special media, 5% CO_2
Botulism	*Clostridium botulinum* (6 toxigenic types: A, B, and E, humans: C and D, animals; F, fish)	Gram-positive, anaerobic, sporeforming rod
Food poisoning	*Clostridium perfringens*	As above (normal inhabitant of intestinal tract)
Staphylococcus enterotoxemias	*Staphylococcus aureus,* coagulase positive	Gram-positive cocci
Hepatitis	Type A, infectious hepatitis virus (Type B, serum hepatitis, is transmitted via direct contact; has longer incubation time and gradual onset of symptoms)	20-nm and 40-nm virions; acid-resistant
Acute infectious nonbacterial gastroenteritis	Adenoviruses, Coxsackieviruses, polioviruses, ECHO viruses. (Norwalk agent: small, ether-stable virus)	
Amebiasis	*Entamoeba histolytica*	20–40 μm; motile; cysts 7–15μm; 4 nuclei in mature cysts
Dental caries	*Streptococcus mutans;* also *Actinomyces, Rothia,* and *Nocardia* sp.	*S. mutans* are gram-positive cocci in chains

PATHOLOGY, SYMPTOMS, TOXINS	TREATMENT (CONTROL)	EPIDEMIOLOGY
Pathogenic in other tissues	Antibiotics	In weakened individuals
Penetrate and multiply in mucosa (dysentery syndrome)	Antibiotics	Infant diarrhea
Profuse watery discharge	Antibiotics; replace fluids	
Dysentery syndrome; incubation period 6–48 h		1974—about 2,400 isolations in U.S.
Intestinal ulcers; enlarged spleen; rose-spot eruption on abdomen; toxemia; incubation period 10–14 days	Antibiotics (vaccine)	Widal test. Associated with poor sanitary conditions
Dysentery syndrome; incubation period 7–66 h		On increase in U.S.; about 10,000 isolations per year
Most severe dysentery; potent exotoxin		
Severest vomiting, diarrhea; incubation period, a few hours to a few days; self-limiting; murine toxin	Sulfonamides; replace fluids and salts (poor vaccine)	Endemic in southeast Asia; pandemic in 1971
Diarrhea; vomiting; incubation period 12–24 h		Contaminated shellfish
Incubation period 5–30 or more days; aches, chills, undulating fever; chronic disease	(Animal control; pasteurization)	Animals → humans by contaminated food and dairy products; 1974, 246 cases in U.S.
Extremely potent neuroexotoxin; complete paralysis; with treatment, about 25% fatal; incubation period 2–190 h (average 1–2 days)	Antitoxin; respirators (toxin destroyed by boiling)	About 25 cases/year in U.S. Most from food ingestion; some wound?
Mild illness: diarrhea and abdominal pain without vomiting; incubation period 8–22 h (enterotoxic exotoxin)	Recovery in a few hours without treatment	
Nausea, vomiting, diarrhea from heat-stable toxin produced by staphylococci growing in poorly handled foods; incubation period 1–7 h	Complete recovery in 24–48 h; death only in weak persons; intravenous administration of fluids to weak persons	From food handlers with pyogenic infections or carriers
Abrupt onset of fever over 100.4°F, often jaundice (attacks liver); fatigue, abdominal discomfort; gradual recovery in 2–6 weeks; incubation period 15–60 days	Gamma globulin prophylaxis; rest	Endemic in nursery schools and other institutions or societies where there is risk of fecal contact
Diarrhea, nausea, vomiting, low-grade fever, cramps, headache	Self-limiting (24–48 h)	Second only to common cold in frequency of illness
Diarrhea	Control by recognition of chronic cases and proper sanitation	10 million people in U.S. harbor parasites and 2 million show symptoms
Dental plaques contain bacteria and other material. Acids and other products "punch" holes in teeth	Restrict sugars; oral hygiene; fluoridation	Affects more than 90% of U.S. population

II. The Carrier Problem. Many enteric infections are transmitted by people with inapparent infections (carriers). Transmission may be direct (some eating utensil) or indirect (via public water supplies, flies, etc.).

III. Epidemiology. Even where the standard of living is relatively high, there are still serious outbreaks of water- and foodborne disease (see table pps. 230–231 and text Table 29-1).

Programmed Self-Test

Do not begin this self-test before reading the corresponding chapter in the text.

FOOD- AND WATERBORNE HUMAN INFECTIONS (Text pages 598 to 626)

The K antigen of *E. coli* resides in the _____.	
Clinical isolates of *E. coli* may be conveniently grouped into three categories: _____, _____, and _____.	capsule
Salmonella are seriologically typed and grouped according to the _____ scheme.	opportunistic; enteropathogenic; enterotoxin-producing
The largest number of *Salmonella* isolations (infections) occur _____ *(seasons)* _____.	Kauffmann-White
Typhoid fever is caused by _____.	in the summer and fall
The pathogenicity of *S. typhi* appears to depend primarily on its ability to multiply within _____.	*S. typhi*
Dysenteriae, boydii, sonnei, and *flexneri* are species of the genus _____.	phagocytes
Vibrio are gram-_____ rods.	*Shigella*
The last pandemic of cholera occurred in _____ to _____.	negative
Is the cholera vaccine routinely administered?	1971; 1973
Which one *Brucella* biotype cannot oxidize D-glucose?	No

Brucellosis goes by the names _____ or _____ in humans and _____ _____ (_____) in cattle.	*Br. ovis*
The high fatality rate of botulism has been mitigated somewhat in recent years by prompt treatment with _____ and the use of _____.	Malta fever; undulant fever; contagious abortion; Bang's disease
One gram of type A botulism exotoxin could kill about _____ mice.	antitoxin; respirators
Between 1970 and 1973, _____ percent of the botulism cases were fatal.	33 million
Type F toxigenic *Cl. botulinum* is found in _____ environments.	23
Types A and B botulism toxins appear to interfere with the mechanism of _____ release from the endings of the motor nerves of (predominantly) the parasympathetic system.	aquatic
The enterotoxin of *Staphylococcus aureus* is relatively heat-_____.	acetylcholine
Serum hepatitis is caused by hepatitis virus type _____.	stable
The nucleic acids of the hepatitis viruses are *(DNA or RNA).*	B
The main causative organism of dental caries is believed to be _____.	RNA
	Streptococcus mutans

Multiple-Choice Test

Underline the correct answer.

1. Which of the following diseases is not ordinarily insect-borne? (a) Cholera; (b) bubonic plague; (c) western equine encephalitis; (d) yellow fever.

2. One of the few gram-negative bacteria that produce exotoxin is: (a) pneumococcus; (b) *Proteus mirabilus;* (c) *Treponema pallidum;* (d) *Shigella dysenteriae.*

3. Infectious hepatitis, caused by the hepatitis A virus, is most commonly passed from person to person via: (a) contaminated food and drink; (b) blood transfusions or nonsterile instruments; (c) arthropod bites; (d) airborne droplets.

4. An organism that does *not* cause severe dysentery is: (a) Streptococcus Group A; (b) *Salmonella typhosa;* (c) *Vibrio cholerae;* (d) *Shigella flexneri.*

5. Cholera is treated with: (a) antibiotics; (b) antibiotics and intravenous administration of salt-containing fluids; (c) interferon; (d) antibiotics and intravenous administration of properdin.

6. Circle the letters corresponding to the three organisms that are transmitted primarily by food or drink. (a) *Salmonella typhi;* (b) *Shigella* species; (c) *Neisseria meningitidis;* (d) influenza virus; (e) ECHO virus.

7. Most reported foodborne outbreaks in 1974 were of _____ etiology. (a) Bacterial; (b) parasitic; (c) viral; (d) unknown.

8. Which of these genera is not a member of the Enterobacteriaceae? (a) *Escherichia;* (b) *Proteus;* (c) *Klebsiella;* (d) *Vibrio;* (e) *Shigella.*

9. Which disease is *not* caused by *Clostridium botulinum?* (a) Gas gangrene; (b) botulism; (c) limberneck; (d) forage poisoning.

Answers: 1. (a); 2. (d); 3. (a); 4. (a); 5. (b); 6. (a), (b), (e); 7. (d); 8. (d); 9. (a).

Chapter 30

Human Contact Diseases

INTRODUCTION: This is the third chapter dealing with infectious diseases of humans. There are essentially three types of contact diseases: sexually transmitted (STD), wound infections, and arthropod-borne. The information covered in some 25 pages of your text is summarized here in three tables corresponding to the three categories of contact diseases. Again these tables serve as references, memory aids, and guides.

Some of the diseases mentioned here are of overwhelming importance. Gonorrhea may be more common than the common cold, bubonic plague has caused the only decrease in the population in western history, and malaria is still killing more than 3 million people annually. Thus, this information is more than a compilation of what organism causes what disease; it outlines the unending struggle for survival.

Programmed Self-Test

Do not begin this self-test before reading the corresponding chapter in the text.

SEXUALLY TRANSMITTED DISEASES (STD) (Text pages 628 to 638)

The prevalence of STD is highest in the _____ to _____ age group.	
Syphilis is caused by the spirochete _____?	20; 24
In the tertiary stage, syphilis affects the central nervous system, resulting in progressive paralysis called _____.	*Treponema pallidum*
_____ is the drug of choice for syphilis.	paresis

Sexually Transmitted Diseases (STD)

DISEASE	CAUSATIVE ORGANISM(S)	DESCRIPTION OF CAUSATIVE ORGANISM(S)	PATHOLOGY, SYMPTOMS, TOXINS	TREATMENT (CONTROL)	COMPLICATIONS (COMMON)	EPIDEMIOLOGY
Syphilis	*Treponema pallidum*	Spirochete; tightly coiled, 3 by 10 μm	1. Incubation period 3–6 weeks 2. Primary: chancre; itching; burning 3. Secondary: general infection 4. Latent stage: may last years 5. Tertiary stage: nerves impaired	Penicillin administration for period of weeks	Congenital syphilis death of fetus; senility; heart damage	Over 100,000 cases in U.S. each year and increasing in frequency
Gonorrhea	*Neisseria gonorrhoeae* (gonococcus)	Gram-negative diplococcus; adjacent sides flattened; organisms in neutrophils	70–80% of infected women and 10–20% of infected men are asymptomatic; urogenital inflammation and pus	Penicillin and other antibiotics	Sterility; arthritis; conjunctivitis of newborn	Estimated millions of cases in U.S. each year; may be most common disease
Genital herpes	Herpes simplex type 2 virus	Icosahedral; double-stranded DNA; enveloped	Genital ulcerative lesions; may be fever	No treatment (vaccine in in development)	Cancer of cervix?; serious neonatal disease	Second most common STD after gonorrhea
Chancroid	*Haemophilus ducreyi*	Very small gram-negative, non-motile rod	Pustule surrounded by edema appears 3–10 days after exposure	Sulfonilamides or other broad-spectrum antibiotics	Destruction of tissue; lymph-node infection	Rare in many western countries; common elsewhere
Lymphogranuloma venereum	*Chlamydia trachomatis*	Elementary body: coccus 300 nm in diameter; spherical body: 1000 nm	Incubation period 5–25 days; growths in lymphatic ganglions of groin; may be ulceration; flulike symptoms	Chloramphenicol and sulfonamides and tetracyclines	Long and very disabling disease	Most common in tropical regions; also in Europe
Urethritis	*Trichomonas vaginalis*	Protozoa	Inflammation of vagina and/or urethra			
Urethritis	*Candida albicans*	Yeast	Inflammation of the bladder and/or mucosa of uterus	Antifungal agents		

Diseases Contracted through Wounds or Abrasions

DISEASE	CAUSATIVE ORGANISM(S)	DESCRIPTION OF CAUSATIVE ORGANISM(S)	PATHOLOGY, SYMPTOMS, TOXINS	TREATMENT (CONTROL)	EPIDEMIOLOGY
Erysipelas	Predominantly beta-hemolytic *Streptococcus*, Lancefield serogroup A	Gram-positive cocci in chains. Extracellular products: strepto-lysins, streptokinases, DNAases, hyaluronidase	Initial lesion is small, bright red spot at site of infection. Later, general skin "rash." Acute infection: chills, fever, and prostration	Antibiotics, scarlet fever antitoxin	Open wound exposed to strep patient, carrier, or fomite
Impetigo contagiosum			Dermititis; lesions on face and hands and sometimes cover body; staphylococci also involved	Topical treatment; antibiotic ointment	Children most susceptible; endemic in schools and camps
Pueperal fever			Streptococci in reproductive tract at childbirth	Antibiotics	Aseptic child births
Boils, abscesses, sore throats, pneumonias, fatal septicemias, and other infections	Staphylococcus (mostly coagulase-positive); many resistant to penicillin	Gram-positive cocci. Extracellular products: alpha hemolysin (rabbit, not human, RBC); beta hemolysin (human RBC); leucocidin, coagulase, fibrinolysin, hyaluronidase	The organisms are often part of the normal flora. In great concentrations or in a weakened individual the organism may invade and cause serious disease	Treatment is by antibiotics like semisynthetic penicillins. Control is by proper hygiene	Was endemic in hospitals (e.g., neonatal wards). Today gram-negative opportunists (e.g., *Pseudomonas*) are a greater endemic problem in hospitals
Tetanus	*Clostridium tetani* (normal soil organism and saprophytes in gut of herbivores)	Gram-positive anaerobic rod; swollen terminal spores (drum-stick appearance)	Organisms gain entrance into deep anaerobic wound. Produce tetano-spasmin exotoxin, which gains entrance to CNS. Muscle spasms and thoracic paralysis follow. Untreated cases: mortality 50%	Antitoxins, antibiotics, and life support systems (tetanus toxoid)	Incidence has steeply declined due to toxoid vaccine
Gas gangrene	*Cl. perfringens* (most virulent) *Cl. novyi; Cl. septicum*	Gram-positive, anaerobic, sporeforming rods	Deep wounds. Soil organisms gain access, multiply, and produce exotoxins (e.g., lecithinase) that destroy tissue	Antitoxins; surgical removal of dead tissue	

Diseases Transmitted by Arthropods

DISEASE	CAUSATIVE ORGANISM(S)	DESCRIPTION OF CAUSATIVE ORGANISM(S)	PATHOLOGY, SYMPTOMS, TOXINS	TREATMENT (CONTROL)	VECTORS	EPIDEMIOLOGY
Bubonic plague	*Yersinia pestis*	Small gram-negative (oval) rods; irregular staining; pleomorphic; coccoid forms (0.5 μm × 1.0 μm); rod forms (1.5-5.0 μm long); single or short or long chains	Chills, fever, vomiting, weakness; enlarged lymph glands (bubos) filled with *Y. pestis*	Elimination of reservoirs and vectors; treatment by antibiotics (vaccine provides immunity for 6–12 months). When untreated, the fatality rates are extremely high	Rat fleas	Wild rodents still harbor the infection (sylvan plague in the western U.S.); several cases reported in U.S. each year. Disease of filth and overcrowding (e.g., city slums). Rodent control essential
Primary septicemic plague			Like bubonic plague, but no bubos, and organisms are always present in bloodstream			
Pneumonic plague			Severe pneumonia, infrequent occurrence during epidemics of bubonic plague		None, airborne	Historically important as disease has killed more people (western civilization and Asia) than any other
Tularemia	*Francisella tularensis*	Very small, extremely pleomorphic, gram-negative rod	Incubation period 3–4 days, then abrupt appearance of chills, fever, headache, pains; swollen, tender, infected lymph nodes; 5–8% fatality rate	Antibiotics and immune serum. Controlled by avoiding contact with infected animals	Ticks, the deer fly, and mosquitoes	Also transmitted to humans by handling infected animals, but not transmitted person to person
Pseudo-tuberculosis	*Yersinia pseudotuberculosis*	Pleomorphic; gram-negative, bipolar staining (see plague)	Diarrhea, wasting away, death in a month; white nodules on organs; septicemia causes death in 1-2 days		Inset bite; also through skin breaks and intestinal tract	
Urban yellow fever	Yellow fever virus	Arbovirus (togavirus B_{111}) single-stranded RNA	Some cases are mild, others severely affect organs; 3–6 days after infection, aches and fever, then symptoms subside; 3–5 days later, albuminuria, hemorrhage, and jaundice	Control depends on eradication of vectors (vaccine)	Aedes aegypti mosquito	Fatality rate: 25–30%; "tropical disease"
Jungle yellow fever					Other than above	

Diseases Transmitted by Arthropods: Protozoan Diseases

DISEASE	CAUSATIVE ORGANISM(S)	DESCRIPTION OF CAUSATIVE ORGANISM(S)	PATHOLOGY, SYMPTOMS, TOXINS	TREATMENT (CONTROL)	VECTORS	EPIDEMIOLOGY
Malaria	*Plasmodium vivax* (tertian malaria) *P. malariae* (quartan malaria) *P. falciparum* (malignant tertian and blackwater fever)		Chills, fever, sweating, thirst, exhaustion; swollen, tender spleen; anemia; relapses common	Quinine; quinacrine (atabrine), Chloroquine (Aralen)	Anopheline mosquito	300 million new cases and 3 million deaths/yr (most for any infectious disease). Eliminated from U.S. by control of vector
Kala azar	*Leishmania donovani*	(See Chap. 18)	Incubation period 2–4 months; onset gradual or sudden; disease acute or chronic. Symptoms resemble malaria. Untreated cases complicated by secondary infection → death	Controlled by elimination of insect vector and destruction of parasite-harboring animals; treatment with antimony compounds	Sandflies; protozoa harbored by dogs and/or other animals	Encountered in India, China, Africa, Central and South American countries, and the Mediterranean basin
Oriental sore	*L. tropica*		Crusted ulcers which may lead to mutilation			
Espundia	*L. braziliensis*					
Sleeping Sickness	*Trypanosoma gambiense*		Early stages: fever, headache, rash, anemia; later stages: CNS involvement (tremors, coma). Untreated cases are usually fatal	Prompt use of tryparsamide (arsenical preparation); control of vector	Tsetse fly	Endemic in tropics
Chagas' disease	*T. cruzi*		Fever and enlarged liver and spleen. Fatality due to meningoencephalitis or heart failure	As above	Reduviid bug	Endemic in South America and Mexico. More common in children

Diseases Transmitted by Arthropods: The Viral Encephalitides

GENERAL CHARACTERISTICS APPLICABLE TO ALL VIRAL ENCEPHALITIDES	DISEASE	VIRUS SIZE, nm	PRIMARY HOST	RESERVOIR	VECTOR	HUMAN CASE MORTALITY RATE, %	OCCURRENCE
These are all RNA viruses belonging to togavirus A or B groups, arenaviruses, or ungrouped. They all attack neurons, causing brain inflammation. Symptoms are fever, lethargy, and visual disturbances. Humans are usually secondary hosts, animals being primary hosts. Main, but not sole, route of transmission is by insects (arboviruses or arthropod-borne viruses). There are no effective vaccines for humans, and treatment is only symptomatic. Comas and convulsions typically occur, and recovery may be complete, partial (paralysis), or none	St. Louis encephalitis	20–30	Humans	Chickens and birds	*Culex* mosquitoes	5–30	Central and western United States; summer
	Japanese B. encephalitis	15–20	Humans	Chickens, birds, and mammals	*Culex* mosquitoes	50(?)	Japan and Far East; warm seasons
	Western equine encephalitis	25–40	Horses, mules, and humans	Chickens and fowl	*Culex tarsalis*	3	United States and Canada; July through September
	Eastern equine encephalitis	25–40	Birds and mammals	Birds	*Aedes* mosquitoes	50–70	Mid-Atlantic States and eastern United States; summer and fall
	Venezuelan equine encephalitis	60–75	Horses and mules (equines)	Rodents	Droplet infection or *Culex* or *Aedes* mosquitoes	0.5	Northern South America, Panama, and Southern United States
	Russian Far East encephalitis	15–20	Young adult human males	Wild mammals and birds	Wood tick (*Ixodes persulcatus*)	30	Far East provinces of Soviet Union, spring and summer
	Lymphocytic choriomeningitis	40–60	Mice and humans in the 20–30 age range	Mice (*Mus musculus*)	Infects humans by respiratory route	Fatalities are rare	United States and possibly elsewhere; winter and spring
	Louping ill	15–22	Sheep	Sheep	Tick (*Ixodes ricinus*)	?	Scotland and northern England
	California encephalitis	?	Children		Mosquito	Low	North and South America; Czechoslovakia; Mozambique

Note: Rickettsial diseases are discussed in Chap. 14, and dermatophytic infections are summarized in Table 30–5 of the text (page 654).

The most common STD (by far) is _____,	Penicillin
Neisseria are gram-_____ _(morphology)_ .	gonorrhea
Which STD agent has been linked to incidences of cancer?	negative; cocci
_____ is the causative agent of chancroid (soft cancre).	Herpes virus 2
Chlamydia trachomatis causes _____.	*Haemophilus ducreyi*
The Frei test is used to confirm diagnosis of _____.	lymphogranuloma venerum

DISEASES CONTRACTED THROUGH WOUNDS OR ABRASIONS (Text pages 638 to 644)

Hemolytic streptococci may enter the body through breaks in the skin and mucous membranes and cause such infections as _____, _____, and _____.	lumphogranuloma venereum
The least serious (but possibly disfiguring) of the above diseases is _____.	erysipelas; impetigo contagiosum; puerperal fever
The pathogenic species of *Staphylococcus* is _____.	impetigo contagiosum
Most strains of staphylococci isolated in hospitals are resistant to _____.	*aureus*
Strains of *S. aureus* may be differentiated by testing the susceptibility of strains to specific types of _____.	penicillin
Staphylococcal alpha-hemolysin acts on cell _____.	bacteriophage
Name one species of *Clostridium* that does not ferment glucose, lactose, and sucrose but does reduce nitrate.	membranes
The neurotropic toxin produced by *Cl. tetani* is called _____.	*tetani*
Mortality in untreated cases of tetanus is as high as _____ percent.	tetanospasmin
Cl. perfringens, Cl. novyi, and *Cl. septicum* cause _____.	50

DISEASES TRANSMITTED BY ARTHROPODS (Text pages 644 to 654)

_____ causes plague in humans, while _____ causes tularemia in humans and rabbits.	gas gangrene
Bubonic plague is transmitted to humans by the bite of infected _____.	*Yersina pestis;* *Francisella tularensis*
When wild rodents harbor *Y. pestis,* the "disease" is called _____ plague.	rat fleas
Urban yellow fever is transmitted among people by the _____ mosquito.	sylvan
The "triad of yellow fever intoxication" is albuminuria, hemorrhage, and _____.	*Aedes aegypti*
The most virulent (fatal) viral encephalitis is _____.	jaundice
"Arbo" stands for _____.	eastern equine
A particularly serious manifestation of infection with *Plasmodium falciparum* in which there is rapid destruction of red cells is called _____.	arthropod-borne
Quinacrine (Atabrine) is used to treat _____.	blackwater fever
P. vivax causes _____ malaria.	malaria
Three specific leishmaniases are _____, _____, and _____.	tertian
Symptoms of kala azar often resemble those of _____.	kala azar; oriental sore; espundia
Sleeping sickness is caused by protozoan parasites belonging to the genus _____.	malaria
Do "ringworm fungi" sometimes cause fatal disease?	*Trypanosoma*
Microsporum audouini causes epidemic ringworm of the _____ (usually) in children.	No
	scalp

Multiple-Choice Test

Underline the correct answer.

1. Many bacteria are now known to produce toxin only when carrying a specific prophage. Which one of the following is *not* known to be phage-converted? (a) *Staphylococcus aureus;* (b) *Treponema pallidum;* (c) *Streptococci,* Group A; (c) *Clostridium botulinum.*

2. Which of the following organisms produces a toxin that is protein and, therefore, heat-labile; that is highly specific in its mode of action; and that is released by living cells? (a) *Streptococcus pneumoniae;* (b) *Haemophilus ducreyi;* (c) *Clostridium welchii;* (d) all pathogens produce such a toxin.

3. Which of the following viruses is *not* transmitted by either airborne or waterborne routes? (a) Mumps; (b) polio; (c) yellow fever; (d) influenza.

4. One of these groups of bacteria does not have members that cause venereal disease. Which one? (a) *Yersinia;* (b) *Treponema;* (c) *Chlamydia;* (d) *Neisseria.*

5. Which bacterial disease has caused the most mortality? (a) Rabies; (b) diphtheria; (c) malaria; (d) gonorrhea.

6. Which virus, during an established infection, always kills its human host? (a) Rabies; (b) polio; (c) Venezuelan equine encephalitis; (d) rhino.

7. The DPT vaccine does *not* confer immunity against: (a) diphtheria; (b) tuberculosis; (c) tetanus; (d) whooping cough.

8. This passage, taken from October 4, 1975, CDC *Morbidity and Mortality,* describes the outbreak of a disease in this country that is caused by a gram-negative bacteria:

   "All 7 patients lived in New Mexico when they became ill (3 in Santa Fe County, 3 in Rio Arriba County, and 1 in Lincoln County), all had onset of symptoms in September, and all are females between 3 and 30 years of age. All had fever (temperature range: $102°$ to $104°$F) and tender or enlarged lymph nodes in the groin (5) or neck (1). Other signs and symptoms were malaise (4), chills (3), anorexia (2), vomiting, dizziness, meningism, headache, and inflammation of the pharynx (1 each).

   Histories of possible exposure were also similar. None of the six patients had handled rodents, but all had come in contact with dogs or cats. One patient recalled having been bitten by fleas, and 2 others had skin lesions that resembled insect bites."

   The genus of the causative organism is: (a) *Bubonia;* (b) *Streptococcus;* (c) *Haemophilus;* (d) *Yersinia;* (e) *Trypanosoma.*

9. A patient complains of itching and soreness in the urogenital tract. Pus is taken from the area and gram-stained and examined microscopically. Inside of white blood cells, gram-negative diplococci are seen. This observation is presumptive evidence that the patient has: (a) Herpes-caused venereal disease; (b) syphilis; (c) gonorrhea; (d) lymphogranuloma venereum.

10. Which of the following diseases is generally considered noncommunicable? (a) Syphilis; (b) tetanus; (c) scarlet fever; (d) typhoid fever.

11. Which of the following diseases is usually transmitted by direct contact with another host (or extremely high airborne concentrations of the organism)? (a) Measles; (b) rabies; (c) mumps; (d) cholera.

12. Which of the following viral diseases that affect the nervous system is *least* lethal to humans? (a) Western equine encephalitis (WEE); (b) Venezualian equine encephalitis (VEE); (c) eastern equine encephalitis (EEE); (d) rabies.

13. The causative agent of which of the following diseases is *not* a gram-positive, anaerobic, sporeforming rod? (a) Bubonic plague; (b) botulism; (c) gas gangrene; (d) tetanus.

Answers: 1. (b); 2. (c); 3. (c); 4. (a); 5. (c); 6. (a); 7. (b); 8. (d); 9. (c); 10. (b); 11. (b); 12. (b); 13. (a).

Bacterial Disease Fill-in Chart

Fill in the chart with the appropriate words.

ORGANISM (GENUS AND SPECIES)	MORPHOLOGY (IN STAIN)	MAIN ROUTE OF TRANSMISSION	DISEASE
Streptococcus pneumoniae	Gram-positive; cocci in pairs	Airborne (droplet)	1.
2.	Gram-negative cocci (pairs); some intra-cellular	Direct contact *only*	3.
4.	Gram-negative rod	5.	Bubonic plague
6.	Thin *acid-fast* rods	Airborne (droplet)	7.
8.	Thin *acid-fast* rods	Prolonged contact	9.
Shigella dysenteriae	10.	Food, drink	Dysentery
11.	12.	13.	Typhoid fever
14.	15.	Droplet	Rheumatic fever
Clostridium botulinum	16.	Contaminated food	Botulism

Answers:
1. Pneumonia
2. *Neisseria gonorrhoeae*
3. Gonorrhea
4. *Yersinia pestis*
5. Rat-flea bite
6. *Mycobacterium tuberculosis*
7. Tuberculosis
8. *Mycobacterium leprae*
9. Leprosy
10. Gram-negative rod
11. *Salmonella typhosa*
12. Gram-negative rod
13. Food, drink
14. Streptococcus; serological group A (rarely B or D)
15. Gram-positive cocci, chains
16. Gram-positive, sporeforming rods

Chapter 31

Infectious Diseases
of Animals

INTRODUCTION: Diseases of animals are important because they result in economic loss and because some animal diseases can be transmitted to humans (*zoonoses*). The zoonoses may be caught by those people that have close contact with animals (veterinarians, farmers, etc.), but they are seldom transmitted from one person to another. Usually zoonoses produce a similar disease in both humans and lower animals. Some zoonoses have been discussed in previous chapters. These include equine encephalitis (virus), tularemia (bacteria), and Chagas' disease (protozoa). This fourth chapter on infectious disease, therefore, completes the discussion of human illness and goes on to elaborate on some diseases specific for lower animals. Finally, information is included on avian disease, insect diseases (especially in regard to control of insect populations), and control of animal and fowl diseases.

The animal diseases will be tabulated in this guide. Those that are zoonotic will be so indicated. One table will include bacterial diseases, and another will include both viral and protozoan diseases. The remaining information will be presented in regular outline form.

Expanded Outline and Summary

I. Diseases of Fowl and Birds.
  A. Importance.
    1. Cause loss of domestic fowl and products (e.g., chickens and eggs).
    2. Transmission to humans.
      a. Salmonellosis.
      b. "Hitchhiking" ticks carry infectious viruses and rickettsias.
      c. Pigeons carry, and disseminate in their droppings, *Histoplasma capsulatum* (continued on p. 248).

Bacterial Diseases of Animals

DISEASE	CAUSATIVE ORGANISM(S)	DESCRIPTION OF CAUSATIVE ORGANISM	PATHOLOGY, SYMPTOMS	TREATMENT (CONTROL)	ANIMALS INVOLVED	HUMAN INVOLVEMENT (IF ZOONOTIC)
Anthrax	*Bacillus anthracis*	Gram-positive, aerobic, sporeforming; square ends	Infection of intestinal tract; some septicemia.	Control by sterilization of infected animals and articles; protective clothing; vaccine only for animals	Herbivorous	Farmers and wool/hide workers, boil at site of infection; if untreated with antibiotics, leads to septicemia and death
Blackleg	*Clostridium chauvoei*	Gram-positive, anaerobic, sporeformers	Muscular swelling of legs; affected tissues are moist with black streaks	Sterilize carcasses; antiserums and (vaccine)	Ruminants	
Glanders	*Pseudomonas mallei*	Gram-negative rod	Ulcerations in respiratory tract; death may occur 2–3 weeks after onset of symptoms	Sulfonamides	Equines (horse)	Transmitted to humans.
Leptospirosis	*Leptospira interrogans*	Thin, tightly coiled, flexible spirochetes (6.0 –20 μm long)	Incubation period: 1–2 weeks; chills, high fever, headache, aches; sometimes (10%) complications; kidney damage, jaundice, and anemia	Eradication of rodents (organisms excreted in urine); (vaccine); antibiotics	Serotype *pomona* (swine); serotype *canicola* (dogs); rats and mice (some are carriers)	Serotype *icterohaemorrhagie* (Well's disease); *canicola* causes jaundice in humans; occupational disease for animal handlers; 836 cases in U.S. from 1964–1973
Listeriosis	*Listeria monocytogenes*	Gram-positive, nonsporulating rod; some filament formation	Neurological; acute encephalitis; high fatality rate	Tetracyclines (no vaccine)	26 or more species of mammals and birds	Transmitted to humans
Erysipeloid (humans)	*Erysipelothrix rhusiopathiae*	Small gram-positive straight or curved rods; some filaments		Penicillin	Rodents may act as reservoirs for swine infection	Erysipeloid is a self-limiting migrating dermatosis
Mastistis	*Staphylococcus aureus; Streptococcus; Pseudomonas* sp.	See previous chapters	Inflammation of mammary gland; poor or no milk; may be fatal	Early treatment with antibiotics	Bovine mastitis (cows)	
Rat-bite fever	*Spirillum minus* (Orient); *Streptobacillus moniliformis* (United States)	*S. moniliformis*: long branching rods or coccoid filaments	Swelling of regional lymph nodes; undulant fever; some secondary infections that may be fatal	Penicillin	Rodents	Transmitted by rodent bite or by contaminated food

Viral and Protozoan Diseases of Animals

DISEASE	CAUSATIVE ORGANISM AND DESCRIPTION OF CAUSATIVE ORGANISM	PATHOLOGY; SYMPTOMS	TREATMENT; CONTROL	ANIMALS INVOLVED	HUMAN INVOLVEMENT (IF ZOONOTIC)
Hog cholera	Viscerotropic virus	Septicemia, hemorrhages in kidneys and lymph nodes; mortality rate 100%	Several vaccines	Swine	Not susceptible
Foot-and-mouth disease	Rhinovirus (RNA; diameter 23 ± 2 nm)	Vesicles of mucosa of mouth, on feet, etc.; low mortality rate	Animal vaccine in endemic areas; disease eliminated in United States	Cloven-hoofed	Humans susceptible; fever, salivation; enters through abrasions in skin or airborne
Swine influenza	Influenza group A; *Haemophilis suis*, a bacterium, enhances severity	Acute disease of respiratory tract; fatality due to secondary infection may occur	1976 vaccine for people	Swine	1918 pandemic hit millions of swine and then killed 20 million people. 1976 outbreak at Fort Dix, N.J. (possibly person-to-person transmission)
Rabies	Rhabdovirus	Incubation period 10 days to several months; Negri bodies	Humans: vaccine after suspect bite; pets: routine vaccination in United States	Dogs, bats, cats, and skunks most frequently infect humans. Bats may recover and become carriers	Mammal bite; severe headache and high fever; alternating stages of excitement and depression; difficulty in swallowing; spasms; death follows paralysis or convulsions; only 5–15% of rabid bites cause rabies; fatality 100%
Tick fever	*Prioplasma bigemina*; Protozoa closely related to malarial parasite *P. equi* (horses); *P. ovis* (sheep)	Tick vector	Kill vectors	Cattle	Not susceptible
Anaplasmosis	*Anaplasma marginale*; coccus like protozoan (0.2–0.8 d)	25–50% of RBC of infected animals contain the parasite	Kill vectors (flies, ticks, mosquitoes)	Cattle	Not susceptible
Coccidiosis	*Eimeria* (12 different species) cause disease			Cattle, sheep, chickens, rabbits	Not susceptible

B.   Some infectious diseases of poultry and birds.

DISEASE	CAUSATIVE AGENT	REMARKS
Fowl cholera	*Pasteurella multocida*	Acute or chronic septicemia; highly communicable; acute form highly fatal
Fowl typhoid	*Salmonella gallinarum*	Affects chickens, turkeys, guinea fowl; other domestic fowl quite resistant; transmitted by active cases and carriers
Pullorum disease (bacillary white diarrhea)	*S. pullorum*	Affects chicks and is transmitted from infected hen to egg; great economic importance, detection of infected birds by agglutination test
Paratyphoid (salmonellosis)	*Salmonella* spp.	About 50 species of *Salmonella* may infect fowl; when transmitted in eggs, can cause salmonella food poisoning in humans
Infectious coryza (roup)	*Haemophilus gallinarum*	Principal symptoms are bloody and mucous exudates in nose; inflammation of eyes and sticking together of eyelids; mortality variable, but infected birds should be destroyed
Avian tuberculosis	*Mycobacterium avium*	Chronic in domestic and wild birds; pigs, rats, and mice are susceptible; humans are resistant; control by eradication of infected birds
Limberneck	*Clostridium botulinum*	Botulism in fowl is characterized by paralysis of neck muscles; other poisons may cause similar symptoms; all are called limberneck
Psittacosis	*Chlamydia psittaci*	Affects many cage birds, turkeys, and other fowl; may be transmitted to humans by contact or in air
Newcastle disease (avian pneumoencephalitis)	Virus	Virus attacks chickens of all ages; main symptom is respiratory distress; reduced egg production and causes death in 10 to 50% of flocks
Laryngotracheitis (influenza)	Virus	Birds have respiratory difficulty; trachea becomes clogged with exudate, causing death by suffocation
Aspergillosis	*Aspergillus fumigatus A. niger*	Affects lungs; a cause of brooder pneumonia in young chicks
Favus	*Achorion gallinarum*	Contact disease characterized by white spots on head and comb
Thrush	*Oidium albicans*	Characterized by lesions in mouth, crop, and esophagus

DISEASE	CAUSATIVE AGENT	REMARKS
Coccidiosis	*Elmeria* sp. (Coccidia)	Spread by contaminated feed, water, and soil; recovery confers immunity to the species causing the infection
Trichomoniasis	*Trichomonas* sp.	Pigeons are asymptomatic carriers; flies may spread the parasite
Enterohepatitis	*Histomonas meleagrides*	Liver and cecum are affected and bird's head becomes discolored; hence the popular name blackhead

II.   Control of Animal and Fowl Diseases. The text elaborates on specific methods. Generally, they involve immunization, quarantine, disinfection, and antibiotic treatment.

III.   Diseases of Insects.
   A.   Kinds (bacterial, viral, fungal, and protozoan). Two examples:
      1.   Foulbroods of bees (*Bacillus*).
      2.   Dysentery and septicemia in locusts (*Enterobacter*).
   B.   Biological control (using microorganisms to kill insects).
      1.   Advantages over pesticide use.
         a.   Spores are relatively permanent.
         b.   Usually low cost.
         c.   Safety (specificity)—most organisms that damage insects do not harm plants or animals.
      2.   Use.
         a.   Bacteria.
            i.   Japanese beetle—milky disease (*B. popilliae* and *B. lentimorbus*).
            ii.   Moths, caterpillars, etc.—*B. thuringiensis*.
         b.   Viruses (16 hold imminent promise as insecticides).
         c.   Fungi—50 species cause insect epidemics, but diseases are too self-limiting to hold much promise.

Programmed Self-Test

Do not begin this self-test before reading the corresponding chapter in the text.

THE ZOONOSES; BACTERIAL DISEASES (Text pages 656 to 664)

Zoonoses are diseases that can be transmitted from

_____ .

Anthrax occurs in _____ animals.   animals to people

The causative agent of anthrax is _____.   herbivorous

Clostridium chauvoei is the causative agent of _____.	*Bacillus anthracis*
Are animals immune to glanders after recovering from the infection?	blackleg
Pathogenic and parasitic strains of leptospires belong to the group _____.	No
Listeriosis is a disease of the _____.	interrogans
Erysipelothrix are gram-_____, slender, curved or straight _____.	nervous system
Mastitis is an inflammation of the _____.	positive; rods
Rat-bite fever, in the United States, is caused by _____.	mammary gland

VIRAL AND PROTOZOAN DISEASES (Text pages 664 to 669)

The mortality rate of hog cholera approaches _____ percent.	*Streptobacillus moniliformis*
What kind of virus causes foot and mouth disease?	100
The severity of swine influenza is enhanced by the bacterium _____.	Rhinovirus
It has been estimated that only _____ to _____ percent of all persons bitten by a rabid animal contract rabies.	*Haemophilus suis*
Diagnosis of rabies is confirmed by the demonstration of inclusion bodies called _____.	5; 15
_____ are the only animals known to recover from virulent rabies. They can thus become carriers of the disease.	Negri bodies
Tick fever is caused by a protozoan parasite, *Piroplasma bigemina,* which is closely related to the parasite that causes _____.	Bats
P. bigemina infects cattle, while _____ infects sheep.	malaria
Eimeria sp. are protozoa that cause _____ in cattle.	*P. ovis*

DISEASES OF BIRDS; DISEASES OF INSECTS; CONTROL OF ANIMAL AND FOWL DISEASES
(Text pages 669 to 675)

When botulism occurs in fowl, it is called _____.	coccidiosis
Tetracycline antibiotics have been used in the feed of birds and fowl for the prevention of _____.	limberneck
The Japanese beetle has been successfully controlled by introducing _____ disease, caused by _____ _____, in their grubs.	psittacosis (ornithosis)
	milky; *Bacillus popilliae* or *B. lentimorbus*

Multiple-Choice Test

Underline the correct answer.

1. Which of these diseases is not characterized as zoonotic? (a) Anthrax; (b) rabies; (c) brucellosis; (d) whooping cough.

2. Glanders fever is caused by a: (a) pseudomonad; (b) leptospira; (c) virus; (d) fungus.

3. Which of these diseases is not caused by a leptospira? (a) Weil's disease; (b) listeriosis; (c) swineherd's disease; (d) leptospirosis.

4. Which one of these biological agents has been most effective in controlling insects? (a) Insect viruses; (b) fungi; (c) sporeforming bacteria; (d) protozoa.

5. Mammals are susceptible to rabies, and virulent infections are usually fatal, except that _____ may recover from the disease and become carriers. (a) People; (b) bats; (c) rats; (d) skunks.

6. An animal disease that is transmitted by vector is: (a) foot and mouth; (b) rabies; (c) mastitis; (d) anaplasmosis.

Answers: 1.(d); 2.(a); 3.(b); 4.(c); 5.(b); 6.(d).

Chapter 32

Infectious Diseases
of Plants

INTRODUCTION: Plant diseases have been and are the cause of many disasters and much hardship. This chapter emphasizes bacterial, viral, and fungal diseases of plants. Their development, symptoms, and control are discussed.

Expanded Outline and Summary

I. Causative Agents of Plant Infections.
   A. Agents (these are usually specific pathogens of plants).
      1. Viruses – more than 300 plant viruses have been identified.
      2. Bacteria – cause fewer than 200 known diseases.
      3. Fungi – cause of most plant disease.
      4. Algae – cause relatively few plant diseases.
      5. Nematodes.
      6. Parasitic higher plants.
   B. Factors relating to pathogenicity.
      1. Pathogen dissemination – wind, water, insects, etc.
      2. Environmental factors.
         a. Temperature (e.g., Texas root rot of cotton is limited to the southern United States because fungus cannot withstand cold).
         b. Moisture.
      3. Seasonal survival of pathogen (i.e., winter survival).
         a. Spores in soil.
         b. Tissues of host (e.g., apple scab fungus in leaves; potato blight fungus in tubers; others in seeds; others in another host).
         c. In insect vector.

II. Symptoms of Plant Diseases (almost all show as differences in appearance of the plant; symptoms may be characteristic of a given disease and, thus, may aid in diagnosis). See also text Table 32-2 for complete characterization.
   A. Necrosis – death of all or any plant part.

    B. Wilt — drooping.

    C. Hypertrophy and hyperplasia — overgrowths.

    D. Hypoplasia — stunted growth.

    E. Blight — rapid death of leaves.

    F. Cankers — wounds and lesions.

    G. Galls — overgrowth ("plant tumors").

    H. Chlorosis — loss of chlorophyll (stripping, spotting, curling, and/or crinkling).

III. Bacterial Plant Pathogens. These genera contain some species that are pathogenic for plants. Some examples are presented:

    A. *Pseudomonas.*

        1. Tobacco wilt — *P. solanacearum.*

        2. Stone fruit canker — *P. syringae.*

    B. *Xanthomonas.*

        1. Bacterial spot of peaches — *X. pruni.*

    C. *Agrobacterium.*

        1. Crown gall of broad-leafed plants — *A. tumefaciens.*

    D. *Corynebacterium.*

        1. Alfalfa wilt — *C. insidiosum.*

        2. Tomato canker — *C. michiganense.*

    E. *Erwinia.*

        1. Apple and pear cankers — *E. amylovora.*

    F. *Streptomyces* spp. — potato scab.

IV. Virus Diseases of Plants.

    A. Diseases (high losses in sugar cane, beets, fruits, tomatoes, etc.).

        1. Mosaic diseases (mottling or spotting of leaves).

            a. Cucumber and tobacco mosaic diseases.

            b. Tomato spotted wilt.

            c. Breaking in tulips (ornamental horticulture).

        2. Leaf curls and yellows (also dwarfing and excessive branching).

            a. Sugar beet curly top.

            b. Peach yellows.

            c. Strawberry stunt.

    B. Transmission.

        1. Insects — aphids, leafhoppers, whiteflies, and mealybugs.

        2. Propagation of infected plants.

        3. Infected seed — 10 percent of plant viruses (e.g., bean mosaic) are transmitted this way.

    C. The nature of plant viruses.

        1. Nucleic acid (usually single-stranded RNA).

        2. Shape.

            a. Anisometric (usually rods like TMV).

            b. Isometric (usually small icosahedrons with 20 sides like alfalfa mosaic virus).

V. Fungus Diseases of Plants (numerous epidemics resulting in complete crop failure leading to disaster, e.g., 1845–1846 potato blight of Ireland).

    A. Plant susceptibility — all plants are susceptible to at least one fungal infection.

Table 32-1. Characteristic Diseases Caused by Some Fungi (Read once and use as reference)

Phycomycetes:

Plasmodiophora	Clubroot of crucifers
Spongospora	Powdery scab of potato tubers
Aphanomyces	Root rot of vegetables
Olpidium	Diseases of cabbage
Pythium	Damping-off of seedlings
Phytophthora	Late blight of potato
Albugo	White rust of crucifers
Plasmopara	Downy mildew of grapes
Rhizopus	Soft rots of fruits and vegetables

Class Ascomyceteae:

Erysiphe (and four other genera)	Powdery mildews
Ceratocystis	Dutch elm disease
Endothia	Chestnut blight
Roselinia	Root diseases of fruit trees
Claviceps	Ergot of rye
Nectria	Twig and stem cankers of trees
Mycosphaerella	Leaf spots on many plants
Venturia	Apple scab
Sclerotinia	Brown rot of stone fruits

Form-class Deuteromyceteae:

Phomopsis	Blights and stem cankers of trees
Colletotrichum	Anthracnose of field crops
Alternaria	Leaf spots and blights
Aspergillus	Rots of stored feeds
Botrytis	Grey mold and blights
Cladosporium	Leaf mold of tomato
Fusarium	Wilt diseases
Penicillium	Rot of fleshy organs

Class Basidiomyceteae:

Sphacelotheca	Loose smut of sorghum
Tilletia	Bunt, or stinking smut, of wheat
Urocystis	Smut of onion
Ustilago	Smut of corn
Cronartium	White pine blister rust
Puccinia	Rust of cereals
Uromyces	Rust of beans

SOURCE: Adapted from George N. Agrios, *Plant Pathology,* Academic, New York, 1969. By permission.

VI. Pathogenesis in Plants (general development of plant disease).
    A. Inoculation — pathogen contacts plant.
        1. Directly through soil.
        2. Airborne or insect-borne (fungal spores).
        3. Waterborne.
    B. Penetration.
        1. Wounds or bites.
        2. Leaf stomata.
        3. Root system.
    C. Incubation (time required for pathogen to cause characteristic symptoms after penetra-

tion) — organisms travel to selected tissues and begin to multiply (bacteria, intercellularly; viruses, intracellularly; fungal mycelia, inter- or intracellularly). Incubation period may be days or months. Host resistance factors brought into play.
- D. Infection — pathogen established in host and causes abnormal physiology. Multiplication of pathogen.
- E. Spread — now-numerous pathogens infect new plant tissues.

VII. Control of Plant Diseases.
- A. Chemical control — work to prevent invasion of the plant, not afterward.
  - 1. Fungicides — harmful to plant as well as to fungi. Sprayed on leaves, stems, and fruits. Contain heavy metals, detergents, phenols, etc.
  - 2. Bacteria and especially viruses more difficult to control by chemical means.
- B. Disease resistance in plants (antibiotics ineffective).
  - 1. Outer defenses (mainly structural).
    - a. Stomata structure.
    - b. Thick coverings.
    - c. Structures that promote rapid drying.
  - 2. Inner defenses (mainly physiological and biochemical).
    - a. Antimicrobial chemicals.
      - i. Enzymes.
      - ii. Phytoalexins (chlorogenic and caffeic acids).
      - iii. Toxin neutralizers.
    - b. Molecular adaptation — e.g., *Helminthosporium sacchari* toxin, helminthosporoside, binds to specific protein in sugar cane cell membranes to kill cells via ion balance upsets. Resistant cane does not have this binding protein.
  - 3. Climatic factors. Examples:
    - a. Ohio potatoes escape blight if they mature early.
    - b. Similarly, cowpeas maturing very early may escape wilt and root knot.
- C. Plant breeding for resistance (hybridization) — 75 percent of field crops and over 50 percent of vegetable crops of the United States are disease resistant. Examples: cereals, potatoes, and sugar beets.
- D. Disease control by crop rotation. Principle: remove host for a period of time and dependent pathogens will die.
- E. Effects of soil fertility on plant diseases — thousands of factors are involved. Generally, as with people, optimum nutrition and climate produce optimum resistance.
- F. Inspection and quarantine — laws prohibit the shipping of uninspected (and potentially new-disease-carrying) plants across national and even state lines.

Programmed Self-Test

Do not begin this self-test before reading the corresponding chapter in the text.

CAUSATIVE AGENTS AND SYMPTOMS OF PLANT DISEASES (Text pages 677 to 681)

Some plant pathogens cause food intoxications when eaten by humans or animals. An example is ergotism, caused by a _____, *Claviceps purpurea,* which grows on cereal grains and some grasses.

CAUSATIVE AGENTS AND SYMPTOMS OF PLANT DISEASES (Text pages 677 to 681)

The causative agent of _____ is *Phymatotrichum amnivorum*.	fungus
The apple scab fungus winters in _____ ; potato blight fungus winters in _____ .	Texan root rot of cotton
Cancerlike growths in plants are called _____.	leaves; tubers
A virus that reduces potato yields is the _____ .	galls

BACTERIAL, VIRAL, AND FUNGAL DISEASES OF PLANTS (Text pages 681 to 689)

Bacterial wilts are caused by _____-producing bacteria that plug the passages in the plant through which water passes.	potato X virus
Bacterial canker of tomatoes is caused by _____ _____ .	slime
Streptomyces spp. cause the disease _____ .	*Corynebacterium michiganense*
Most viruses cause _____-type plant diseases.	potato scab
Is alfalfa mosaic virus structurally related to tobacco mosaic virus?	mosaic
Smuts and rusts are generally caused by _____ .	No
Dutch elm disease is caused by a fungus belonging to the class _____ .	fungi

PATHOGENESIS AND CONTROL OF PLANT DISEASES (Text pages 689 to 697)

"Many small lesions on leaves or stems" refers to plant _(type of disease)_ .	Ascomycetes
Nearly all fungicides are injurious to _____ as well as to fungi.	rusts
The fungicide Bordeaux mixture causes increased _____ in tomatoes.	plants

Helminthosporium sacchari must produce helminthosporoside in order to cause _____ disease of _____ .	transpiration
Unfortunately, several plant pathogens were introduced into the United States before inspection and quarantine were required, resulting in epidemics of chestnut blight, _____ , and bacterial canker of citrus crops.	eyespot; sugar cane
	Dutch elm disease

Multiple-Choice Test

Underline the correct answer.

1. Which agent causes more plant diseases, more frequently, than the others? (a) Bacteria; (b) viruses; (c) fungi; (d) algae.

2. *Puccinia graminis* has two hosts. One is wheat, the other is: (a) rye; (b) barberry; (c) potatoes; (d) ginger.

3. A plant with hypoplasia is: (a) droopy; (b) mottled; (c) stunted; (d) overgrown.

4. Bacterial corn wilt is caused by: (a) *Erwinia stewartii;* (b) *Pseudomonas syringae;* (c) *Agrobacterium tumefaciens;* (d) *Xanthomonas pruni.*

5. Chemical control of plant diseases is most widely used for, and most effective on: (a) bacteria; (b) viruses; (c) fungi; (d) protozoa.

6. Phytoalexins are produced by _____ to inhibit _____ . (a) Bacteria – seed germination; (b) fungi – photosynthesis; (c) plants – plant growth; (d) plants – plant pathogens.

7. Plant viruses generally contain: (a) single-stranded DNA; (b) double-stranded DNA; (c) single-stranded RNA; (d) double-stranded RNA.

Answers: 1. (c); 2. (b); 3. (c); 4. (a); 5. (c); 6. (d); 7. (c).

Chapter 33

Fundamentals of
Microbial Ecology

INTRODUCTION: Chapters 25–32 of the text stressed some harmful activities of microorganisms; chapters 33–40 will cover beneficial activities of organisms, including the indispensable contributions of the protista in maintaining soil fertility and aquatic stability and in recycling waste products. The final three chapters will show how microorganisms are manipulated to serve humanity on an immense scale.

Chapter 33 provides the introductory information necessary to understand and study many of these life-sustaining activities. Your "microscope" should be switched from the high-power study of one organism (in some detail) to a panoramic view of communities of organisms, products, and econiches.

Expanded Outline and Summary

I. Microbial Ecology and the Ecosystem.
   A. Microbial ecology — relation of groups of microorganisms to one another, to higher organisms, and to the environment.
   B. The ecosystem (the largest such system is earth — the biosphere).
      1. Biotic inhabitants.
      2. Abiotic components.

II. The Genome as a Component of the Ecosystem (genome-controlled phenotypes in relation to their ecosystems).
   A. Evolutionary adaptation — change of genotype (mutation or recombination) and selection of a particular genotype (e.g., drug-resistant mutants survive chemotherapy).
   B. Physiological or phenotypic adaptation — response of all individuals of a species (with limits of genotype) to temporary environmental changes (e.g., loss of flagella at higher temperatures).
   C. Genome-environment interactions.
      1. Fixed genome in a variable environment — adaptation in this case is physiological or phenotypic (e.g., *Neurospora crassa* grows above 26°C only when adenine is an available nutrient).

2. Variable genome in a fixed environment — organism mutates or genetically recombines, but external conditions do not change.
3. Variable genome in a variable environment — altered genotype may better cope with the new environment, leading to selection and evolution.

III. Microorganisms and Their Ability to Cause Changes. Microorganisms have great potential to alter their environment (use substrate and produce end products) because:
  A. High surface area/volume ratio (more contact with outside components).
  B. Rapid growth rate and immense populations.
  C. Diverse enzyme capabilities (microorganisms may degrade compounds that other organisms cannot degrade).

IV. Some Characteristics of Microbial Ecosystems. Microorganisms are ubiquitous, and their ecosystems are numerous.
  A. Habitat size — macroscopic (visible).
  B. Nutrient supply.
    1. Quantity: usually less than in laboratory media, resulting in slower growth.
    2. Fluctuates, resulting in population shifts.

V. Microbial Associations (Symbiosis). Symbiosis used here to describe (a general) close association between individuals of different species.
  A. Neutral associations (neutralism) — two species do not compete for nutrients (or anything) and, therefore, *may occupy the same environment and not affect one another* (neither organism gains or loses).
  B. Positive associations.
    1. Mutualism — each organism benefits.
      a. Syntrophism (exchange of nutrients between two species), e.g., *Lactobacillus arabinosus* produces folic acid, which is required by *Streptococcus faecalis,* and *S. faecalis* produces phenylalanine, which is required by *L. arabinosus.*
      b. Two organisms producing a product(s) that neither can produce alone, e.g., *Thiobacillus ferrooxidans* (fixes CO_2) and *Beijerinckia lacticogenes* (fixes N_2) together leach metals from ores.
      c. Mutualistic disease phenomena, e.g., swine influenza is due to the action of a virus and *Haemophilus suis.*
      d. Associations of two organisms to function (essentially) as one organism, e.g., lichens.
    2. Commensalism — one organism benefits while the other remains unaffected. These examples are cited in the text.
      a. Yeast reducing sugar concentrations so that other organisms may grow.
      b. Facultatives creating anaerobic conditions for anaerobes.
      c. *Staphylococcus* supplying *Haemophilus* with NAD.
      d. Organisms in biogeochemical cycles (Chap. 34).
  B. Negative associations.
    1. Antagonism — one organism adversely affecting the environment of another organism. Antagonisms are quite common in nature (e.g., antibiotics), enabling one organism to predominate in an econiche. Examples offered in the text are:
      a. *Staphylococcus aureus* and *Pseudomonas aeruginosa* each produce substances that inhibit *Aspergillus terreus.*

   b. Soil organisms (myxobacteria and streptomycetes) produce lytic enzymes.
  2. Competition — organisms competing for the same nutrient or other ecocondition, e.g., many bacteria are found in the early stages of sauerkraut fermentation, but *Lactobacillus plantarum* alone survives at the end.
  3. Parasitism — one organism (parasite) living in (or on) another organism and at the expense of the other organism (host). Numerous examples were presented in the previous section of the text. Bacteria also have parasites:
   a. Bdellovibrio — bacteria that lyse other bacteria.
   b. Phage.
  4. Predation — killing and eating of one species by another. Unlike parasite, predator actually ingests another living organism (rather than just stealing its food and/or contents).

VI. Techniques for the Study of Microbial Ecosystems. (These methods allow one to monitor heterogeneous populations. Pure-culture techniques, yielding homogeneous populations, are not, alone, suitable for studying dynamic, diverse ecosystems.)
 A. Submerged-slide technique — useful for studying niches containing *periphytes* (organisms that attach to solid surfaces, multiply, and form microcolonies). Other organisms also attach to "periphytic films." The slides may be observed microscopically and the films cultured to grow representative organisms.
 B. Scanning electron microscopy (SEM) — materials (in "natural state") placed under the three-dimensional scope and observed. This micrograph, for example, shows fungi on plant leaves.

 C. Measurement total of microbial substance (biomass) or microbial activity. (It is not yet possible to routinely count the number of *each* individual type of organism in the ecosystem.)
  1. Measurement of ATP (gaining wide usage for monitoring the environment).
   a. All *living* cells contain ATP.
   b. About 1 μg ATP = about 250 μg carbon.
   c. Using the firefly luciferase system, one can measure as little as 10^5 μg ATP/ liter of sample.
  2. Determination of $^{14}CO_2$ — the relationship between CO_2 utilization and cell biosynthesis makes it possible to quantitate cell mass by monitoring radioactive carbon.

VII. The Rumen — A Specialized Animal Ecosystem. (Ruminants are herbivorous mammals — cattle, sheep, goats, and camels — with a compartmentalized stomach. The first compartment is the rumen.)

A. The rumen as a continuous culture system.
   1. Nutrient largely cellulose (grass and hay).
   2. Billions of bacteria and protozoa digest cellulose.
B. Rumen microbiota (anaerobic).
   1. Cellulose decomposers — bacteria, e.g., *Bacteroides succinogenes.*
   2. Starch decomposers — bacteria, e.g., *Bacteroides amylophilus.*
   3. Fatty acid producers — bacteria, e.g., *Selenomonas ruminantium.*
   4. Methane producer — bacterium, *Methanobacterium ruminantium.*
   5. Protozoa — e.g., ciliates like *Entodinium* feed upon the bacteria.
C. The rumen environment (relatively constant).
   1. Temperature — $39°C$
   2. pH — 5.8-6.8 (acid end products, but saliva is buffered)
   3. Gas — CO_2 and CH_4.
D. The mutualistic relationship.
   1. Ruminant provides environment and nutrients that enable the microbes to survive.
   2. Microbes provide nutrients — fatty acids, carbohydrates, amino acids, proteins, and vitamins — that sustain the ruminant.

VIII. Germfree and Gnotobiotic Life. Animals are born sterile, and normal microflora does not develop if the environment and food are sterilely maintained. Gnotobiotic animals are those living in association with one or more known organisms. Research applications are:
A. The effect of normal flora on the growth and development of animals.
B. The contribution of intestinal flora to proper nutrition.
C. The role of bacteria in causing dental caries.
D. The mechanism of animal growth stimulation by antibiotics.
E. Synergism of protozoa and bacteria in amebic dysentery.

IX. Microbial Interactions as Natural Phenomena in Ecosystems. Pure cultures are artificially created laboratory situations, for in nature loose and specialized microbial associations exist. Microorganisms in mixed culture probably behave differently from those in pure culture. Little research has been done on mixed associations of microorganisms.

Programmed Self-Test

Do not begin this self-test before reading the corresponding chapter in the text.

FUNDAMENTALS OF MICROBIAL ECOLOGY (Text pages 701 to 721)

_____

The biosphere is _____ .
_____

Ecology comprises two major components, namely _____   earth
and _____ .
_____

Physiological or _____ adaptation represents the response of the organism to temporary changes in the environment.	the biotic inhabitants; the abiotic components
Neurospora crassa grows without an external supply of _____ at temperatures up to 26°C, but at 33°C it will grow only if the nutrient is supplied in the medium.	phenotypic
The text defines _____ as a condition in which the individuals of a species live in close association with individuals of another species.	adenine
Lactobacillus arabinosus cannot synthesize the amino acid _____ .	symbiosis
Beijerinckia lacticogenes is able to fix _____ , while *Thiobacillus ferrooxidans* is able to fix _____ .	phenylalaline
Will *Entamoeba histolytica* cause disease in an animal that is otherwise germ-free?	N_2 ; CO_2
The V factor, required by *Haemophilus influenzae,* is _____ .	No
Certain *Pseudomonas* pigments affect *Aspergillus* by inhibiting _____ .	nicotinamide adenine dinucleotide (NAD)
_____ is defined as one organism adversely affecting the environment of another organism.	spore germination
Myxobacter is antagonistic to other organisms because it often _____ them.	Antagonism
A genus of bacteria whose members parasitize other bacteria is _____ .	lyses
Organisms that attach to solid surfaces, grow, and form microcolonies are referred to as _____ .	*Bdellovibrio*
Are significant quantities of ATP found in dead organisms?	periphytes
In viable organisms, 1 μg ATP is equivalent to about _____ μg carbon.	No
The temperature of the rumen is slightly higher than that of other parts of the animal and is about _____ °C.	250

The gas on top of the rumen is composed mainly of _____ and _____ .	39
Germ-free animals living in association with one or more known organisms are termed _____ .	carbon dioxide; methane
Do germ-free animals develop dental caries?	gnotobiotic
	No

Multiple-Choice Test

Underline the correct answer.

1. An exchange of nutrients between two species is defined as: (a) syntrophism; (b) parasitism; (c) commensalism; (d) antagonism.

2. Rumen contain: (a) no microorganisms (sterile); (b) thousands of microorganisms per milliliter; (c) billions of microbes per milliliter; (d) bacteria but no protozoa.

3. Rumen are: (a) aerobic; (b) anaerobic; (c) microaerophilic; (d) alkaline.

4. Which of the following is *not* a negative association between organisms? (a) Antagonism; (b) parasitism; (c) competition; (d) commensalism.

5. The relationship between organisms in which one organism lives in or on another species and at the expense of the other species is defined as: (a) commensalism; (b) antagonism; (c) parasitism; (d) competition.

6. *Streptococcus lactis, Leuconostic dextranium,* and *L. citrovorum* are often associated in: (a) rumen; (b) the soil; (c) aquatic econiches; (d) industrial starter cultures.

7. Myxobacteria and streptomycetes have this in common – both groups are: (a) fungi, (b) filamentous; (c) mutualistic with algae; (d) secretors of lytic enzymes.

Answers: 1. (a); 2. (c); 3. (b); 4. (d); 5. (c); 6. (d); 7. (d).

Chapter 34

Soil Microbiology

INTRODUCTION: Fertile soil teems with microbes that produce, prey upon, digest, degrade, and transform substances that sustain life. In this chapter you will "meet" prominent soil microorganisms, learn how some organic matter is recycled, and be introduced to the bacteria that make soil fertile as they cooperate to mediate the carbon, sulfur, and nitrogen cycles.

As you read this section of the Study Guide, you will find that the nitrogen cycle is discussed in atypically great detail. This is to provide a concrete example to enhance general comprehension. It is also emphasized because humanity's struggle to provide sufficient food is intimately intertwined with the cycle and our knowledge of it.

Expanded Outline and Summary

I. History
   A. Beijerinck (1851–1931) — enrichment-culture technique; isolated *Rhizobium* and *Azotobacter;* sulfur cycle.
   B. Winogradsky (1856–1953) — enrichment-culture technique; autotrophic bacteria; nitrogen and sulfur cycles.

II. The Soil Environment (region of earth's crust where geology and biology meet).
   A. Mineral particles.
      1. Composition — compounds of silicon, aluminum, and iron; lesser amounts of the other minerals.
      2. Size — small clay particles (0.002 mm or less) to large pebbles.
      3. Types.
         a. Mineral soils — largely inorganic solid matter (most of the foregoing information relates to this type).
         b. Organic soils — very little inorganic matter (bogs and marshes).
   B. Organic residue — plant, animal, and much microbial mass. *Humus* — material in the last stages of decomposition not readily decomposed by microorganisms — improves the buffering and water-holding capacities of soils.
   C. Water — also contains dissolved nutrients.

D. Gases — exist in spaces between soil particles, and CO_2 is dissolved in water in relatively large amounts.

E. Biological systems — plant roots, animals, and tremendous numbers of microorganisms.

III. The Microbiota of the Soil.

A. Diversity — billions of organisms per gram of soil. Wide diversity of types.

Table 34-1. Soil Population in a Fertile Agricultural Soil

TYPE	NUMBER PER GRAM
Bacteria:	
Direct count	2,500,000,000
Dilution plate	15,000,000
Actinomycetes	7,000,000
Fungi	400,000
Algae	50,000
Protozoa	30,000

SOURCE: A. Burges, *Microorganisms in the Soil,* Hutchinson, London, 1958.

B. Variability — different soils and soil conditions have a bearing on the kinds and numbers of microorganisms present.

C. Microbiota.

1. Bacteria — greater numbers and more species than other microorganisms; thousands of species representing numerous physiological types are found. A prominent group, Actinomycetes (Genera: *Nocardia, Streptomyces,* and *Micromonospora*), responsible for "earth odor," degrade complex chemicals and thus play an important role in soil fertility.

2. Fungi — hundreds of species. Abundant near surface (aerobic). Active decomposers of plant tissues; add *"crumb structure"* to the soil.

3. Algae — smaller populations than bacteria or fungi (greens and diatoms). Help reestablish fertility of "dead" soils.

4. Protozoa (flagellates and amoebas) — primary predators (on bacteria).

5. Viruses — plant viruses and phages.

D. The rhizosphere — region where soil and roots make contact. Microflora, especially bacteria, most abundant here because plants supply some nutrients.

IV. Biogeochemical Activity of Microorganisms in Soil. Bacteria play an indispensable role in recycling, and making available to other forms of life, compounds containing nitrogen, carbon, sulfur, and phosphorus. The following sections relate to each of these cycles in turn.

V. Transformation of Nitrogen Compounds: The Nitrogen Cycle.

A. Importance — all animals are dependent on plants for survival. Plant growth (abundance), in turn, is limited by many factors, but perhaps the most limiting nutrient is usable nitrogen. This is because:

1. Plants cannot use atmospheric nitrogen (N_2).

2. Nitrogen compounds are not naturally abundant in rocks and soils.

3. "Usable" nitrogen compounds (NH_3, NO_2, NO_3) are soluble and therefore leached (washed away by water).

4. "Usable" nitrogen compounds are volatile and escape into the atmosphere.
5. "Usable" nitrogen compounds are decomposable. Therefore, the nitrogen-compound content of soils must be continuously replenished (especially soils used for the new high-yield crops). While fertilizer is becoming more expensive, bacteria have naturally replenished the soil for millions of years.

B. The nitrogen cycle (the major processes are listed below and then discussed in turn).

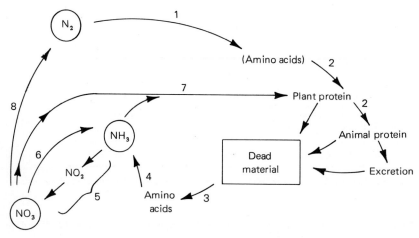

PROCESS	REACTIONS	ORGANISMS	CONDITIONS
1. Nitrogen fixation	N_2 gas $\longrightarrow$ combined N	Few; heterotrophic	Aerobic; anaerobic more in tropics
2. Protein synthesis	AA $\longrightarrow$ protein	All	—
3. Proteolysis	protein $\longrightarrow$ AA	Many	Exoenzymes
4. Ammonification	AA $\xrightarrow{\text{deaminase}}$ ammonia	Many	Excess N to C ratio
5. Nitrification	$NH_3 \longrightarrow NO_2$ (nitrite)	*Nitrosomonas*	Autotrophic; aerobic
	$NO_2 \longrightarrow NO_3$ (nitrate)	*Nitrobacter*	Autotrophic; aerobic
6. Nitrate reduction	$NO_3 \longrightarrow NO_2 \longrightarrow NH_3$	Many	Variety; low O_2
7. Nitrogen assimilation	inorganic N $\longrightarrow$ AA $\longrightarrow$ protein	Many	Variety
8. Denitrification	$NO_3 \longrightarrow N_2 \uparrow$	Certain heterotrophs	Anaerobic (wet) soil

1. Nitrogen fixation – The conversion of molecular nitrogen into nitrogenous compounds.

$$(N = N \xrightarrow[\text{nitrogenase}]{3H_2} 2NH_3)$$
or
high temperature (pressure)

If there is one limiting reaction that regulates the ultimate abundance of life, it is this one. Many organisms carry out other necessary reactions (e.g., combining ammonia into carbon compounds to make amino acids), but relatively few species convert nitrogen into "usable" ammonia.

   a. Methods of detecting nitrogen fixation.
      i. Using labeled nitrogen ($^{15}N_2$).
     ii. Detecting nitrogenase by monitoring the conversion of acetylene to ethylene.
   b. Types of nitrogen fixation.
      i. Physical
        A. Lightening or other severe environmental phenomena.
        B. Industrially, using the Haber-Bosch process (requires very high temperatures and pressures, both of which demand use of costly fuels).
     ii. Nonsymbiotic — carried out by several dozen species of bacteria (see text Table 34-3). *Azotobacter* sp. and *Clostridium pasteurianum* were the first studied, and *Klebsiella pneumoniae* is also being intensively studied.
    iii. Symbiotic — rhizobium in association with legumes (soybeans, clover, peas, alfalfa, etc.). Bacteria "infect" root system through *infection thread*. Bacteria and plant cells divide, forming nodule (soybean nodules shown). Together the bacteria and the plants fix nitrogen, though neither can do so alone. Specific *Rhizobia* interact with specific legumes.

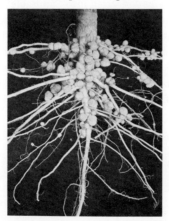

   c. Increasing food production (investigations underway).
      i. Using nitrogenase in lieu of extreme physical conditions in the Haber-Bosch process.
     ii. Establishing symbiotic nitrogen-fixing relationships in crops other than legumes (e.g., corn and *Spirillum lipoferum*).

2. Protein synthesis — carried out by all life (see Chapter 11).

3. Protoeolysis — proteins (most complex nitrogen-containing compounds) cannot be utilized by plants and must be recycled. These degradative steps, proteins $\xrightarrow{\text{proteinases}}$ peptides $\xrightarrow{\text{peptidases}}$ amino acids, are mediated by exoenzymes, produced by many species of bacteria and fungi. The clostridia are among the most active proteolytic enzyme producers.

4. Amino acid degradation — ammonification. The amino acids, released from proteolysis, may be deaminated (removal of the amino group) by many organisms. There are

several ways this can occur. One way, oxidative deamination, is used as an example. The ammonia may escape into the atmosphere or be solubilized (NH_4) and used by plants or oxidized to nitrates.

$$CH_3CHNH_2COOH + \tfrac{1}{2}O_2 \xrightarrow{\underset{\text{deaminase}}{\text{alanine}}} CH_3COCOOH + NH_3$$
$$\text{Alanine} \qquad\qquad\qquad \text{Pyruvic acid} \quad \text{Ammonia}$$

5. Nitrification — oxidation of ammonia to nitrate.
   a. Oxidation of ammonia to nitrite by *Nitrosomonas*:
   $$2NH_3 + 3O_2 \rightarrow 2HNO_2 + 2H_2O$$
   b. Oxidation of nitrite to nitrate by *Nitrobacter:*
   $$HNO_2 + \tfrac{1}{2}O_2 \rightarrow HNO_3$$
   Selected heterotrophic fungi may also mediate these reactions. The end product, nitrate, is a choice "plant food" because it is soluble and easily assimilated, and because it is not volatile, so that it remains in the soil. Nitrification occurs in aerobic (well tilled and drained) soil at pH 7.0.
6. Reduction of nitrate to ammonia — occurs in anaerobic conditions (e.g., waterlogged soil). The process involves several reactions (reaction: $HNO_3 + 4H_2 \rightarrow NH_3 + 3H_2O$).
7. Nitrogen assimilation — inorganic nitrogen (e.g., NH_3, NO_2, and NO_3) may be incorporated into organic carbon to make amino acids, which are used in plant and microbial protein. Animals depend on this protein to supply essential amino acids.
8. Denitrification — nitrates converted into "unusable" nitrogen gas or nitrous oxide. This process is not prominent in well-aerated soils that are not overloaded with organic matter and nitrates. In this overall reaction, $NO_3 \rightarrow NO_2 \rightarrow N_2O \rightarrow N_2$, nitrate (not O_2) is used as a final electron acceptor. Some organisms carrying out these reactions are:
   a. *Thiobacillus denitrificans* — autotroph.
   b. *Micrococcus denitrificans, Serratia* sp, *Pseudomonas* sp, and *Achromobacter* sp. — heterotrophs.

VI. Transformation of Carbon Compounds: The Carbon Cycle.
   A. Schematic of the carbon cycle showing the role of microorganisms.

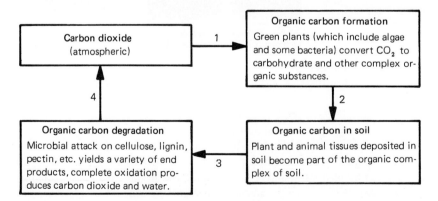

   B. The processes.
   1. Carbon dioxide fixation — CO_2 fixed (or incorporated) into organic matter. Process is carried out, most abundantly, by green plants and algae via photosynthesis (see Chap. 11). Bacteria also fix CO_2.

    a. Phototrophs, etc. (see Chap. 11).

    b. Chemosynthetic types. Reaction example:

$$CO_2 + 2H_2 \rightarrow (CH_2O)_x + H_2O$$

    c. Heterotrophs. Reaction example:

$$\underset{\text{Pyruvic acid}}{CH_3COCOOH} + CO_2 \rightarrow \underset{\text{Oxaloacetic acid}}{HOOCCH_2COCOOH}$$

2. Plant and animal tissues deposited in the soil.

3. Organic carbon degradation — done principally by bacteria and fungi.

4. One of the most abundant plant compounds is cellulose. It is degraded as shown:

$$\text{Cellulose} \xrightarrow[\text{cellulase}]{\text{enzyme}} \text{cellobiose (2 glucose units)}$$

$$\text{Cellobiose} \xrightarrow[\beta\text{-glucosidase}]{\text{enzyme}} \text{glucose}$$

$$\text{Glucose} \xrightarrow[\substack{\text{of many micro-}\\\text{organisms}}]{\text{enzyme systems}} \substack{\text{carbon dioxide, water}\\\text{and/or other end products}}$$

VII. Transformation of Sulfur Compounds: The Sulfur Cycle.

    A. Schematic of the sulfur cycle, showing the role of microorganisms.

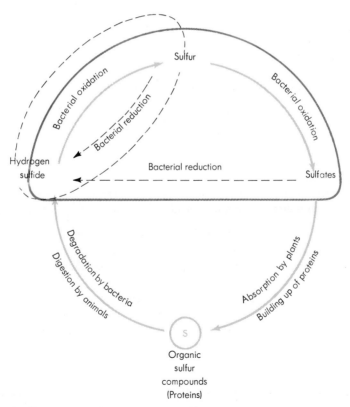

    B. The processes.

       1. Oxidation of elemental slfuur — elemental sulfur (S_o) cannot be used by plants or animals. Certain bacteria oxidize it to sulfates. E.g., *Thiobacillus thiooxidans:*

$$2S + 2H_2O + 3O_2 \rightarrow 2H_2SO_4$$

2. Assimilation and incorporation of sulfates — plants take up sulfates and use them to biosynthesize sulfur-containing amino acids (e.g., cysteine and methionine).

3. Digestion and degradation of organic sulfur — plant material is degraded by bacteria, releasing, among many other products, the three sulfur-containing amino acids. These amino acids in protein and as units are used by animals to build their protein. Eventually, plant and animal protein is degraded, and the sulfur may be released from the sulfur-containing amino acids. Such reactions are mediated by many heterotrophic bacteria, e.g.,

$$
\begin{array}{l}
CH_2SH \\
| \\
CHNH_2 + H_2O \longrightarrow \\
| \\
COOH \\
\text{Cysteine}
\end{array}
\qquad
\begin{array}{l}
CH_3 \\
| \\
C = O + H_2S + NH_3 \\
| \\
COOH \\
\text{Pyruvic} \quad \text{Hydrogen} \\
\text{acid} \quad \text{sulfide}
\end{array}
$$

4. Hydrogen sulfide oxidation — this reaction, $CO_2 + 2H_2S \xrightarrow{\text{light}} (CH_2O)_x + H_2O + 2S$, carbohydrate
is characteristic of the purple and green photosynthetic sulfur bacteria (*Chromatium* and *Chlorobium*) which use H_2S as the election donor to reduce CO_2. The nonsulfur purple bacteria (e.g., *Rhodospirillum*) can also mediate the reaction.

5. Sulfur reduction — a few bacteria may convert S_o to H_2S.

6. Sulfate reduction — the cycle may be shunted (away from some plant involvement) by certain soil bacteria. For example, organic acids serve as the electron donors for the reduction of sulfates and sulfites to hydrogen sulfide by anaerobic sulfate-reducing bacteria like *Desulfotomaculum* that mediate this reaction:

$$\text{Organic acids} + SO_4 \rightarrow H_2S + CO_2$$

C. Winogradsky column — experimental simulation of the soil sulfur cycle (text pages 742 to 743).

VIII. Transformation of Compounds of Other Elements.
A. Solubilization of phosphates from insoluble metal compounds.
B. Solubilization of iron and manganese oxides by coverting them to salts.
C. Release of phosphates from nucleic acid.

IX. Degradation of Pesticides. Pesticides destroy pests like weeds, insects, and pathogens. An ideal pesticide would act quickly and then be easily degraded into nontoxic substances. Nonbiodegradable (nonbacteriodegradable) pesticides have caused problems.

Programmed Self-Test

Do not begin this self-test before reading the corresponding chapter in the text.

HISTORY; THE ENVIRONMENT AND MICROBIOTA OF THE SOIL (Text pages 724-731)

_____ and _____ developed the enrichment-culture technique.

Organic soils are typically found in _____ .	Beijerinck; Winogradsky
Plant and animal remains in the last stages of decomposition are called _____ . This is a dark-colored, amorphous substance composed of residual organic material not readily decomposed by microorganisms.	bogs and marshes
Nocardia and *Streptomyces* belong to the bacterial group _____ .	humus
In the soil, fungi are most abundant near the _____ .	Actinomycetes
Most soil protozoa are flagellates or _____ .	surface
The region where the soil and roots make contact is called the _____ .	amebas
Of all the types of microorganisms found in the soil, _____ predominate.	rhizosphere

THE NITROGEN CYCLE (Text pages 731 to 739)

The enzymatic hydrolysis of proteins is called _____.	bacteria
Do proteinases normally function within the cell?	proteolysis
One end product of deamination is always _____ .	No
The process by which ammonia is oxidized to nitrate is called _____ .	NH_3
Two genera of bacteria that nitrify are _____ and _____ .	nitrification
Nitrate is normally reduced to ammonia under _____ conditions.	*Nitrosomonas; Nitrobacter*
The transformation of nitrates to N_2 or N_2O is called _____ .	anaerobic
An autotroph that converts nitrates to atmospheric nitrogen is _____ .	denitrification

_____ symbiotically fixes nitrogen in association with legumes.

Thiobacillus denitrificans

An aerobic nonsymbiotic nitrogen fixer is the bacteria __(genus)__ .

Rhizobium

Rhizobia-infected legumes characteristically have abnormal growths, called _____ , on the root system.

Azotobacter

The enzyme _____ catalyzes this reaction:
$N = N \xrightarrow{3H_2} 2NH_3$.

nodules

THE CARBON AND SULFUR CYCLES (Text pages 739 to 743)

Can elemental sulfur be utilized by plants or animals?

nitrogenase

Thiobacillus thiooxidans oxidizes elemental sulfur to _____.

No

Many heterotrophic bacteria degrade cysteine to pyruvic acid and _____ .

sulfates

Chromatium oxidizes hydrogen sulfide to _____.

hydrogen sulfide

Cellobiose is a degradation product of _____ and contains two _____ units.

elemental sulfur

Organic carbon degradation in the soil is done principally by bacteria and _____ .

cellulose; glucose

CYCLES OF OTHER ELEMENTS: DEGRADATION OF PESTICIDES (Text pages 743 to 744)

Bacteria change insoluble oxides of iron and manganese to soluble _____ .

fungi

Which pesticide is not readily degraded by bacteria? 2,4,5-T or 2,4-D?

salts

2,4,5-T

Multiple-Choice Test

Underline the correct answer.

1. The type of microbe that is most numerous in soil is: (a) viruses; (b) bacteria; (c) fungi; (d) algae; (e) protozoa.

2. Which plant is not susceptible to infection by a specific species of *Rhizobium*? (a) Wheat; (b) soybean; (c) clover; (d) alfalfa.

3. Alfalfa is a leguminous plant. It is used in crop rotation: (a) to replenish the water content of the soil; (b) to replenish the nitrogen content of the soil; (c) because it has very deep roots and will prevent erosion; (d) to replenish the sulfur content of the soil.

4. *Nitrosomonas:* (a) oxidizes NO_2 to NO_3; (b) reduces NO_3 to NH_3; (c) fixes nitrogen; (d) oxidizes NH_3 to NO_2.

5. Which of these is the best plant food (fertilizer) because it can easily be assimilated by plants and because it is less volatile than the others? (a) NO_3; (b) N_2; (c) NH_3; (d) KCN (potassium cyanide).

6. Which of these processes is the antithesis of nitrogen fixation? (a) Protein synthesis; (b) nitrate reduction; (c) denitrification; (d) nitrification.

7. The process whereby nitrate (NO_3) in the soil is converted to ammonia is called: (a) nitrification; (b) nitrosification; (c) nitrogen fixation; (d) nitrate reduction.

8. Nitrate reduction is most likely to occur under: (a) aerobic conditions; (b) anaerobic conditions; (c) conditions where *Nitrosomonas* is the predominant organism; (d) conditions of neutral pH.

9. Which one of the following amino acids contains sulfur? (a) Methionine; (b) arginine; (c) histidine; (d) tryptophan.

10. The top layer of bacteria in the Winogradsky column is: (a) nonsulfur purple bacteria; (b) Thiobacilli; (c) purple sulfur bacteria; (d) green sulfur bacteria.

Answers: 1. (b); 2. (a); 3. (b); 4. (d); 5. (a); 6. (c); 7. (d); 8. (b); 9. (a); 10. (a).

Chapter 35

Microbiology
of Air

INTRODUCTION: The air may carry microorganisms but cannot support their growth. Therefore, it is not, in the usual sense, a microbial econiche. However, many microorganisms, including
pathogens (Chap. 28) and fungal spores, are disseminated via the air. Usually, the flora of the air
reflects the flora of nearby terrestrial/aquatic habitats, although some organisms (e.g., fungal
spores) may be transported across vast distances. Some microbial species may survive in the air for
only seconds, while others may survive indefinitely.

Facilities such as health centers, disposal plants, and laboratories often need to monitor and
control airborne flora. This chapter covers these topics.

Expanded Outline and Summary

I. Techniques for Microbiological Analysis of Air.
   A. Solid impingement devices — microorganisms collected (impinged) on solid surface (agar
      medium; filter disk).
      1. The settling-plate technique — simple procedure of exposing petri plate to air. Used
         to isolate airborne organisms and perhaps to determine the kinds of fungi and bac-
         teria present in the air and the approximate extent of airborne contamination.
      2. Sieve-type sampler — a measured volume of air is drawn through a perforated cover
         and onto petri dishes containing agar medium.
      3. Slit-type samplers — petri dish is rotated at uniform speed under a slit through which
         air is drawn. When the air is postulated to contain many organisms, the petri plate is
         rotated rapidly; when it is postulated to contain few organisms, the plate is rotated
         slowly. This is an efficient quantitative technique.
      4. Membrane filters — air is filtered through a membrane, and organisms become trap-
         ped on the membrane's surface. The membrane is then placed on a growth-support-
         ing medium and incubated until colonies are apparent.
   B. Liquid impingement devices — known volumes of air are forced through fluid, which is
      subsequently plated.

II. The Microbial Content of Air. This study provides a general pattern of bacterial airborne populations in various locales. Outdoors, fungi are often as populous as or more populous than bacteria.

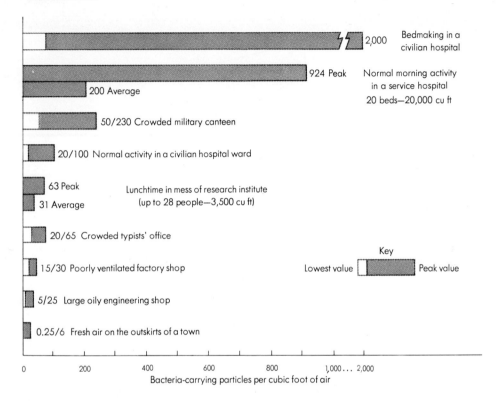

Figure 35-4. Bacterial content of air in civilian and military establishments as measured with the slit sampler.

A. Indoor air: Room air.
  1. Some factors influencing microbial levels.
    a. Ventilation.
    b. Number of people (or animals).
    c. Activity of people.
      i. Coughing and sneezing produce bacteria-laden droplets.
      ii. Bedclothes have microorganisms, so bedmaking adds to microbial populations.
      iii. Hospital flora reflects that of the patients.
      iv. Laboratory-produced aerosols result from inoculations, centrifugations, etc.
B. Outdoor air: the atmosphere.
  1. Dust particles contain soil microorganisms.
  2. Water droplets contain water microorganisms.
  3. Facilities (sprinklers, sewage treatment plants, etc.) spew microorganisms into the air.

4. Urban industrial areas have this type of airborne microflora distribution:

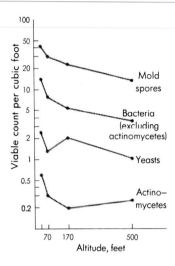

Figure 35-10. The influence of altitude on the concentration of different types of microorganisms from urban air.

5. Upper air (origin: soil and sea) — bacteria and molds are distributed globally in air masses from 0 to more than 16,500 ft above sea level.

III. Control of Microorganisms in the Air. Physical and chemical techniques, presented earlier (Chaps. 22 and 23), apply here.
   A. Ultraviolet radiation — germicidal lamps (wavelengths: 250 to 260 nm). Humans must not be directly exposed, as eye and even skin damage may result.
      1. Direct irradiation in unoccupied rooms or rooms occupied for only short periods of time (e.g., laboratory inoculation rooms).
      2. Indirect irradiation in occupied rooms (e.g., schools, hospitals, etc.).
      3. In air circulating systems (in air ducts).
   B. Chemical agents — rooms must be evacuated until aerosol chemical agents (noted in Chap. 23) have sterilized or disinfected the area and have dissipated (or been rendered nontoxic).
   C. Filtration — materials are fibrous (e.g., cotton or glass); series of filters retards clogging.
   D. Laminar-airflow system (unidirectional airflow) — air passes through high-efficiency particulate air (HEPA) filters of cellulose acetate pleated around aluminum foil. Particles as small as 0.3 μm can be removed. These systems are now used in the electronics and aerospace industries, and are gaining wide use in medical, microbiology, and pharmaceutical laboratories.
   E. Miscellaneous methods and practices.
      1. Control of dust.
      2. Proper ventilation.

Programmed Self-Test

Do not begin this self-test before reading the corresponding chapter in the text.

MICROBIOLOGY OF AIR (Text pages 747 to 759)

Do microorganisms grow when in the air?	
In slit sampling, when the air contains few organisms, the plate is rotated at _____ speed.	No
Fine sprays producing droplets that remain suspended in air for a time are called _____ .	slow
Most microorganisms live in the upper surface layer of water, which is called the _____ . This layer is less than _____ in depth.	aerosols
Among the airborne molds, species of _____ were found to predominate.	microlayer; 0.1 mm
Are bacteria routinely isolated 3,000 m above sea level?	*Cladosporium*
Ultraviolet irradiation is most germicidal at wavelengths of _____nm.	Yes
HEPA stands for _____.	250 to 260
	high-efficiency particulate air

Multiple-Choice Test

Underline the correct answer.

1. Which of the following techniques for microbiological analysis of the air is simplest in design and requires the least specialized equipment? (a) Settling plate; (b) sieve and slit sampling; (c) membrane filter; (d) liquid impingement.

2. Triethylene glycol, lactic acid, and β-propiolactone are each: (a) found in liquid impingement media; (b) used to soak HEPA filters; (c) aerosol or gaseous disinfectants (sterilizers); (d) used to clean lab benches.

3. Which genus of bacteria has not been isolated from the upper atmosphere? (a) *Bacillus;* (b) *Micrococcus;* (c) *Sarcina;* (d) *Neisseria.*

4. In which of these places would the most bacteria normally be found? (a) Hospital operating room; (b) hospital ward; (c) air over a city; (d) 1,000 m above an ocean.

Table 35-1. Number of Bacteria and Molds Which Developed on Plates of Seawater and Freshwater Media Exposed for 1 h at Different Distances from Land

DISTANCE FROM LAND, NAUTICAL MILES	SEAWATER MEDIUM		FRESHWATER MEDIUM		RATIO SW/FW	
	BACTERIA	MOLDS	BACTERIA	MOLDS	BACTERIA	MOLDS
0–10	45	115	20	200	2.25	0.57
10–150	48	79	13	69	3.69	1.14
150–400	71	20	39	36	1.82	0.56

SOURCE: Data from C. E. Zobell, "Microorganisms in Marine Air," Aerobiology, *AAAS Publ.* 17, 1942.

5. Based on the data from this table, which *generalization* is accurate? (a) There are more airborne bacteria over seawater than over freshwater; (b) there are more airborne molds over seawater than over freshwater; (c) as one samples further from land, the number of airborne molds decreases; (d) levels of airborne molds and bacteria drop substantially as one samples further than 400 nautical miles from land.

Answers: 1. (a); 2. (c); 3. (d); 4. (b); 5. (c).

Chapter 36

Aquatic
Microbiology

INTRODUCTION: Our standard of living — and even our survival — is intertwined with the health of the waterways. Yet as we and our technology progress, we place greater stress and demands upon these resources. Only recently have we become aware that not even the great oceans can yield to all our demands or receive all our "garbage" and still remain in balance. So, whether we are talking about a creek or the Pacific Ocean, we need to understand its ecology if we are to utilize its resources without damaging it, possibly beyond repair.

Our knowledge of many aquatic ecosystems is still rather primitive, but some scientific approaches have been developed, some basic facts are evident, and some interactions can be predicted. This chapter emphasizes the microbial aspects of the developing aquatic sciences.

Expanded Outline and Summary

I. Natural Waters. Water or hydrolytic cycle: 80,000 cubic miles annual ocean evaporation + 15,000 cubic miles annual land and lake evaporation = 24,000 cubic miles annual precipitation.
   A. Atmospheric water — many microorganisms that are airborne are washed back to the surface during precipitation.
   B. Surface water — great variety of microflora that fluctuates and depends on:
      1. The ecosystem in question.
      2. Nutrient conditions.
      3. Climatic conditions.
   C. Ground (subterranean) water — due to filtrations, it has low microbial content.

II. The Aquatic Environment. A few of the many conditions that influence microbial populations are described.
   A. Temperature.
      1. Polar regions — around $0°C$ — psychrophiles.
      2. Equatorial regions — 30 to $40°C$ — mesophiles.
      3. Hot springs — $60°C$ and up — thermophiles.
   B. Hydrostatic pressure — increases 1 atm/10 m. Barophilic microorganisms (require pressure) have been isolated at 1,000 m.

    C. Light — required by primary producers (mostly algae). Photic zone varies and is usually confined to the upper 50 to 125 m.

    D. Salinity (dissolved salts).

        1. Freshwater — less than 0.5 percent. Organisms halophobic (cannot grow if salt concentration exceeds 1.0 percent).

        2. Seawater — 3.3 to 3.7 percent. Many marine organisms are halophilic (or halotolerant), growing at 2.5 to 4.0 percent salt concentrations.

        3. Salt lakes — saturated with salt. Populated with halophilic microorganisms.

    E. Turbidity — affects photosynthetic zone. Affected by:

        1. Land minerals.

        2. Detritus (particulate organic materials such as cellulose).

        3. Suspended microorganisms.

    F. Hydrogen-ion concentration (pH) — aquatic organisms can be grown at pH 6.5 to 8.5; optimum usually 7.2 to 7.6.

        1. Sea: 7.5 to 8.5.

        2. Lakes and rivers: more variable pH than sea.

    G. Inorganic and organic constituents.

        1. Inorganic — nitrates and phosphates are important, especially for algae.

        2. Organic — required for saprophytic bacteria and fungi.

III. Distribution of Microorganisms in the Aquatic Environment (some terminology and generalizations). Microorganisms are ubiquitous, with the highest populations occurring in "surface water" and inshore sediments.

    A. Plankton — floating and drifting microbial life.

        1. Phytoplankton — algae.

        2. Zooplankton — protozoa.

    B. Benthic microorganisms — aquatic bottom organisms. Higher numbers and more kinds of organisms exist in an inshore estuarine-marine system.

    C. Mixing of waters (upwelling) — caused by wind, tide, and currents. Mixes nutrient-containing sediment with water.

IV. Techniques for the Study of Aquatic Microorganisms.

    A. Problems.

        1. Finding a suitable growth medium.

        2. Many marine organisms require solid surfaces.

        3. Viability lost during sampling-culturing hiatus.

        4. Special sampling equipment required.

        5. Marine viruses cannot yet be routinely isolated.

    B. Procedures (these methods were previously discussed).

        1. To identify and enumerate organisms:

            a. Submerged-slide technique.

            b. Plate cultures.

            c. Membrane-filter technique.

        2. To isolate specific physiological types:

            a. Enrichment culture.

        3. Measurement of total biomass or biochemical activity.

            a. Algae — dry weight or total chlorophyll.

            b. Total ^{14}C uptake or ATP content of flora.

V. Aquatic Microorganisms.
   A. Lakes and ponds (limnology: study of ecology of lakes, ponds, and streams).
      1. Zones.
         a. Littoral — along shore; light penetrates to bottom; rooted vegetation.
         b. Limnetic — open areas; depth determined by light compensation level (depth of effective light penetration).
         c. Profundal — deeper regions of open water (little light; little photosynthesis).
         d. Benthic — bottom areas; light lacking; soft mud or ooze.
      2. Microbial populations.
         a. Littoral — great variety of physiological types (photo- and chemoautotrophs, heterotrophs, etc.). Mostly aerobic or facultative.
         b. Limnetic — as above, but lower population densities.
         c. Profundal — mostly heterotrophic, anaerobic decomposers and facultatives.
         d. Benthic — as above, but higher population densities.

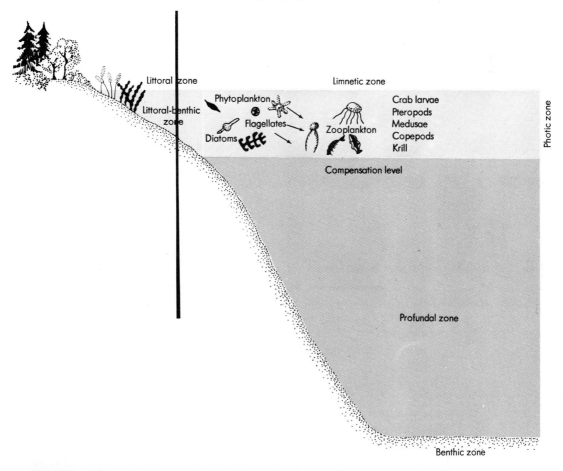

Fig. 36-6. Schematic diagram of a lake illustrating zonal regions.

      3. Stratification and mixing (due to temperature differences) — stratification is barrier to nutrient and oxygen exchange, especially in still waters.

   a. Summer — top layers warmer; stratification.

   b. Winter — top layers colder (if less than 4°C); stratification.

   c. Spring and fall — mixing of layers (e.g., in spring ice thaws and sinks to bottom when it warms to over 4°C) results in increased dissolved nutrients and oxygen and increased microbial growth (e.g., algal blooms).

B. Streams — inflow from surrounding terrestrial econiches and lakes and ponds. In "virgin" streams, the microbiota reflects this input.

C. Estuaries (semienclosed coastal bodies of water that have free connections to the open sea).

   1. Inputs and outputs (a great variety of interactions — see diagram — makes it difficult to generalize about conditions and biota). Physical and biological conditions nearest the seas resemble the seas, while nearest rivers, estuaries resemble rivers.

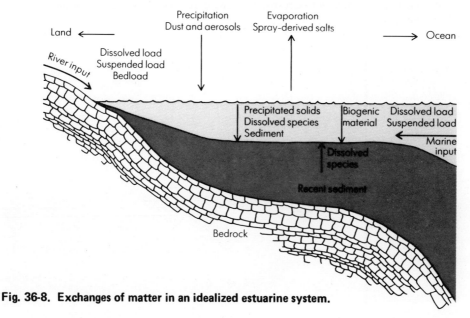

Fig. 36-8. Exchanges of matter in an idealized estuarine system.

   2. Case study: The Chesapeake Bay.

      a. Receiving basin for nine major rivers (in New York, Pennsylvania, Maryland, and Virginia).

      b. Shoreline: 4,600 miles, ranging from highly industrialized areas to uninhabited marshlands.

      c. Salinity: less than 1 percent near rivers to 3.5 percent (normal seawater) at its mouth.

      d. It has wilderness regions and many human inputs from agriculture, industry, commerce, and recreation.

      e. Bacterial populations — some general examples:

         i. Areas of high domestic input — coliforms, fecal streptococci, species of saprophytes (e.g., *Bacillus*, *Proteus*, etc.).

        ii. Nutritionally poor areas — soil bacteria and budding/appendaged bacteria among many species.

D. The sea — relatively stable ecosystem, and hence relatively stable populations of microorganisms are found almost everywhere.
  1. Algae and blue-green algae.
    a. Marine plankton — algae and blue-green algae (phytoplankton) are the primary converters of radiant energy to chemical energy. Directly or indirectly support all other marine life.
    b. Blooms — enormous populations of algae and blue-green algae.
  2. Bacteria — psychrophiles and slight to moderate halophiles or halotolerant.
    a. Photosynthetic zone — tied to plankton for their nutrients and the surfaces they provide. Some genera (often pigmented) are *Pseudomonas, Vibrio, Flavobacterium*. Population is sparse because of the light intensity. More bacteria are found just beneath this zone.
    b. Above sea floor — very sparse populations.
    c. Benthic zone — many anaerobes and facultative heterotrophs are present at sediment-water interface. As indicated in Table 26-2 of your text, more than 1 million bacteria per gram of sediment are routinely isolated.
  3. Zooplankton (protozoa such as foraminifera and radiolaria) — these feed on algae, bacteria, and detritus. By night, they surface feed (e.g., on phytoplankton); by day they sink below the photic zone.
  4. Fungi — also routinely isolated.

VI. The Role and Importance of Aquatic Microbial Ecosystems.
  A. Productivity of aquatic ecosystems (in terms of food supply).
    1. Food web in a shallow estuary.
      a. Primary producers — phytoplankton make a small contribution; shoreline plants, the principal contribution.
      b. Converters to detritus — bacteria and fungi.
      c. Eaters of detritus — protozoa, crustaceans, insect larvae, a few fish, etc.
    2. Fertility of the ocean.
      a. Primary producers — phytoplankton (light, nitrogen, and phosphorus are limiting factors).
      b. Cyclers — bacteria remineralize and make available some of the inorganic nutrients required by phytoplankton.
      c. Second step in chain — crustaceans (e.g., krill).
      d. Apices of chain — krill (etc.) are food for fish, sea birds, seals, whales, etc. Some of these animals, in turn, are food for other animals.
  B. Biogeochemical transformations (mineralizations, i.e., the dissimilation of organic compounds to CO_2, H_2O, and inorganic salts).
    1. Biogeochemical cycles — see Chap. 34 for nitrogen, carbon, sulfur, and phosphorus cycles.
    2. Marine sediments — phytoplankton skeletons of silica and calcium are found (often in enormous concentrations) in various parts of the sea (e.g., the chalk beds of England and France are foraminifera remains).
      a. Procaryotes precipitate calcium carbonate $\longrightarrow$ limestone.
      b. Procaryotes involved in the mineralization of iron, manganese, and sulfur.
      c. Procaryotes involved in the formation of petroleum.

Programmed Self-Test

Do not begin this self-test before reading the corresponding chapter in the text.

AQUATIC MICROBIOLOGY (Text pages 761 to 779)

Hydrostatic pressure increases with depth at a rate of 1 atm/_____ m.	
Generally photosynthetic activity of aquatic environments is confined to the _____ zone, which in turn is generally confined to the upper _____ to _____ m.	10
The salinity of seawater averages about _____ percent.	photic; 50; 125
Many species of marine bacteria, called _____ , characteristically grow while attached to a solid surface.	3.5
The aggregation of floating and drifting microbial life in the surface region of the aquatic ecosystem is called _____ .	periphytes
Plankton comprising primarily algae is called _____, while plankton comprising primarily protozoa is called _____ .	plankton
Microbial inhabitants of the bottom region of a body of water are collectively referred to as the _____ organisms.	phytoplankton; zooplankton
A phenomenon called _____ occurs in an ocean when water rises from a deeper to a shallower depth.	benthic
Are marine viruses routinely isolated?	upwelling
The microbiology of freshwater constitutes a part of the science of _____ , which is the study of life and conditions for life in lakes, ponds, and streams.	No
The water around shorelines is referred to as the _____ zone.	limnology
The upper waters of the open sea, where photosynthesis may occur, constitutes the _____ zone.	littoral
The deeper waters of the open sea constitute the _____ zone.	limnetic

A massive growth of algae is called a _____ .	profundal
Lakes or ponds enriched with nutrients, particularly nitrogen and phosphorus (a condition referred to as _____), are likely to support excessive algal growth.	bloom
The characteristic color of the Red Sea is associated with heavy blooms of the blue-green alga _____*(genus)*_____ .	eutrophication
At night zooplankton commonly graze on _____ at the surface, and during the day they sink below the _____ zone.	*Oscillatoria*
Are the main primary producers of a shallow estuary usually algae? Are the main primary producers in the oceans usually algae?	phytoplankton; photic
The terrestrial environment produces 1 to 10 g of dry organic matter per square meter per day, compared to _____ g in the offshore ocean areas. Does the total productivity of the oceans exceed that of the land?	No; Yes
The red shrimplike crustacean *Euphausia superba* (commonly called _____) feeds upon phytoplankton.	0.5; Yes
The "_____ Ocean" is described as being richer in life than any other major oceanic area.	krill
The chalk beds of England are chiefly the remains of _____ .	Antarctic
	foraminifera

Multiple-Choice Test

Underline the correct answer.

1. Bottom-dwelling aquatic organisms reside in the _____ zone. (a) Profundal; (b) benthic; (c) littoral; (d) limnetic.

2. Sphaerotilus is a(n): (a) protozoa; (b) fungus; (c) alga; (d) bacterium.

Questions 3 and 4 refer to this figure.

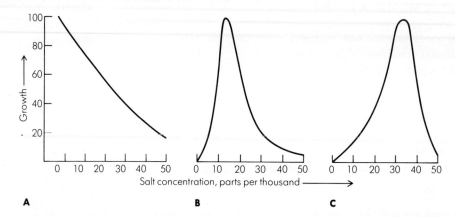

A   B   C

3. The organism in graph A is: (a) halophilic; (b) halophobic; (c) halotolerant; (d) psychrophilic.

4. The organism in graph _____ requires the highest salt concentration for growth. (a) A; (b) B; (c) C.

5. In a river, the highest concentrations of bacteria are found: (a) in midstream; (b) within 10 in of the surface; (c) in the bottom mud or bank; (d) from 10 to 20 in below the surface.

6. Where are the greatest concentrations of bacteria found? (Assume no pollution.) (a) Rivers; (b) lakes; (c) oceans; (d) rhizosphere.

7. Which one of the following is not a primary producer? (a) Algae; (b) krill; (c) blue-green algae; (d) mangrove leaves.

Answers: 1. (b); 2. (d); 3. (c); 4. (c); 5. (c); 6. (d); 7. (b).

Chapter 37

Microbiology of
Domestic Water
and Sewage

INTRODUCTION: Human waste products are unbalancing many aquatic ecosystems. Toxic products may render food resources poisonous or kill them along with microorganisms. Once microorganisms are eradicated, recycling ceases, and the water system may quickly become a quagmire or sewer.

Likewise, should the organic load of a waterway exceed the ability of bacteria to aerobically degrade it, the water will become toxic and filled with detritus. Furthermore, human waste consists largely of bacteria, some of which may be pathogenic. For these reasons it is essential that human wastes be treated (decomposed, "depathogenized," and even deionized) before they reach waterways en masse.

This chapter covers the monitoring of water, microbiological safety standards, and methods of treating domestic sewage. Microbiology is, indeed, a key in assessing the quality of water and in purifying it.

Expanded Outline and Summary

I. Water Purification.
   A. Definitions.
      1. Potable water—free of disease-producing microorganisms and chemical substances deleterious to health.
      2. Nonpotable water—contaminated with domestic or industrial wastes.
   B. Individual water supplies.
      1. Underground sources (wells and springs) away from toilets and barnyards are usually safe.
      2. Rainwater caught and stored in cisterns is potable.
      3. Surface water may not be potable and should be treated.

C. Municipal water supplies (treatment processes).

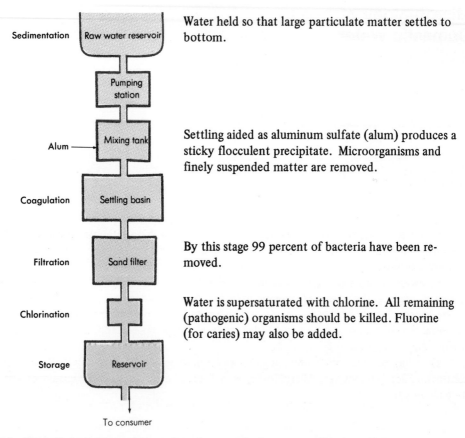

Sedimentation — Raw water reservoir — Water held so that large particulate matter settles to bottom.

Pumping station

Alum → Mixing tank — Settling aided as aluminum sulfate (alum) produces a sticky flocculent precipitate. Microorganisms and finely suspended matter are removed.

Coagulation — Settling basin

Filtration — Sand filter — By this stage 99 percent of bacteria have been removed.

Chlorination — Water is supersaturated with chlorine. All remaining (pathogenic) organisms should be killed. Fluorine (for caries) may also be added.

Storage — Reservoir

To consumer

Figure 37-1. Flow diagram of usual procedures in municipal water-purification plant.

II. Determining Sanitary Quality.
    A. Sanitary surveys (inspection of water system).
        1. Parameters.
            a. Inspection of the quality of raw water.
            b. Observation of the treatment and holding systems.
            c. Check of distribution to consumers.
        2. Purpose—to see whether the engineering is conducive to the output of potable water.
    B. Bacteriological evidence of pollution.
        1. Why pathogens are not directly monitored.
            a. Sporadic entrance into water.
            b. Relatively short survival period in water.
            c. Present in water in low numbers and thus elude detection.
            d. Lengthy, costly laboratory detection procedures.
        2. Indicator organisms—fecally contaminated water contains normal intestinal

bacteria. Thus, presence of coliforms, fecal streptococci, and *Clostridium perfringens* indicate that the water has been contaminated and may contain intestinal pathogens.

3. Why indicator organisms serve as "fingerprints" of fecal contamination.
   a. Billions are present in animal intestinal tracts.
   b. Relatively long survival in most water.
   c. Established laboratory identification procedures exist.
4. The coliform group (all are not anaerobic or sporeformers; all are gram-negative rods that ferment lactose → acid + gas).
   a. Examples of genera.
      i. *Escherichia.*
      ii. *Enterobacter.*
   b. Differentiation of *Escherichia* from *Enterobacter* (IMViC).

| | TEST | | | |
ORGANISM	Indole	Methyl Red	Voges-Proskauer	Citrate
Escherichia coli	+	+	−	−
Enterobacter aerogenes	−	−	+	+

C. Bacteriological techniques.
   1. Sampling the water.
      a. The sample must be collected in a sterile bottle.
      b. The sample must be representative of the supply from which it is taken.
      c. Contamination of the sample must be avoided during and after sampling.
      d. The sample should be tested as promptly as possible after collection.
      e. If there is a delay in examination of the sample, it should be stored at a temperature between 0 and 10°C.
   2. Test for coliforms. (See Fig. 37-2.)
   3. Standard plate count—determines total viable, aerobic heterotrophic bacteria (also fungi). Good-quality water usually has fewer than 100 such organisms per milliliter.
   4. Membrane-filter technique (see text page 788 and recall Chap. 35, Microbiology of Air).
D. Microorganisms other than coliform bacteria (of significance in water microbiology).
   1. Fecal streptococci—in intestines of warm-blooded animals; also indicate fecal pollution.
   2. Slime-forming bacteria—clog pipes and cause unpleasant taste.
   3. Iron bacteria—precipitate metals, clogging pipes and altering color and taste.
   4. Sulfur bacteria.
      a. *Thiobacillus*—produces sulfuric acid, lowering pH.
      b. *Desulfovibrio*—produces H_2S, causing unpleasant taste.
   5. Algae—in large numbers ruin taste and color; may produce toxins.
   6. Viruses—enteric viruses in sewage get into bodies of water.
      a. Picorna group: polio-, coxsackie- and ECHO viruses.
      b. Detection methodology is being developed.

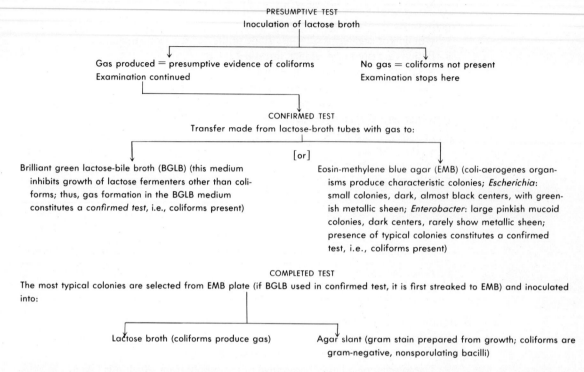

PRESUMPTIVE TEST
Inoculation of lactose broth

Gas produced = presumptive evidence of coliforms
Examination continued

No gas = coliforms not present
Examination stops here

CONFIRMED TEST
Transfer made from lactose-broth tubes with gas to:

[or]

Brilliant green lactose-bile broth (BGLB) (this medium inhibits growth of lactose fermenters other than coliforms; thus, gas formation in the BGLB medium constitutes a confirmed test, i.e., coliforms present)

Eosin-methylene blue agar (EMB) (coli-aerogenes organisms produce characteristic colonies; *Escherichia*: small colonies, dark, almost black centers, with greenish metallic sheen; *Enterobacter*: large pinkish mucoid colonies, dark centers, rarely show metallic sheen; presence of typical colonies constitutes a confirmed test, i.e., coliforms present)

COMPLETED TEST
The most typical colonies are selected from EMB plate (if BGLB used in confirmed test, it is first streaked to EMB) and inoculated into:

Lactose broth (coliforms produce gas)

Agar slant (gram stain prepared from growth; coliforms are gram-negative, nonsporulating bacilli)

Fermentation of lactose broth and demonstration of gram-negative, nonsporulating bacilli constitutes a positive completed test demonstrating the presence of some member of the coliform group in the volume of sample examined

Figure 37-2.

III. Swimming Pools.
  A. Transmission of diseases (e.g., eye, nose, throat, intestinal, and skin infections).
  B. Control of disease by proper chlorination and filtration.

IV. Water Pollution (Control Act administered by EPA). Law (1972) states that the United States must substantially clean its waters by 1983 and eliminate all water-pollutant emissions by 1985.

V. Sewage (used water supply of a community).
  A. Contents.
    1. Domestic wastes (e.g., wash water and excrement).
    2. Industrial wastes (e.g., acids, oils, etc.).
    3. Ground, surface, and atmospheric water.
  B. Kinds of sewer systems.
    1. Sanitary sewers—carry domestic and industrial sewage.
    2. Storm sewers—carry surface and storm water.
    3. Combined sewers—carry all sewage through single system.
  C. Chemical characteristics.

1. Water—99.9 percent.
2. Suspended solids—0.02 to 0.03 percent (major municipal plant may handle 100 tons of solids daily).
3. Inorganics—e.g., phosphates, nitrates, ammonium compounds.
4. Organics—also from slaughterhouses, paper mills, etc.
   a. Nitrogenous compounds: urea, proteins, amines, and amino acids.
   b. Nonnitrogenous compounds: carbohydrates, fats, and soaps.
D. Biochemical oxygen demand (BOD)—a measure of the amount of oxygen microorganisms require to oxidize and cycle wastes into cellular components. It is important that wastes be oxidized prior to reaching a waterway (sewage treatment) so that the waterway's entire oxygen supply is not diverted away from fish, plants, etc., and into bacterial sewage degradation.
E. Microbiological characteristics—contains soil, intestinal, and a wide variety of other microbes.

VII. Sewage-Treatment Processes.
  A. Single dwelling units (or motels, shopping centers, etc.)
    1. Septic tank—designed to retain solids so that they may be anaerobically (and incompletely) degraded. Serves as settling and partial sludge digestion tank. Material released into absorbtion field has high BOD, is odorous, and may contain pathogens. Diagram of septic tank and installation:

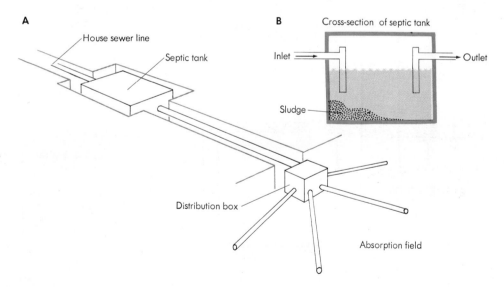

Figure 37-7.

    2. Evapotranspiration system—used when septic tank installation is not feasible because of high water table or impermeable soil. Sewage is piped into soil that cannot absorb it. Sewage, by capillary action, goes to the surface of soil where it is degraded by aerobic bacteria and used by green plants that transpire the liquid.

Installation diagram:

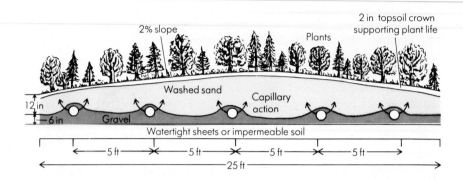

Figure 37-8.

B.   Municipal treatment processes. (Numbers refer to outline explanation)

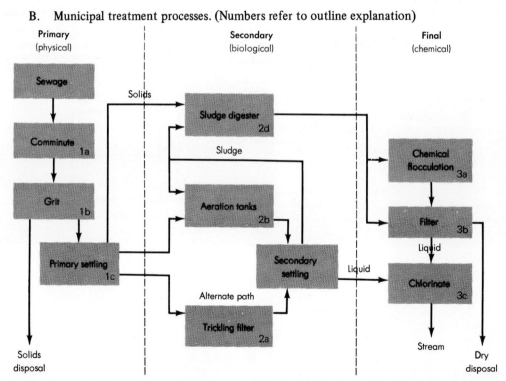

Figure 37-9. Flow diagram of major steps in modern sewage-treatment plant. (Numbers refer to outline explanation.)

1.   Primary treatment— *physical* removal of coarse solids.
    a.   Screening—removes largest solids (e.g., boxes, tires, etc.). Material may be in-
        cinerated, or material may be ground and/or used for landfill.

   b. Grit chambers—remove smaller solids (e.g., pebbles, etc.).
   c. Sedimentation (primary settling)– removes smaller particulate material (e.g., fecal matter, paper, etc.). This particulate material (sludge) is often treated biologically (e.g., anaerobic degradation in sludge digester).
2. Secondary (*biological*) treatment—degradation of organic matter to reduce the BOD. One or more of the following methods might be engineered into a facility.
   a. Trickling filter—sewage sprayed (this aerates it) over rock beds, which contain populations of bacteria that decompose the sewage as it trickles through.

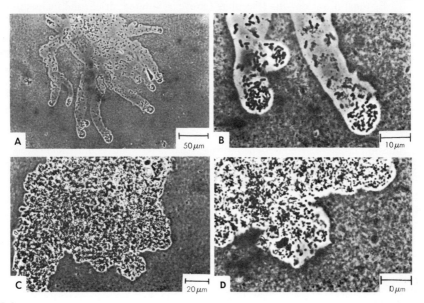

Figure 37-12.

   b. Activated-sludge process—vigorously aerated sewage coalesces into particles teeming with aerobic microbial degraders. Done in aeration tanks and followed by further sedimentation.

Figure 37-13. Activated sludge aeration tank.

    c. Oxidation ponds (lagoons)—in these 2 to 4 ft-deep ponds, algae (e.g., *Chlorella*) use sewage nutrients and provide oxygen for aerobic degradation.

    d. Sludge digestion (of solids accumulated during primary treatment and sometimes after secondary treatment). Anaerobes digest sludge in deep tanks, yielding methane (may be used as heating fuel), carbon dioxide, and smaller amounts of nitrogen and hydrogen. Anaerobic sewage degradation is slow, requiring weeks.

  3. Final (chemical) treatment.

    a. Chemical flocculation—removes much of the remaining particulate matter.

    b. Final filtration—the flocculate (above) is filtered, dried, and incinerated. It may alternatively serve as landfill or even fertilizer.

    c. Chlorination—the final liquid effluent is chlorinated to kill microorganisms, some of which may have been pathogenic. This low-BOD, nonoffensive, "nonhazardous" liquid may now (in good conscience) be drained to natural waterways.

VIII. Microorganisms and Sewage-Treatment Procedures. During secondary treatment, microorganisms recycle sewage into environmentally acceptable substances. The specifics of their activities have been tabulated on page 802 of your text.

 IX. The Pollution Problem. Well-designed sewage-treatment facilities must serve every community or adjacent bodies of water won't. Many new facilities have been built, but many more are required.

Programmed Self-Test

Do not begin this self-test before reading the corresponding chapter in the text.

WATER PURIFICATION; DETERMINING SANITARY QUALITY; SWIMMING POOLS; WATER POLLUTION (Text pages 781 to 791)

Water that is free of disease-producing microbes and chemical substances dangerous to health is called _____ water.

The principal operations employed in a municipal water purification plant to produce water safe for human consumption are sedimentation, filtration, and _____ .

potable

When water is bacteriologically monitored, are pathogens usually the object of the search?

chlorination

One of the IMViC reactions, Vi stands for the _____ test, which measures the production of the compound _____ .

No

Sphaerotilus is surrounded by a sheath that is sometimes encrusted with insoluble compounds of _____.	Voges-Proskauer; acetyl-methylcarbinol
Polio, coxsackie, and ECHO are names of enteric viruses that belong to the _____ group of viruses.	iron
Water in swimming pools is disinfected with _____.	picorna
The Federal Water Pollution Control Act is administered by the _____Agency.	chlorine

SEWAGE: CHARACTERISTICS, TREATMENT, DISPOSAL, TREATMENT PROCESSES, AND DEGRADATION BY MICROORGANISMS (Text pages 791 to 804)

Combined sewers have the input of both _____ sewers and _____ sewers.	Environmental Protection
Sewage consists of about _____ percent water.	sanitary; storm
The principal nitrogenous compounds in sewage are proteins, amines, amino acids, and _____.	99.9
BOD stands for _____.	urea
The more oxidizable the material, the _____ is the BOD.	biochemical oxygen demand
The processes that occur in a septic tank are _____ and _____ of the sludge.	higher
Final sewage treatment is chemical; secondary treatment is _____.	sedimentation; (anaerobic) degradation
Distribution arm, stone bed, and effluent collection trough are part of the _____ apparatus.	biological
The removal of nitrogen (NH_3) from sewage is a two-step process. The aerobic reaction process is _____, and the anaerobic process is _____.	trickling filter
An important alga in sewage oxidation ponds (lagoons) is _____.	nitrification; dentrification

The principal end-product gas of anaerobic sludge digestion is _____.	*Chlorella pyrenoidosa*
Given enough time and oxygen, aerobes convert sewage carbohydrates and fats to _____.	methane
	$CO_2 + H_2O$

Multiple-Choice Test

Underline the correct answer.

1. Which genus is part of the coliform group? (a) *Proteus;* (b) *Enterobacter;* (c) *Pseudomonas;* (d) *Clostridium.*

2. Which is an aerobic sewage treatment process (facility)? (a) Septic tank; (b) sludge digestion chamber; (c) evapotranspiration system.

3. The *least* amount of water is consumed by: (a) municipalities; (b) industry; (c) agriculture.

4. All other factors remaining equal, as the BOD increases, the dissolved oxygen (DO): (a) increases; (b) decreases; (c) remains the same.

5. "If air is forced into the system, particles of suspended matter flocculate into small gelatinous masses, swarming with aerobic microscopic life and capable of oxidizing organic matter readily." This is a description of: (a) activated sludge; (b) a trickling filter; (c) tertiary sewage treatment; (d) the intermittent sand filter.

6. Drinking water is examined for the prsence of *E. coli* mainly because this is: (a) an intestinal pathogen; (b) a lactose fermenter, all of which are dangerous; (c) a normal intestinal inhabitant; (d) an exotoxin producer.

7. The major purpose of primary sewage treatment is to: (a) reduce the BOD; (b) remove some of the suspended and floating particles; (c) remove pathogens; (d) raise the BOD.

8. The action of the secondary sewage treatment is: (a) physical; (b) chemical; (c) biological.

9. What are the long-term effects of a continuously high BOD upon a waterway? (a) High DO; (b) increased degradation of sewage; (c) decreased degradation of sewage as the DO decreases; (d) proliferation of fish.

Answers: 1. (b); 2. (c); 3. (a); 4. (b); 5. (a); 6. (c); 7. (b); 8. (c); 9. (c).

Chapter 38
Microbiology
of Foods

INTRODUCTION: It should be recalled that there are metabolic similarities between heterotrophic microorganisms and the higher animals. Therefore, it should not be surprising that our
food constitutes a good growth medium for many microbes.

When microorganisms grow on food, they may "spoil" it by converting macromolecules into
less palatable end products. Worse, they may cause disease and/or produce toxins that cause disease.

Historically some microorganisms have contaminated foods and have produced end products
that have inhibited the growth of other microorganisms and thus preserved the food. These end
products turned out not to be harmful to humans who acquired tastes for them. Today such
microbial action is controlled in the making of pickles, sauerkraut, cheeses (next chapter), etc.

This chapter deals with these topics. It covers the microbial flora of foods, the ways this
flora spoils foods, ways to prevent this spoilage, and how some organisms act on foods to produce
products that are both palatable and relatively resistant to spoilage (fermented foods).

Finally, one way of combating food shortages is mentioned: the cultivation of microbes as a
food crop (single-cell protein).

Expanded Outline and Summary

I. Microbial Flora of Fresh Foods. The inner tissues of most foods are generally free of micro-
organisms. High concentrations of microorganisms usually result from improper handling
and storage and lead to faster spoilage.
   A. Fresh meats—cutting provides new surfaces and contaminants (including skin, intesti-
      nal, and soil organisms).
   B. Poultry—major contaminants are pseudomonads.
   C. Eggs—usually sterile unless cracked.
   D. Fruits and vegetables—may harbor bacteria, fungi, and/or viruses or become contami-
      nated with them during post-harvest handling. The low pH (2.3 to 5) of fruits helps
      preserve them from bacterial spoilage.

E. Shell- and finfish—flora generally reflects the flora of the waters in which they were harvested. Ingestion of raw seafood has led to a number of disease outbreaks (e.g., dysentery, hepatitis).

II. Microbial Spoilage of Foods.
  A. Processes and products.
    1. Degradation processes.
      a. Protein foods + proteolytic microorganisms → amino acids + amines + ammonia + hydrogen sulfide.
      b. Carbohydrate foods + carbohydrate-fermenting microorganisms → acids + alcohols + gases.
      c. Fatty foods + lipolytic microorganisms → fatty acids + glycerol.
    2. Microbial products.
      a. Pigments.
      b. Viscous polysaccharides (capsules).
      c. Toxins.
  B. Spoilage of noncanned foods—Table 38-1 of your text lists the types (appearance) of spoilage of many foods and the causative organisms. You should read through the table once and thereafter use it as a handy reference.
  C. Spoilage of canned foods—many times, anaerobic sporeformers are involved (clostridia), since they can resist high temperatures and grow in the anaerobic atmosphere of the can. The sporeformers, however, do not survive proper canning temperatures. Tables 38-2 and 38-3 list kinds of spoilage, organisms involved, and the signs of spoilage. You should read through the tables once and thereafter use them as handy references.

III. Microbiological Examination of Foods. The type of growth medium and the specific technique varies with the food, the kind(s) of organism being monitored, the conditions of food storage, etc. A general approach is presented in Fig. 38-1.

IV. Preservation of Food (techniques). All prevent or remove contamination and/or inhibit microorganisms and/or kill them. Smoking, salting, and drying were ancient processes, to which have been added modern processes like refrigeration, canning, and pasteurization. All processes must eliminate pathogens and minimize microbial populations, because the more microorganisms there are, and the more active they are, the more quickly the food will spoil.
  A. Aseptic handling.
  B. Heat.
    1. Boiling the food (kills vegetative cells and destroys some toxins).
    2. Canning—steam under pressure at the proper temperature for the proper time kills all vegetative cells and spores and destroys all toxins.
    3. Pasteurization (see Chap. 39)—kills most pathogens and reduces microbial populations but does not eliminate all microorganisms. Thus, subsequent refrigeration is required.
  C. Low temperatures—usually bacteriostatic.
    1. Refrigeration—no higher than 3.3°C to retard all but psychrophilic organisms.
    2. Freezing.
      a. Frozen foods—produce is steamed (blanched) to inactivate enzymes and then quick-frozen (-32°C or lower).

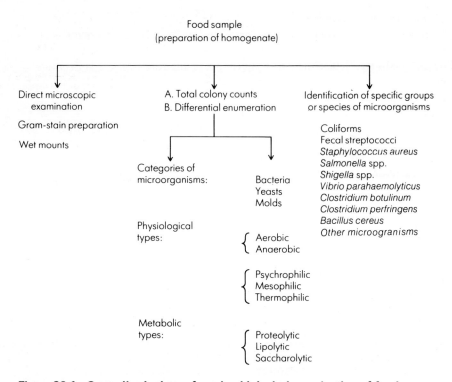

Figure 38-1. Generalized scheme for microbiological examination of food.

b. Home freezing—no higher than –10 to –20°C for long-term storage. General guidelines:

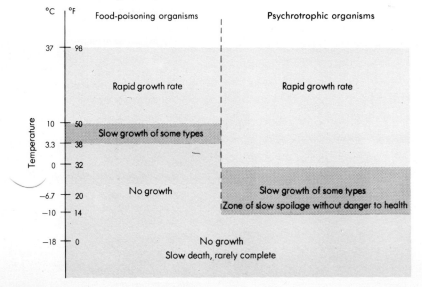

Figure 38-3.

D.   Dehydration (usually bacteriostatic).
E.   Osmotic pressure (cells plasmolyzed—water exits, leading to dehydration—and metabolism is arrested).
  1.   Concentrated sugar (jellies and jams)—much more inhibitory to bacteria than to fungi.
  2.   Brine (salted meats, etc.).
F.   Chemicals.
  1.   Organic acids—sorbic and propionic acids inhibit mold growth in bread. Also, benzoic, acetic, and lactic acids preserve fermented foods.
  2.   Smoking—cresols, etc., penetrate the meat and preserve it.
  3.   Nitrates and nitrites—used in curing meats. Preserve color and inhibit some anaerobic bacteria.
G.   Radiation.
  1.   Ultraviolet—in some meat processing plants.
  2.   Ionizing radiations—gamma rays and high-energy electron beams are being experimentally tested for "cold sterilization." *Radiation pasteurization* kills more than 98 percent but less than 100 percent of all microflora.

V.   Fermented Foods. Starter cultures (industrial—sometimes patented—inocula), often consisting of lactic acid–producing organisms, are used to mediate these (and other) processes.

Table 38-5. Some Examples of Fermented Food Products

FERMENTED FOOD	STARTING PRODUCT	MICROORGANISMS INVOLVED
Sauerkraut	Shredded cabbage	Early stage: *Enterobacter cloacae* *Erwinia herbicola* Intermediate stage: *Leuconostoc mesenteroides* Final stage: *Lactobacillus plantarum*
Pickles	Cucumbers	Early fermentation: *Leuconostoc mesenteroides* *Streptococcus faecalis* *Pedicoccus cerevisiae* Later fermentation: *Lactobacillus brevis* *L. plantarum*
Green olives	Olives	Early stage: *Leuconostoc mesenteroides* Intermediate stage: *Lactobacillus plantarum* *L. brevis* Final stage: *L. plantarum*
Sausage	Beef and pork	*Pediococcus cerevisiae* *Micrococcus* spp.

VI. Microorganisms as Food—Single-Cell Protein.
  A. Growth—on industrial waste products (byproducts) like hydrocarbon wastes (petroleum industry), beet molasses, and spent sulfite liquors (paper industry).
  B. Advantages.
    1. Rapid growth, high yield (several thousand times that of meat; at least 10 times that of crops).
    2. High protein content (20 to 70 percent).
    3. Proteins contain all essential amino acids.
    4. Some microorganisms (yeasts) have a high vitamin content.
    5. Recycling of industrial wastes and byproducts.

Programmed Self-Test

Do not begin this self-test before reading the corresponding chapter in the text.

MICROBIOLOGY OF FOODS (Text pages 807 to 821)

_____*(Genus)*_____ species constitute the major contaminants on the skin of freshly dressed poultry.

The _____ of fruits restricts bacterial, but not fungal, growth. | *Pseudomonas*

Vibrio parahaemolyticus, an enteric pathogen, may cause disease in people that eat _____, | low pH (acidity)

Does mold contamination of canned foods cause the can to swell? | seafood

---

Are wet mounts usually a part of the microbial examination of food? | No

---

The organism it is most important to eliminate from canned foods is _____. | Yes

---

Before freezing, the frozen food industry blanches (which means _____) fresh produce to inactivate enzymes. | *Clostridium botulinum*

Is freezing generally a bactericidal process? | steams

_____ and _____ acids are commonly used to inhibit mold growth in bread. | No

---

_____is a term describing the killing of over 98 percent but not 100 percent of the organisms by intermediate doses of radiation. | Sorbic; propionic

---

The starting product of sauerkraut is _____, and that of pickles is _____.	Radiation pasteurization
The genus of bacteria that is usually involved in the final stage of food fermentation is _____.	shredded cabbage; cucumbers
Pediococcus cerevisiae is an organism used as a starter culture in the preparation of _____.	*Lactobacillus*
Single-cell protein is a term that describes the use of _____ _____ as a food.	fermented sausage
Some microorganisms, particularly _____, have a high vitamin content.	microorganisms
	yeasts

Multiple-Choice Test

Underline the correct answer.

1. A food poisoning organism that has been reported to grow at temperatures as low as 3.3°C is: (a) *Clostridium botulinum,* types A and B; (b) *Staphylococcus aureus;* (c) *Salmonella typi;* (d) *Cl. botulinum,* type E.

2. Which process of food preservation is bactericidal? (a) Dehydration; (b) canning; (c) pasteurization; (d) freezing.

3. Which type of microorganism is most likely to multiply on the surface of jelly? (a) Mold; (b) bacteria; (c) virus; (d) protozoa.

4. Which organism has the highest (%) protein content? (a) Yeasts; (b) algae; (c) *Pseudomonas* sp.

5. Which one of the following genera is most likely to survive in canned food? (a) *Bacillus;* (b) *Clostridium;* (c) *Staphylococcus;* (d) *Streptococcus.*

6. Pickles are preserved by: (a) their high acid content; (b) their high salt content; (c) their low pH; (d) a relatively anaerobic environment; (e) all the above.

Answers: 1. (d); 2. (b); 3. (a); 4. (c); 5. (b); 6. (e).

Chapter 39

Microbiology of Milk and Milk Products

INTRODUCTION: This chapter is a sequel to the previous one, covering similar information and homing in on a frequently consumed and important food. Just as milk is an excellent mammalian nutrient, so it is a superb medium for the growth of heterotrophic microbes. Therefore, contamination is a very serious concern.

This chapter covers the flora of milk, the laboratory monitoring of that flora, the elimination of excess populations of bacteria and all pathogens, and the microbial conversion of milk into other dairy products.

Expanded Outline and Summary

I. Sources of Microorganisms in Milk. Milk is sterile but washes out organisms on and in the teat canal. It becomes further contaminated during processing and storage.
   A. The cow—must be in good health (small number of saprophytes) and not infected (large number of pathogens).
   B. The milking area—must be clean.
   C. Milking equipment—most important source of contamination. Machines, cans, tanks, etc., must be sanitized.
   D. Personnel—must be healthy and sanitary.

II. Types of Microorganisms in Milk.
   A. Biochemical types—all other factors remaining equal, the more bacteria in milk, the more quickly it will spoil. *Streptococcus lactus* and some *Lactobacillus* sp. produce lactic acid (homofermentative, or one end product), which sours the milk, though it may remain somewhat palatable. Other biochemical types produce end products that in sufficient quantities render milk unpalatable. The following is a summary of the major biochemical types found in milk, their origin and products. Read the table several times to gain a *general* knowledge of its content.

Table 39-1. Biochemical Types of Microorganisms in Milk

BIOCHEMICAL TYPES	REPRESENTATIVE MICROORGANISMS	SOURCE OF MICROORGANISMS	SUBSTRATE ACTED UPON AND END PRODUCTS	ADDITIONAL REMARKS
Acid producers	Streptococci, e.g., *Streptococcus lactis* *S. cremoris*	Dairy utensils, silage, plants	Lactose fermented to lactic acid or lactic acid and other products such as acetic acid, ethyl alcohol, and carbon dioxide	Acid producers that produce only lactic acid are referred to as *homofermentative* types; those which produce a variety of products are called *heterofermentative* types
	Lactobacilli, e.g., *Lactobacillus casei* *L. plantarum* *L. brevis* *L. fermentum*	Feeds, silage, manure	Lactose is fermented to lactic acid and other products. Some species of lactobacilli are homofermentative; others are heterofermentative	
	Microbacteria, e.g., *Microbacterium lacticum*	Manure, dairy utensils, and dairy products	Lactose fermented to lactic acid and other end products; do not produce as much acid as the streptococci or lactobacilli	Some of these bacteria can survive exposure to very high temperature, e.g., 80–85°C for 10 min
	Coliforms, e.g., *Escherichia coli* *Enterobacter aerogenes*	Manure, polluted water, soil, and plants	Lactose fermented to a mixture of end products, e.g., acids, gases, and neutral products	The number of coliform bacteria present in milk is an indicator of its sanitary quality
	Micrococci, e.g., *Micrococcus luteus* *M. varians* *M. freudenreichii*	Ducts of cow's mammary gland, dairy utensils	Small amounts of acid produced from lactose (weakly fermentative); micrococci are also proteolytic	Moderately heat resistant; some strains capable of surviving 63°C for 30 min
Gas producers	Coliforms *Clostridium butyricum* *Torula cremoris*	Soil, manure water, feed	Lactose fermented with accumulation of gas; the gas may be a mixture of carbon dioxide and hydrogen, or only carbon dioxide in the case of yeast fermentation	Bulk containers of milk may have their lids lifted by gas pressure in instances where contamination with gas producers is unusually high
Ropy or stringy fermentation	*Alicaligenes viscolactis* *Enterobacter aerogenes*	Soil, water, plants, feed	Organisms synthesize a viscous polysaccharide material that forms a slime layer	Milk favors the formation of capsular material; sterile skim milk is frequently

Table 39-1. Biochemical Types of Microorganisms in Milk (continued)

BIOCHEMICAL TYPES	REPRESENTATIVE MICROORGANISMS	SOURCE OF MICROORGANISMS	SUBSTRATE ACTED UPON AND END PRODUCTS	ADDITIONAL REMARKS
Ropy or stringy fermentation (continued)	*Streptococcus cremoris*		or capsule on the cells	used as the culture medium when capsule formation is sought
Proteolytic	*Bacillus* spp. e.g., *B. subtillis* *B. cereus* *Pseudomonas* spp.	Soil, water, utensils	Proteolytic organisms degrade the casein to peptides, which may be further dissimilated to amino acids; proteolysis may be preceded by coagulation of the casein by the enzyme rennin	End products of proteolysis may impart abnormal flavor or odor to the milk; *Pseudomonas* spp. may produce coloration of milk
	Proteus spp.			
	Streptococcus liquefaciens			
Lipolytic	*Pseudomonas fluorescens* *Achromobacter lipolyticum* *Candida lipolytica* *Penicillium* spp.	Soil, water, utensils	Lipolytic microorganisms hydrolyze milk fat to glycerol and fatty acids	Some fatty acids impart rancid odor and taste to milk

B. Temperature characteristics—temperature optima of the flora of milk determine the populations that exist after pasteurization and holding. Thermoduric organisms withstand pasteurization and may multiply during storage. You will gain general insights from reading this chart:

Table 39-2. Effect of Holding Temperature of Raw Milk on Numbers and Types of Bacteria

HOLDING TEMPERATURE, °C	CHANGES IN NUMBERS	PREDOMINANT ORGANISMS
1–4	Slow decline first few days followed by gradual increase after 7 to 10 days	True psychrophiles, e.g., species of *Achromobacter, Flavobacterium, Pseudomonas,* and *Alcaligenes*
4–10	Slight change in number during first few days followed by rapid increase in numbers; large populations present after 7 to 10 days or more	As above, changes produced on holding are of the following types; ropiness, sweet curdling, proteolysis, etc.
10–20	Very rapid increase in numbers; excessive populations reached within few days or less	Mainly acid-producing types such as lactic streptococci

Table 39-2. Effect of Holding Temperature of Raw Milk on Numbers and Types of Bacteria (continued)

HOLDING TEMPERATURE,°C	CHANGES IN NUMBERS	PREDOMINANT ORGANISMS
30-37	High populations develop within hours	Coliform group favored
37 and above	High populations develop within hours	Some mesophiles, thermophiles, e.g., *Bacillus coagulans* and *B. stearothermophilus*

C. Pathogenic types—do not appear in milk if the cows and handlers are healthy, if the milk has been properly collected and stored, and if the milk is properly pasteurized.
  1. Pathogens from cows—e.g., tuberculosis and brucellosis.
  2. Pathogens from humans—e.g., typhoid fever, diphtheria, dysentery, scarlet fever.

III. Microbiological Examination of Milk. High bacterial counts indicate contamination or improper cooling and/or holding. Both raw and processed milk is examined.
  A. The standard plate count (number of colonies per milliliter)—not all viable bacteria grow on the selected medium and under specified conditions of incubation.
  B. The direct microscopic count—microorganisms in a known quantity (0.01 ml) of milk are stained and counted. Counts are converted to number of bacteria per milliliter. This count is rapid and technically uncomplicated, but low population densities are difficult to count and dead cells may also be counted.
  C. Reductase test—milk exposed to air has an oxidation-reduction potential (O/R) of about +300 mV. Growing bacteria lower the O/R potential to a negative value. This shift can be measured with dyes:

POSITIVE MILK O/R (LITTLE OR NO GROWTH):	NEGATIVE MILK O/R (GROWTH):
OXIDIZED FORM OF DYE IN MILK	REDUCED FORM OF DYE IN MILK
Methylene blue (blue)	Leuco methylene blue (colorless)
Resazurin (slate blue)	Resorufin (pink)
	Dihydroresorufin (colorless)

  D. Special techniques for specific types of microorganisms. Rather than estimates of total microbial populations, the procedures outlined in Table 39-3 on page 833 of the text specifically measure:
  1. Thermoduric bacteria.
  2. Psychrophilic bacteria.
  3. Thermophilic bacteria.
  4. Coliform bacteria.
  5. Proteolytic bacteria.
  6. Pathogenic streptococci (beta-hemolytic).
  7. Yeasts and molds.

IV. Pasteurization of Milk. This must substantially reduce total microbial populations (retard spoilage) and kill most pathogens like the causative agent of Q fever (*Coxiella burnetii*). There is a medium balance between maximal destruction of microorganisms and minimal destruction of nutritional value.
   A. Pasteurization processes.
      1. Low-temperature holding (LTH) or vat pasteurization–145°F (62.8°C) for 30 min.
      2. High-temperature short time (HTST)–161°F (71.7°C) for 15 s.
   B. The phosphatase test–phosphatase is present in raw milk and many tissues. The test is based on the fact that pasteurization destroys the enzyme:

$$\text{Disodiumphenyl phosphate} + \text{phosphatase} \rightarrow \text{phenol} + \text{phosphate}$$

| Substrate | Enzymes from milk | Products |

The amount of phenol (phosphatase activity) is estimated by a reagent that turns blue in the presence of phenol. "Lack" of phenol is attributed to proper pasteurization.

V. Sterilization of Milk (e.g., 300°F for 1 to 2 s).
   A. Advantages.
      1. No refrigeration required.
      2. Long-term storage.
   B. Disadvantages (remedies are currently being sought).
      1. Poor flavor.
      2. Loss of nutrients.

VI. Grades of Milk. Regulation codes are based on all phases of processing and distribution of milk and on bacterial counts. The following is an example of such standards:

Table 39-4. Chemical, Bacteriological, and Temperature Standards for Grade A Milk and Milk Products

PRODUCT	TEMPERATURE	BACTERIAL LIMITS	OTHER
Grade A raw milk for pasteurization	Cooled to 50°F or less and maintained thereat until processed	Individual producer milk not to exceed 100,000/ml prior to commingling with other producer milk	Antibiotics: less than 0.05 unit/ml
Grade A pasteurized milk and milk products (except cultured products)	Cooled to 45°F or less and maintained thereat	Milk and milk products; 20,000/ml	Coliform limit: not exceeding 10/ml; phosphatase: less than 1 μg/ml by Scharer rapid method (or equivalent by other means)
Grade A pasteurized cultured products	Same as above	Exempt	Same as above

SOURCE: Grade "A" Pasteurized Milk Ordinance, 1965 Recommendations of the U. S. Public Health Service, Washington, 1967.

VII. Dairy Products Manufactured with the Aid of Microorganisms
   A. Fermented milks and related products—"souring" (by organisms in milk) of milk to preserve milk and to provide a new product. Today special inocula (starter cultures) mediate the souring. The products, organisms, and processes are summarized below.
   1. Organisms commonly found in starter cultures.

ORGANISMS	END PRODUCTS	FUNCTION OF END PRODUCTS
Streptococcus lactis *S. cremoris*	Lactic acid	Preservation; tangy taste
Leuconostoc citrovorum *L. dextranicum*	Volatile acids and neutral products: acetic acid, acetylmethyl carbinol, diacetyl	Characteristic flavor and aromas
Lactobacillus acidophilus *L. bulgaricus* *L. lactis*	Lactic acid	Preservation; tangy taste

   2. The products.

FERMENTED PRODUCT	PRINCIPAL MICROORGANISMS RESPONSIBLE FOR FERMENTATION	GENERAL REMARKS
	Leuconostoc Involved	
Commercial cultured buttermilk	*Streptococcus lactis* or *S. cremoris* and *Leuconostoc citrovorum* or *L. dextranicum*	Inoculation of pasteurized skim milk
Butter	As above	Processing of butterfat granules
Cultured sour cream	Same as used for cultured buttermilk, i.e., streptococci and leuconostocs	Not strictly a fermented milk but manufacture resembles that of cultured buttermilk. Cream is inoculated and incubated until the desired acidity develops. Flavor and aroma compounds are also contributed by the starter culture.
	Leuconostoc not involved	
Bulgarian milk	*Lactobacillus bulgaricus*	Incubation of inoculated milk at 37° C, but otherwise similar to cultured buttermilk. Product differs from commercial buttermilk in having higher acidity and lacking aroma
Acidophilus milk Sweet acidophilus milk (initial product is low-fat pasteurized milk)	*L. acidophilus*	Milk for propagation of *L. acidophilus* and the bulk milk to be fermented is sterilized, since this organism is easily overgrown by contaminating bacteria. Incubation is at 37° C; acidity allowed to develop to 0.6 to 0.7%.

FERMENTED PRODUCT	PRINCIPAL MICROORGANISMS RESPONSIBLE FOR FERMENTATION	GENERAL REMARKS
Leuconostoc not involved (continued)		
Yogurt laban & dahi (Greece, Romania, Hungary, Turkey)	***Streptococcus thermophilus*** ***L. bulgaricus***	Made from milk in which solids are concentrated by evaporation of some water and addition of skim milk solids. Product has consistency resembling custard
Kefir	***S. lactis*** ***L. bulgaricus*** Lactose-fermenting yeasts	A mixed lactic acid and alcoholic fermentation; bacteria produce acid (0.6 to 1.0% lactic acid), and yeasts produce alcohol (0.5 to 1.0% ethanol). The organisms conglomerate to form small granules called **kefir grains**. The granules are used as the starter culture in the Balkans, the fermentation is carried out in leather bags made of goatskin. The fermentation process may be continuous by adding fresh milk as the fermented product is removed. Kefir is made from cow, goat, or sheep milk.
Kumiss	Similar to those found in kefir grains	A mixed acid-alcoholic fermentation product made from mares' milk in certain parts of Russia

B. Cheese—processed from milk, generally by the procedures and organisms diagrammed on the following page. A few examples of types of cheeses are listed.
1. General process (see diagram on next page).
2. Selected examples of ripening.
    a. Roquefort and bleu—curd inoculated with spores of *Penicillium*. Roquefort incubated at 9 to 12°C; high humidity.
    b. Swiss—propionobacter also added before curdling (produces acid + gas creating holes).
    c. Limburger—moist curd placed in ripening room at 20°C, humidity 90-95 percent; curd is periodically rubbed with salt for a few days. Cheese becomes contaminated with organisms (*Brevobacterium linens*), which are then allowed to grow at 10°C.

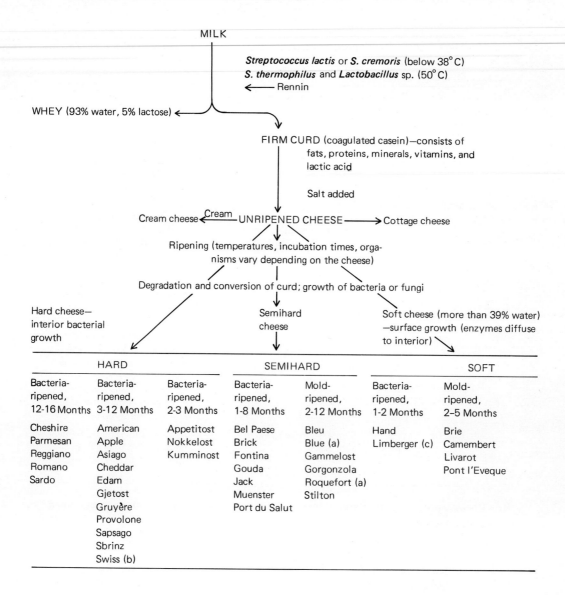

MILK

Streptococcus lactis or *S. cremoris* (below 38°C)
S. thermophilus and *Lactobacillus* sp. (50°C)
←—— Rennin

WHEY (93% water, 5% lactose) ←

FIRM CURD (coagulated casein)—consists of fats, proteins, minerals, vitamins, and lactic acid

Salt added

Cream cheese ←Cream— UNRIPENED CHEESE ——→ Cottage cheese

Ripening (temperatures, incubation times, organisms vary depending on the cheese)

Degradation and conversion of curd; growth of bacteria or fungi

Hard cheese—interior bacterial growth

Semihard cheese

Soft cheese (more than 39% water)—surface growth (enzymes diffuse to interior)

HARD			SEMIHARD		SOFT	
Bacteria-ripened, 12-16 Months	Bacteria-ripened, 3-12 Months	Bacteria-ripened, 2-3 Months	Bacteria-ripened, 1-8 Months	Mold-ripened, 2-12 Months	Bacteria-ripened, 1-2 Months	Mold-ripened, 2–5 Months
Cheshire	American	Appetitost	Bel Paese	Bleu	Hand	Brie
Parmesan	Apple	Nokkelost	Brick	Blue (a)	Limberger (c)	Camembert
Reggiano	Asiago	Kumminost	Fontina	Gammelost		Livarot
Romano	Cheddar		Gouda	Gorgonzola		Pont l'Eveque
Sardo	Edam		Jack	Roquefort (a)		
	Gjetost		Muenster	Stilton		
	Gruyère		Port du Salut			
	Provolone					
	Sapsago					
	Sbrinz					
	Swiss (b)					

Programmed Self-Test

Do not begin this self-test before reading the corresponding chapter in the text.

SOURCES, TYPES, AND EXAMINATION OF MICROORGANISMS IN MILK (Text pages 824 to 833)

At the time of milking, the number of organisms in the milk of a healthy cow ranges between several _____ and several _____ per milliliter.

The most important source of milk contamination is the _____ _____ with which it makes contact.	hundred; thousand
The production of the product _____ is referred to as the normal fermentation of milk.	interior of the equipment
Alcaligenes viscolactis causes ropy fermentation of milk because of its viscous _____, which is composed of polysaccharide.	lactic acid
An organism (genus) that is commonly found in milk and on the ducts of a cow's mammary gland is _____.	capsule
How many end products are produced by homofermentative bacteria?	*Micrococcus*
Holding milk at 30 to 37°C favors the growth of the _____ group of bacteria.	One
SPC stands for _____.	coliform
If methylene blue retains its blue color when added to milk, it means that the milk _____ severely contaminated.	standard plate count
_____ agar is used to detect pathogenic streptococci in milk.	is not

PASTEURIZATION, STERILIZATION, AND GRADES OF MILK (Text pages 833 to 835)

The pasteurization temperature (LTH) was raised 2°F, from 143 to 145°F, in order to kill the causative agent of _____.	Blood
The HTST process employs equipment capable of exposing milk to a temperature of 161°F for _____ seconds.	Q fever
Phosphatase is present in _____ milk but not in _____ milk.	15
In the phosphatase test the concentration of the chemical _____ is monitored.	raw; pasteurized
To date, sterilized milk has had two drawbacks: It is less palatable and less _____.	phenol

The coliform concentration of grade A pasteurized milk may not exceed _____ per milliliter.	nutritious

DAIRY PRODUCTS MANUFACTURED WITH THE AID OF MICROORGANISMS (Text pages 836 to 843)

The diacetyl in butter is produced by the microbial genus _____.	10
Kefir is fermented by _____ that produce ethanol as well as by bacteria.	*Leuconostoc*
Milk curd consists mainly of coagulated _____.	yeasts
In the production of cheese, both the starter culture and the enzyme _____ curdle the milk.	casein
The watery fluid which separates out during the formation of the curd is called _____. It consists of about 93 percent water and 5 percent _____.	rennin
Cottage and cream cheese are _____ cheeses.	whey; lactose
During the manufacture of Roquefort cheese, the curd is inoculated with the spores of the mold _____.	unripened
Interior bacterial growth is characteristic of _____ cheeses.	*Penicillum roqueforti*
	hard

Multiple-Choice Test

Underline the correct answer.

1. The process of pasteurization: (a) kills *Clostridium botulinum;* (b) was invented by Koch; (c) kills *Mycobacterium tuberculosis;* (d) involves the boiling of milk; (e) kills *Bacillus subtilis.*

2. A microorganism commonly found in pasteurized milk is: (a) *Lactobacillus;* (b) *Escherichia;* (c) *Pasteurella;* (d) *Bacillus;* (e) none (pasteurized milk is sterile).

3. A major liquid (waste) product of the cheese industry is: (a) casein; (b) whey; (c) diacetyl; (d) curd.

4. Long ago when there were no refrigerators, herdsmen were forced to drink milk within hours after collecting it. When the milk was left to stand, organisms naturally found in milk soured it and an abundance of *Streptococcus lactis* preserved the milk as a palatable product, paving the way for the discovery of the manufacture of cheese, a product that could be stored for longer periods of time than raw milk. When an abundance of *Leuconostoc* also grew, the product tasted like: (a) Swiss cheese; (b) yogurt; (c) wine; (d) butter.

5. Soft cheeses such as Camembert are ripened by: (a) microbial surface growth; (b) microbial growth throughout and surface growth; (c) microbial growth throughout with surface growth inhibited; (d) protozoa only.

6. Which of the following cheeses requires the least time and is often the cheapest to produce? (a) Swiss; (b) Camembert; (c) kefir; (d) cheddar; (e) cottage.

7. Swiss cheese is ripened by: (a) molds; (b) yeasts; (c) propionic acid bacteria; (d) finisher cultures.

8. Which of the following genera is not employed in dairy industry starter cultures? (a) *Bacillus;* (b) *Streptococcus;* (c) *Leuconostoc;* (d) *Lactobacillus.*

9. One measure of the effectiveness of pasteurization is the assay for: (a) Lactobacilli; (b) coagulase; (c) phosphatase; (d) rennin.

Answers: 1. (c); 2. (a); 3. (b); 4. (d); 5. (a); 6. (e); 7. (c); 8. (a); 9. (c).

Chapter 40

Industrial
Microbiology

INTRODUCTION: The previous three chapters have shown how microorganisms may mediate or impede the treatment of sewage and the production of foods. This final chapter is the sequel to those on applied microbiology, for microorganisms make many products for humanity and also ruin others.

Where chemists cannot match the productivity of living systems, microorganisms produce the products. Some examples include antibiotics and steroids as well as smaller molecules such as alcohols and organic acids. Industry also uses microorganisms to manufacture foods (e.g., alcoholic beverages) and as foods (e.g., yeasts). Species of microorganisms that cause disease may also be used to prevent disease when incorporated into vaccines.

On the other side of the coin, unchecked microbes may prematurely deteriorate paper, textiles, and other products.

This chapter summarizes some of the roles of microorganisms as the most productive (and counterproductive) industrial chemists.

Expanded Outline and Summary

    I. Microorganisms and Industry (overall concepts).
       A. Prerequisites to practical industrial processes (characteristics of a worthwhile system).

$$\text{Substrate (raw material)} \xrightarrow{\text{microorganisms}} \text{products}$$

          1. The organism.
             a. Large amounts of product.
             b. Stable characteristics.
             c. Rapid growth.
             d. Nonpathogenic.
          2. The substrate.
             a. Cheap
             b. Available in large quantities } e.g., whey.

3. The product.
    a. Recoverable.
    b. Purifiable.
B. Major classes of products.
  1. Alcoholic beverages (e.g., wines and beers).
  2. Pharmaceutical chemicals (e.g., antibiotics and steroids).
  3. Food supplements (e.g., yeast and algae).
  4. Chemicals (e.g., ethanol).
  5. Vaccines.

II. Industrial Uses of Bacteria (fermentations).
  A. Spectrum of fermentations—the uses of 14 products produced by various bacteria are presented in the text (Table 40-12; page 846). These selected examples show the diverse involvement of industry with bacteria.
  B. The text expands on three examples as illustrations.
    1. Lactic acid production: Use of whey.
      a. Production steps:

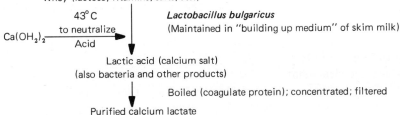

      b. Product uses.
        i. Animal food supplement
        ii. Treatment of calcium deficiency.
        iii. Lacquer solvent (*n*-butyl lactate).
    2. Vinegar production: Frings method.
      a. Production steps.

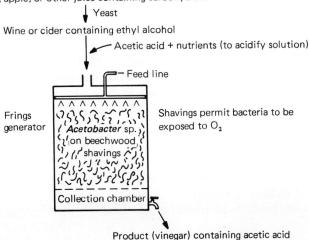

b. Overall reaction.

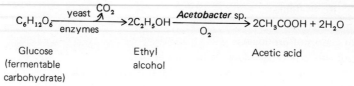

$$C_6H_{12}O_6 \xrightarrow[\text{enzymes}]{\text{yeast} \quad CO_2} 2C_2H_5OH \xrightarrow[O_2]{\textit{Acetobacter} \text{ sp.}} 2CH_3COOH + 2H_2O$$

Glucose   Ethyl   Acetic acid
(fermentable   alcohol
carbohydrate)

3. Amino acid production.
    a. L-lysine: food supplement.

Escherichia coli
———————————→ diaminopimelic acid (DAP) ————————————————→lysine
                                      DAP decarboxylase
                                             from
                                 Enterobacter aerogenes

    b. L-glutamic acid. Monosodium glutamate is a flavor enhancer.

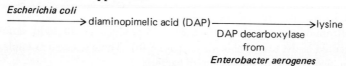

Carbohydrate + peptone ——————→ α-ketoglutaric ——————→Glutamic
    + salts + biotin   acid   acid +
                                                             NAD +
                                                             H_2O

Micrococcus or *Arthrobacter* or *Brevibacterium*; NH_3 $NADH_2$; glutamic acid dehydrogenase

III. Industrial Uses of Yeasts.
    A. Alcohol fermentations.
        1. The substrate—any fermentable carbohydrate. Complex carbohydrates (e.g., starches)
            must first be hydrolyzed by heat or enzymes form barley malt or molds.
        2. The organism—selected strains of *Saccharomyces cerevisiae* that produce and tolerate
            high yields of alcohol.
        3. The reaction:

$$C_6H_{12}O_6 \xrightarrow[\text{enzymes}]{\text{yeast}} 2C_2H_5OH + 2CO_2$$

        Glucose   Ethyl   Carbon
        (fermentable   alcohol   dioxide
        carbohydrate)

        4. Useful products.
            a. Industrial (solvent) and commercial alcohol.
            b. Alcoholic beverages (see Table 40-2, text page 854).
    B. Baker's yeast—selected strains of *S. cerevisiae* that grow rapidly and vigorously ferment
        the sugar in dough are used. The steps in the production of such strains are diagramed on
        page 853 of the text.
    C. Food yeasts—single-cell protein.

IV. Industrial Uses of Molds.
    A. Spectrum of fermentations—the uses of eight products, produced by various molds, are
        presented in the text (Table 40-3, page 855). These examples show the diverse involve-
        ment of industry with molds.
    B. Four mold products are covered in more detail.

1. Penicillin production.
    a. Increasing the yield of penicillin (serves as a model for any product). Increased yields due essentially to obtaining more productive organisms and to better growth and recovery techniques.
    b. Commercial production of penicillin.

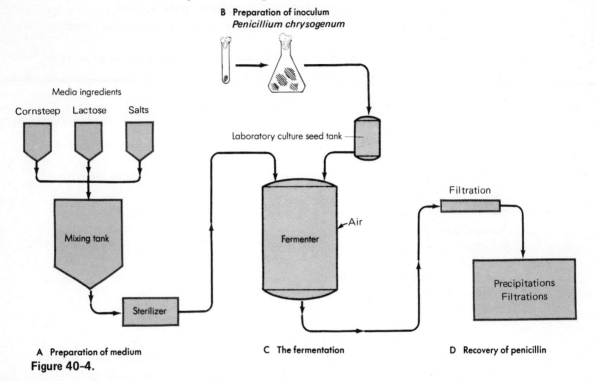

B Preparation of inoculum
Penicillium chrysogenum

Media ingredients

Cornsteep   Lactose   Salts

Laboratory culture seed tank

Filtration

Mixing tank

Air

Fermenter

Precipitations
Filtrations

Sterilizer

A Preparation of medium   **C** The fermentation   **D** Recovery of penicillin

Figure 40-4.

2. Citric acid.
    a. Uses.
        i. In blood for transfusions.
        ii. Flavoring extracts.
        iii. Manufacture of inks and dyes.
    b. Production.

$$\text{Molasses–salt medium} \xrightarrow[\text{O}_2]{\textit{Aspergillus niger}} \text{citric acid}$$

3. Enzyme production.
    a. Organisms: *Aspergillus; Penicillium; Mucor; Rhizopus.*
    b. The products.
        i. Amylases (hydrolyze starch)—used in food, pharmaceutical, and textile industries.
        ii. Invertases (hydrolyze sucrose to glucose and levulose)—used in food industry (e.g., candy manufacturing).

          iii. Protease (mixture of proteolytic enzymes)—used in bating (treatment of hides), in manufacture of glue, in detergents.

          iv. Pectinase—used in the clarification of fruit juices and in the retting of flax and manufacture of linen.

    4. Steroid conversions (steroids useful in treatment of arthritis. rheumatism, and other diseases)—to comprehend the numerous reactions by numerous organisms, see text Fig. 40-7, page 859, which illustrates the conversions of just one of the steroids, progesterone.

V. Biologies for Immunization. This major industry rests on the foundations covered in previous chapters (25–32) on microorganisms and disease.

VI. Petroleum Microbiology. Microorganisms both benefit and harm the industry.
    A. Petroleum formation—microbial hydrocarbons and geochemical involvement produce petroleum.
    B. Petroleum exploration—microbial test system contains all growth ingredients except carbon source.
    C. Petroleum production—*Desulfovibrio* sp. corrode pipes; other bacteria contaminate drilling fluid.

VII. Deterioration of Materials (foodstuffs were previously discussed, as was the retardation of microbial spoilage).
    A. Paper.
        1. Production.
            a. Cellulose fibers are chemically treated to separate and purify them into pulp.
            b. Fibers redeposited in sheet form.
        2. Microbial deterioration.
            a. Pulp slimes—many microorganisms involved, especially bacilli.
            b. Finished paper—cellulose degraders involved.
    B. Textiles and cordage (those of natural fibers like cotton, wool, linen, and silk)—ruined predominantly by molds, especially where there is high humidity and little light.
    C. Painted surfaces (those not containing a fungicide)—"mildewed" by molds like *Pullularia* (most common), *Aspergillus,* etc.

VIII. Analytical Microbiology. Specific organisms are used quantitatively to assay vitamins (auxotrophs), amino acids (auxotrophs), and antibiotics. Very sensitive tests.
    A. Antibiotics—inhibition of growth.
    B. Vitamins and amino acids—amount of growth is proportional to the amount of nutrient added to the assay medium (e.g., *Lactobacillus arabinosus* and niacin).

IX. Future Prospects.
    A. Microbial enzymes.
    B. Single-cell protein.
    C. New pharmacological/chemotherapeutic agents.
    D. Mixed-culture fermentations.
    E. Immobilized enzyme technology (enzymes are fixed on a matrix and substrates are acted upon by the enzyme)—in this technique, enzymes are recoverable, act longer, and do not contaminate the product.

Programmed Self-Test

Do not begin this self-test before reading the corresponding chapter in the text.

INDUSTRIAL MICROBIOLOGY (Text pages 845 to 866)

Industry produces more _____ than any other antibiotic.

Organisms serving industry should grow rapidly and be non-_____.

penicillin

Useful products of *Clostridium actetobutylicum* are _____ and _____.

pathogenic

A use for whey cited by your text is as a substrate for the production of _____.

acetone; butanol

The Frings generator is used to make _____.

lactic acid

Is the conversion of alcohol to acetic acid an aerobic process?

vinegar

DAP decarboxylase converts deaminopimelic acid to _____.

Yes

Glutamic acid is a flavor enhancer when in its salt form, _____.

lysine

The yeast _____ produces high yields of ethyl alcohol.

monosodium glutamate

Baker's yeast grows at a pH of _____, whereas most bacteria do not.

Saccharomyces cerevisiae

The mold _____ is most widely used for the commercial production of citric acid.

4 to 5

Invertase hydrolyzes sucrose to _____ and _____.

Aspergillus niger

Proteases are used for bating (treatment of _____) to provide a finer texture and grain.

glucose; levulose

Corrosion of iron pipe by _____ is a major problem in the petroleum industry.

hides

Paper can be degraded (ruined) by organisms (e.g., *Myrothecium verrucaria*) that degrade the complex polysaccharide _____.	*Desulfovibrio*
Lactobacillus arabinosus requires niacin for growth. It can be used to bioassay _____.	cellulose
Enzymes can be put to work more efficiently than ever before using _____. With this technique enzymes are recoverable, act longer, and do not contaminate the product.	niacin
	immobilized enzyme technology

Multiple-Choice Test

Underline the correct answer.

1. Which organism is not "employed" by industry to make a product(s) for humanity? (a) *penicillium notatum;* (b) *Proteus mirabilis;* (c) *Saccharomyces cerevisiae;* (d) *Lactobacillus bulgaricus.*

2. In the manufacture of beer, malt is converted to wort by the actions of: (a) bacteria; (b) molds; (c) enzymes; (d) yeasts.

3. Streptokinase is produced so that it may be used to: (a) clot blood; (b) dissolve blood clots; (c) preserve foods; (d) bate hides.

4. Industrial steroid conversions are generally carried out by: (a) yeasts; (b) molds and mold-like bacteria; (c) lactobacilli; (d) protozoa.

5. *Pullularia* sp. appear to be the most common cause of mildewed paint. These organisms are: (a) viruses; (b) bacteria; (c) molds; (d) algae.

6. This kind of standard curve results when one is doing the type of test called a(n): (a) standard plate count; (b) antibiotic assay; (c) bioassay; (d) immobilized-enzyme procedure.

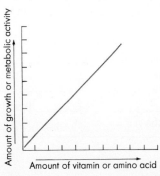

The remainder of the questions (fill in the blank) refer to the following table (table-reading comprehension test).

Table 40-1. Some Industrial Products (Other than Antibiotics) Produced by Bacteria

PRODUCT	MICROORGANISM	USES
Acetone-butanol	*Clostridium acetobutylicum* and others	Solvents; chemical manufacturing
2, 3-Butanediol	*Bacillus polymyxa; E. aerogenes*	Solvent; humectant; chemical intermediate
Dihydroxyacetone	*Gluconobacter suboxydans*	Fine chemical
2-Ketogluconic acid	*Pseudomonas* spp.	Intermediate for D-araboascorbic acid
5-Ketogluconic acid	*G. suboxydans*	Intermediate for tartaric acid
Lactic acid	*Lactobacillus delbrueckii*	Food products, textile and laundry, chemical manufacturing, deliming hides
Bacterial amylase	*Bacillus subtilis*	Modified starches; sizing paper; desizing textiles
Bacterial protease	*B. subtilis*	Bating hides; desizing fibers; spot remover; tenderizing meat
Dextran	*Leuconostoc mesenteroides*	Stabilizer in food products; blood-plasma substitute
Sorbose	*Q. suboxydans*	Manufacture of ascorbic acid
Cobalamin	*Streptomyces olivaceus; Propionibacterium freudenreichii*	Treatment of pernicious anemia; food and feed supplementation
Glutamic acid	*Brevibacterium* spp.	Food additive
Lysine	*Micrococcus glutamicus*	Animal-feed additive
Stretokinase-Streptodornase	*Streptococcus hemolyticus*	Medical use (dissolving blood clots)

7. Which product is a coenzyme or vitamin? _____

8. Which product degrades complex carbohydrates? _____

9. Which product is used in the synthesis of a vitamin? _____

10. Which microorganism, if any, is a yeast? _____

Answers: 1. (b); 2. (c); 3. (b); 4. (b); 5. (c); 6. (c); 7. cobalamin; 8. amylase; 9. sorbose; 10. none.